Avian Physiology

AVIAN
PHYSIOLOGY

By Paul D. Sturkie

PROFESSOR OF POULTRY PHYSIOLOGY

RUTGERS UNIVERSITY

THE STATE UNIVERSITY OF NEW JERSEY

COMSTOCK

PUBLISHING ASSOCIATES

A DIVISION OF CORNELL UNIVERSITY PRESS

ITHACA, NEW YORK, 1954

First Published 1954

PRINTED IN THE UNITED STATES OF AMERICA BY

GEORGE BANTA PUBLISHING CO., MENASHA, WISC.

To my wife

Preface

PHYSIOLOGY may be divided into three main categories: cellular, comparative, and special—i.e., the physiology of special groups of organisms. The physiology of special groups has received the most attention. In the animal field, interest has centered largely on mammalian physiology, with particular emphasis on human physiology and its relationship to medicine. By comparison, the physiology of birds has been neglected. Knowledge in certain areas of avian physiology is limited, fragmentary, and often confused, and little or no new research is being conducted. Much of the physiological research on the bird has been conducted from the comparative viewpoint, which is concerned more with broad functional relationships between groups of animals than with details of a special group. In some areas, however, these fundamental functions have not been definitely established. Even in certain fields, such as endocrinology, where there is considerably more research activity on the bird, there are wide gaps in our knowledge.

This book is the first one in any language devoted to the specialized physiology of birds. It deals mainly with the chicken, the duck, and the pigeon, because most of the research has been conducted on these species and they represent species of economic importance to man.

Inasmuch as physiology provides a rational basis for much of animal husbandry and veterinary medicine, this book should be of especial interest to teachers, students, and research workers in poultry science and husbandry and in veterinary medicine. More knowledge and research in avian physiology, particularly on the domestic species, should have important applications to the poultry industry, which is rapidly expanding in this country. Although few poultry departments at present offer course work on the physiology of birds, it is hoped that this book may be instrumental in increasing the number of institutions offering such work and in stimulating more research. It may serve, also, as a source of reference for the experimental physiologist and should provide pertinent physiological material for courses in comparative physiology, ecology, and ornithology.

The bibliography is extensive but not exhaustive. An attempt was made to select the most important and more recent references, with minor consideration given to priority. The references are cited at the end of each chapter and include the complete title.

The writer is indebted to investigators, journals, and books for many of the illustrations used. Separate acknowledgment is made in the legends to the authors and books or journals from which illustrations came. The original drawings and modifications of illustrations of others were prepared by my wife, to whom I am grateful.

Special thanks are extended to colleagues who read one or more chapters and made helpful suggestions. These are Drs. H. H. Dukes, J. A. Dye, F. B. Hutt, R. M. Fraps, C. S. Shaffner, A. V. Nalbandov, T. C. Byerly, J. H. Leathem, J. B. Allison, W. C. Russell, and H. J. Metzger.

PAUL D. STURKIE

New Brunswick, New Jersey
July, 1953

Contents

Chapter 2

Chemical Constituents of the Blood   24

Chapter 3

Circulation, Blood Pressure, and Blood Volume   41

Chapter 7

Transport of the Blood Gases ___ 111

Chapter 8

Regulation of Body Temperature ___ 118

Chapter 9

Energy Metabolism 138

Chapter 10

Alimentary Canal: Anatomy, Prehension, Deglutition, Passage of Ingesta, Motility 151

Chapter 11

Alimentary Canal: Digestion, Absorption, Secretion of Gastric Juice, pH   164

Chapter 12

Carbohydrate Metabolism   185

Chapter 13

Kidneys and Urine   206

Chapter 14

The Special Senses 229

THE EYE AND VISION

HEARING

TASTE

SMELL

Chapter 15

Reproduction in the Female and Egg Formation 247

Chapter 16

Reproduction in the Male, Fertilization, and Early Embryonic Development

285

Chapter 17

Hypophysis   301

Chapter 18

Gonadal Hormones   327

Chapter 19

Thyroids   348

Chapter 20

Parathyroids, Thymus, Pancreas   381

Chapter 21

Adrenals 398

Avian Physiology

CHAPTER 1

Blood: Formed Elements, Hemoglobin, Physical Characteristics

BLOOD has many functions. Some of these are (1) absorption and transport of nutrients from the alimentary canal to the tissues, (2) transport of the blood gases to and from the tissues, (3) removal of waste products of metabolism, (4) transportation of hormones produced by the endocrine glands, and (5) regulation of the water content of the body tissues. Blood is also concerned in the regulation and maintenance of body temperature and in hydrogen ion concentration (Dukes, 1947).

Blood contains a fluid portion (the plasma), salts and other chemical constituents, and certain formed elements, the corpuscles. The corpuscles comprise the erythrocytes (red cells) and leucocytes (white cells).

ERYTHROCYTES

Erythrocytes of birds are oval-shaped and, unlike those of mammalian blood, are nucleated and are larger (Figure 1). The sizes of the erythrocytes of some avian species are presented in Table 1.

Melampy (1948) has studied the cytochemistry of the erythrocytes of chickens. He found the total nitrogen content on a moisture-free basis of the nucleus to be 12.5 percent and for the cell as a whole 15.8 percent. The average dry weight of a single erythrocyte was

Table 1. Dimensions of bird erythrocytes in microns
(from Groebbels, 1932)

Species	Long diameter	Short diameter	Thick-ness	Author
Chicken				
3 day old	12.5	7.0	3.8	Lange
25 day old	13.0	7.2	3.5	"
70 day old	13.0	6.5	3.5	"
mature (♂ & ♀)	12.8	6.9	3.6	"
Pigeon				
1 day old	13.0	7.7	3.8	"
mature	12.7	7.5	3.7	"
Turkey				
male	15.5	7.5	—	Venzlaff
female	15.5	7.0	—	"
Duck	12.8	6.6	—	Malassez

44.3×10^{-6} micrograms, and of the nucleus, 10.5×10^{-6} micrograms. The cytoplasm contained greater quantities of most of the amino acids than did the nucleus.

Methods of Counting

The erythrocytes are counted directly in a counting chamber (hemocytometer). There are a number of different types of these, but essentially they consist of a glass plate containing squares or cells in which the erythrocytes are counted. A sample of blood is taken and diluted in a red-cell diluting pipette, usually one part blood to 200 parts of the diluting medium. A number of diluting fluids have been used, including Toisson's, Wiseman's, and others. According to Olson (1948), Wiseman's diluting fluid gives satisfactory results. This fluid consists of 50 mg. of phloxine, 5 cc. of neutral formalin, and 95 cc. of Ringer's solution. After the blood has been diluted and mixed thoroughly in the diluting pipette, a drop or two is inserted under the cover slip onto the counting chamber. The diluting fluid stains the erythrocytes a distinct pink color, and they are counted in the squares. Usually the cells are counted in 80 of the smallest squares, including 16 in each of the corners and 16 in the middle of the square. If the dilution of the blood in the pipette is 1–200, then the number of cells counted in the 80 squares is multiplied by 10,000 to give the number of erythrocytes per cubic millimeter of blood. (For details, see Olson, 1948.)

Number

The number of erythrocytes in fowl and other avian species is shown in Table 2. The number of erythrocytes for various breeds of chickens is not significantly different (Groebbels, 1932).

Effects of hormones. Sexually mature males have a higher number of

Table 2. Erythrocyte numbers in birds in millions
per cubic millimeter

Species	Age	Sex		Sex not given	Investigator
		Male	Female		
Chicken	Adult	3.24	2.77		Dukes (1947)
"	"	3.32	2.72		Olson (1937)
"	"	3.26	2.72		Lange (Groebbels, 1932)
"	3 hours			1.84	"
"	3 days			2.23	"
"	12 days			2.65	"
"	26 days			2.77	Cook (1937)
"	32–47 days			2.83	Twisselmann (1939)
"	50 days			2.34	Lange
"	70 days			2.39	"
"	82 days			2.79	Cook
Pigeon	Adult	4.00	3.07		Wastl & Leiner (Groebbels)
"	"	3.23	3.09		Riddle & Braucher (1934)
Dove	"	3.04	2.99		"
Goose (domestic)	"			2.71	Wastl & Leiner (Groebbels)
Duck (domestic)	"			2.80	Malassez (Groebbels)
Turkey (domestic)	"	2.24	2.37		Venzlaff (Groebbels)
Ostrich	"	1.89*			De Villiers (1938)

* Males and females.

erythrocytes than females. This has been shown by Domm and Taber (1946), Juhn and Domm (1930), Newell and Shaffner (1950) in chickens, and others. Before sexual maturity there appears to be no significant difference in the count and little variation due to age up to this time. The fact that the male has more red cells than the female suggests that gonadal hormones may account for the difference. This has been proven experimentally by Domm and Taber (1946), who showed that capons have fewer erythrocytes than normal males. When the capons were treated with testicular hormone (androgen), the erythrocytes approached the number for normal males. Female castrates (poulards) had the same number of erythrocytes as normal females, indicating that the ovarian hormone in physiological amounts has no effect on red cell numbers. Poulards treated with androgen show an increase in red cells, approaching the figure for males, but when treated with large doses of estrogen there was a diminution in red cell count.

	Male	*Female*	*Investigator*
Normal	3,250,000	2,610,000	Domm & Taber (1946)
Castrate	2,480,000	2,600,000	"

That the thyroid hormone (thyroxine) exerts a control over erythrocyte numbers in the male chicken was shown by Domm and Taber (1946) in their experiments on thyroidectomy, as follows:

	Males	*Females*
Completely thyroidectomized	2.43*	2.60
Incompletely thyroidectomized	2.62	2.65
Normal individuals	3.25	2.61

* Millions per cubic millimeter.

The operation had no effect upon numbers in the female.

Thiouracil (a goitrogen or antithyroid drug) is considered to have an effect similar to thyroidectomy, but when it was administered to chickens, it depressed the erythrocyte numbers significantly in males, females, and capons (Domm and Taber, 1946).

Other factors. According to Domm and Taber, the number of erythrocytes of hens is greater in the fall than in the winter and spring, when rate of laying is usually higher. They also observed a diurnal variation in erythrocytes, with high values at midnight and the lowest values at noon. Riddle and Braucher (1934) showed that male doves and pigeons also have higher numbers of red cells than the females. Olson's data (1937) suggest a seasonal variation in red cell count, with values higher in the winter.

Other factors which affect the concentration of erythrocytes in the blood are certain minerals, vitamins, and drugs. Deficiencies in iron and copper produce anemia and a decrease in hemoglobin (Hart, Elvehjem, and Kemmerer, 1930).

Cobalt is not usually considered essential for normal erythropoiesis, but when excessive amounts are administered to certain mammals and ducks, an increase in the number of erythrocytes (polycythemia) occurs. When cobalt chloride, 1 to 4 mg. daily for 14 days, was injected into ducks, the red cell count increased from 2.6 to 3.1 million (Davis, McCullough, and Rigdon, 1945). These authors suggested that the initial rise in count following cobalt administration is due to erythropoietic stimulation, but that the maintenance of the elevated number may be due to a decreased rate of destruction of erythrocytes.

Corpuscular Volume (Hematocrit)

The corpuscles may be separated from the plasma by centrifugation. A sample of blood is placed in a hematocrit tube and centrifuged for 15 to 20 minutes at 3000 or more r.p.m. The tube is graduated so that volume of the cells can be read off. The cell volume is composed largely of erythrocytes, but includes leucocytes as well. The method is subject to an error of about 5 percent due to the fact that some plasma is trapped with the cells as they settle out and that the estimation includes the leucocytes. Values for cell volume in percent are shown as follows:

		Male	Female	Author
Chicken	Sexually immature	29	29	Newell & Shaffner (1950)
"	Adult, sexually mature	45	29	"
"	Adult, laying		28.5	Sturkie & Newman (1951)

Androgen increases cell volume, but estrogen has no effect on it (Newell and Shaffner, 1950; Sturkie and Newman, 1951).

Resistance of Erythrocytes

Hemolysis is the discharging of hemoglobin from the corpuscles into the plasma. A number of factors, such as freezing, thawing, and changes in osmotic pressure of the blood, produce hemolysis. Solutions which have the same osmotic pressure as blood and which do not cause hemolysis are isotonic. Those with lower osmotic pressures than blood are hypotonic solutions, and those with higher pressures are hypertonic solutions. Hypotonic solutions cause hemolysis and bursting by increasing the water content of the cells, and hypertonic solutions cause a shrinking of the corpuscles, because water is lost from the cells. The fragility of red cells is measured by their resistance to solutions of known concentrations and osmotic pressures, usually NaCl solutions. The point at which hemolysis begins is termed minimum resistance, and the point at which all cells are hemolyzed is termed maximum resistance. Figures for the resistance of bird erythrocytes are shown as follows:

Species	Minimum resistance Percent NaCl	Maximum resistance Percent NaCl	Author
Chicken	0.4 to 0.47	—	Kleineberger and Carl (from De Villiers, 1938)
"	0.44	0.28	Demmel (from Dukes, 1947)
Ostrich, males	0.47	0.27	De Villiers (1938)
Ostrich, females	0.48	0.28	"

Formation and Destruction of the Corpuscles

Two theories on the origin of the blood cells have been evolved— monophyletic and polyphyletic. The proponents of the monophyletic theory maintain that there is one specific stem cell developing from the mesenchyme which gives rise to the two main types of blood cells, both white and red. The proponents of the polyphyletic theory of blood cell formation believe that erythrocytes and leucocytes develop from two originally distinct cell types. The erythrocytes are formed from the vascular endothelium of the bone marrow, and the leucocytes from reticular connective tissue cells.

Jordan (1939), who adheres to the monophyletic view, thinks that the bone marrow is the chief hematopoietic center in birds and consequently can give rise to all the different cell types. Krumbhaar (1928) believed that while the bone marrow is the chief site of hematopoiesis in birds the liver may also function in this respect.

The length of life of the erythrocyte in mammals is estimated to be from 28 to 100 days, and in the chicken, 28 days (Hevesy and Ottesen, 1945). According to Rous's conception of erythrocyte destruction, the red corpuscles break up in the blood stream into smaller and smaller pieces, still retaining their hemoglobin. When in a very fine state of division these fragments are taken out by cells of the reticulo-endothelial system, by which the hemoglobin is split into its iron-containing part and its protein fraction. Another way in which the red corpuscles are destroyed is through phagocytosis by the cells of the reticulo-endothelial system. Finally, there remains the possibility that erythrocytes are destroyed by hemolysis in the spleen and perhaps other places. But failure to find large amounts of free hemoglobin makes this view doubtful. In the dog, the main seat of bilirubin formation is the red bone marrow. It is reasonable to suppose, therefore, that this is the principal site of erythrocyte destruction. In man, the spleen is probably of great importance in the process, but in the rabbit and guinea pig it is probably less important; in birds, the liver is the main site, according to Krumbhaar (1928).

Storage of Erythrocytes in the Spleen

Barcroft (1925) demonstrated that the spleen of mammals serves as a reservoir of erythrocytes and that in times of emergency it expels the reserve cells into the general circulation. This function was also ascribed to the spleen of the chicken by Harmon, Ogden, and Cook (1932), who reported that asphyxia induced in normal chickens increases hemoglobin, but not in splenectomized ones. Sturkie (1943), using a more reliable method of hemoglobin determination and a larger number of birds, could not confirm their results. His results showed that while asphyxia in the intact bird appeared to increase the hemoglobin slightly not one of the differences was significant. These results reveal that asphyxia does not stimulate the spleen of the fowl to expel erythrocytes into the general circulation as it does the spleen of mammals. It is known that the high degree of contractility of the mammalian spleen plays an important role in the expulsion of blood into the main circulating channels (Barcroft, 1925; Klemperer, 1938) and is dependent upon the thick muscular capsule and prominent trabeculae of the organ. The spleen of birds has a thin capsule with few muscle fibers and no true trabeculae (Klemperer) and is capable of contraction to only a slight extent.

THROMBOCYTES

The thrombocytes are among the smallest cells in the blood of the fowl. (See Figure 1.) They show considerable variation in size, and their shape may vary from oval to round. The typical thrombocyte is oval, with a round nucleus in the center of a clear cytoplasm. A constant feature is the presence of one or more brightly red-stained granules at the poles of the cell. The chromatin of the nucleus is dense and is clumped into relatively large masses which are distinctly separated by the parachromatin.

Evidence from a number of sources suggests that they are cells belonging to the erythrocyte series. Blount (1939) states that a thrombocyte is an erythrocyte in which the process of hemoglobinization of the cell did not proceed to maturity. All stages of the erythroblast-thrombocyte series can be detected in smears prepared from the bone marrow.

HEMOGLOBIN

Hemoglobin is a complex compound; it is composed of a pigment, reduced heme, which is attached to a protein, globin. Heme is an iron-containing chromogen with the formula $C_{34}H_{32}O_4N_4Fe$. The iron gives the hemoglobin its color. The chromogen radical of the hemoglobins of different species is the same, but the globin fractions vary with the species. This is shown by the differences in crystalline structure of oxyhemoglobin of different species (Reichert and Brown, 1909).

The crystals of chicken oxyhemoglobin are orthorhombic, and the optical character is negative. Among the different species of birds studied, the hemoglobin crystals of the chicken and the quail resemble each other most, but the crystals of the guinea fowl are very different.

The amounts of hemoglobin (in percent) contained in the wet erythrocytes of various avian species are as follows:

Chicken	24.2	Kruger (see Wirth, 1931)
Duck	38.1	"
Goose	22.4	"
Turkey	23.5	"

There is some evidence that avian erythrocytes may contain more than one type of hemoglobin. This is discussed in Chapter 7.

The percentage composition of blood hemoglobin of the chicken and goose has been determined as follows (Hoppe-Seyler, from Reichert and Brown, 1909):

	C	*H*	*N*	*S*	*Fe*	O_2
Chicken blood	52.4	7.19	16.4	0.86	0.33	22.5
Goose blood	54.2	7.10	16.2	0.54	0.43	20.7

These figures are of about the same magnitude as those reported for most mammals.

Amounts of Hemoglobin

The amount of hemoglobin in chicken blood, as observed from the literature, is highly variable. Recent work has demonstrated that much of this variation may be attributed to the methods of determination. Many of the earlier workers used the Newcomer acid-hematin method, but since the erythrocytes of birds are nucleated, this causes a turbidity of the solution following treatment with acid and produces readings which usually are too high. A modification of the Newcomer acid-hematin method by which the blood is first hemolyzed with NH_4OH gives more reliable figures, since the turbidity is eliminated or minimized (Schultz and Elvehjem, 1934). Hunter, Stringer, and Weiss (1940) showed that in slightly acid solutions there is a retention of hemoglobin during osmotic hemolysis of erythrocytes.

The reliability of a number of different methods of determining hemoglobin in the chicken was tested by Bankowski (1942). He worked with chickens 42 to 56 days of age. The amount of hemoglobin in grams per 100 ml. of blood as determined by the various methods follows: (1) Dare, 7.7 grams; (2) Haden-Hauser, 7.8; (3) modified Newcomer, 9.7; (4) photelometric acid hematin, 9.8; (5) alkaline hematin, 12.1; and (6) Sheard-Sanford, 8.91. He stated that methods 3 and 4 were the most reliable.

Table 3. Hemoglobin values (grams percent) of normal chickens

Age	Male	Female	Method	Investigator
21 days	9.16	9.30	Modified Sahli (acid as hemolyzing agent)	Holmes *et al.* (1933)
42 "	9.70	9.60	"	"
63 "	9.70	9.70	"	"
84 "	10.10	9.70	"	"
Adult	13.50	9.80*	Acid hematin (corrected for turbidity)	Dukes & Schwarte (1931)
"	—	9.71*	Modified Newcomer	Bankowski (1942)
"	—	8.90*	"	Sturkie (1943)
"	—	8.90*	"	Schultze & Elvehjem (1936)
"	—	7.44*	Dare	Harmon (1936)
"	—	10.95†	"	"
"	11.76	9.11	Not given	Olson (1937)
"	—	8.00*	Determined Fe in blood	Winters (1936)
"	—	8.10†	"	"

* Laying.   † Nonlaying.

Rostorfer (1949) has shown that there is considerable variation in the density readings of acid hematin of duck blood. Readings at 450 mμ (millimicrons) showed much greater variation than at 410 mμ. He states that most of the determinations of earlier workers were made at wave lengths of 450 mμ., at which the density of acid hematin is somewhat variable. This may account for some of the variation in results obtained.

It is noted from Table 3 that, in chickens as young as 21 days old, hemoglobin almost reaches normal adult value. Cook (1937), who used the Dare method and who measured hemoglobin in chicks from 26 weeks of age to maturity, showed that the values ranged from 62.2 percent at 26 weeks to 67.1 percent at 138 weeks of age (100 percent equals 17 grams). The sex of his birds was not given. The values for adult males are higher than for females, as is expected, since the number of erythrocytes is higher for males.

The hemoglobin (Hb) values of normal small White Holland turkeys are shown in grams percent (Wolterink, Davidson, and Reineke, 1947) as follows:

Age (weeks)	1	4	8	12	16	20	24	28	32	40
Hb. (gm./100 ml.)	7.77	8.11	8.56	9.01	9.46	9.91	10.37	10.82	11.27	12.17

It is apparent that there is considerable variation in the amounts for birds of different ages, but no significant sex difference was observed.

Hemoglobin determinations have been made on a number of other avian species (see Groebbels, 1932; De Villiers, 1938; Olson, 1948), but in many cases, because of unreliable methods, the values are too high. For example, the figures reported by different investigators for pigeon blood are as follows: 10.6, 16.1, 15.2, 13.7, and 15.97 gm./100 ml.

Effect of rate of egg production on hemoglobin. Blood hemoglobin in nonlaying hens is higher than that in laying hens, according to Harmon (1936) and Maughan (1935), but Winters (1936) reported no difference in hemoglobin of laying and nonlaying birds. Schultze and Elvehjem (1936) stated that most of their birds were laying when the determinations were made, but some of them stopped laying and the hemoglobin did not change. Sturkie's results (unpublished) are similar to those of Schultze and Elvehjem.

LEUCOCYTES

Counting

Leucocyte counts of chicken blood and other bird species have been made by many investigators. Olson (1937 and 1948), Twisselmann (1939), and De Villiers (1938) have discussed and summarized the reports of various authors, including their own work. There is considerable variation in the number of the various cell types. Part of these discrepancies may be attributed to the method of making the count and, in many cases, to the small number of birds used.

Total leucocytes include all of the white cells, and counts upon these are made in a counting chamber as described for erythrocytes, except that the blood is usually diluted 1–100 instead of 1–200 before it is placed in the counting chamber. The determination of the total white cell count is attended with difficulty because the red cells are nucleated. Diluting fluids which are ordinarily used on mammalian blood and contain acetic acid to dissolve the red cells are unsatisfactory for bird blood because the stroma of the red cells contracts about the nuclei, making it impossible to discriminate these from some of the leucocytes. If a fluid such as

Toisson's solution is used, which preserves the red and white cells, then again it is difficult to distinguish with certainty between the thrombocytes and the small lymphocytes under the powers of magnification that can be used in conjunction with the counting chamber (De Villiers, 1938).

Several workers have used Toisson's fluid, but have generally found it unsatisfactory. Blain introduced a direct method for the purpose of staining the leucocytes differentially so that they could be counted. He used two solutions. Solution 1 contained neutral red, 1–5000, made up in Locke's solution, and Solution 2 contained 12 percent formalin, also made up in Locke's solution. Both were adjusted to a pH of 7.4 and kept at a temperature of 39°C. while in use. The blood was first mixed with the neutral red solution, and the other solution was then added. The white cells take up the neutral red, whereas the red cells do not. Some other workers, however, have found Blain's method not too satisfactory, since the distinction between the thrombocytes and the small lymphocytes is difficult. (For a review of these methods, see De Villiers, 1938, and also Olson, 1948.)

De Villiers, working on ostrich blood, and Olson (1937 and 1948), working with chicken blood, found Wiseman's stain to be satisfactory for making total leucocyte counts. This stain contains 95 cc. of Ringer's solution, 5 cc. of formalin, and 50 mg. of phloxine. This solution stains the granulocytes a bright red, and this is in contrast with the other cells which stain much less brilliantly. Olson (1937) found that Blain's method on chicken blood gave more consistent results for leucocytes than did Wiseman's method. De Villiers (1938) found Wiseman's fluid fairly satisfactory for ostrich blood. In his review of these methods, De Villiers states that there is no unanimity of opinion among the writers about the best method to use for total leucocyte count.

For the differential count, a number of stains are available, such as the May-Grunewald, Giemsa, Leishman's, Jenner's, Wright's and supravital techniques. According to Twisselmann (1939), the supravital techniques are more reliable because there are no unidentifiable, degenerated cells present, as occurs with Wright's stain. The monocytes can be unmistakably differentiated, and the staining of the cells is always of the same intensity. A comparison of the two methods by Twisselmann (1939) is included in Table 4.

De Villiers (1938) stated that staining with Wright's stain entails little work and the smear is usually ready for examination within 10 minutes. This stain, according to him, gave as good and as uniform results as any of the stains which he used and proved more satisfactory than some of them for the purpose of differentiating between the lymphocytes and monocytes. Olson (1948) seemed to prefer this stain for normal chicken blood, but stated that the May-Grunewald and Giemsa combinations have been found useful, especially with pathological blood.

Olson has shown that in differential counts the error in terms of coefficients of variability are: for the lymphocytes, 8.6 percent; heterophils, 27.9; eosinophils, 58.8; basophils, 62.6; and monocytes, 22.2. The coefficient of variability for total leucocytes was 34.2 percent, using phloxine as the stain.

Description of Cell Types

The description of the cell types which follows is mainly that of Olson (1937). See Figure 1.

Heterophils. This type of leucocyte in the blood of the fowl is sometimes designated polymorphonuclear-pseudo-eosinophilic granulocyte, but for the sake of brevity such cells may be designated as heterophils. This designation as heterophils is also made for the sake of clarity in order to avoid the confusion associated with use of the term "pseudo-eosinophil." In man and in certain other mammals such as the dog, these leucocytes possess neutral-staining granules. In rabbits and birds, the granules of these leucocytes are acid in reaction. The term heterophil then would imply the variableness of the staining reaction of this group of cells in the various species of animals.

The heterophils in the blood of the chicken are usually round and have a diameter of approximately 10 to 15 microns. The characteristic feature of these cells is the presence of many rod-shaped or spindle-shaped acidophilic crystalline bodies in the cytoplasm. Frequently, in routinely stained smears, these cytoplasmic bodies are distorted, and they may then be variable in shape. In cases of such distortion the color reaction must be used as a criterion for their distinction. The bodies are distinct and usually dull red,

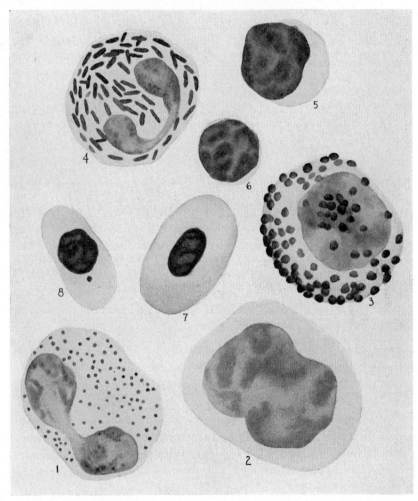

Figure 1. Drawing of mature blood cells of the bird.

　1, eosinophil; 2, monocyte; 3, basophil; 4, heterophil; 5 and 6, large and small lymphocytes; 7, erythrocyte; 8, thrombocyte.

against a background of colorless cytoplasm. The nucleus is poly-morphic with varying degrees of lobulation.

　Eosinophils. Polymorphonuclear eosinophilic granulocytes are of about the same size as the heterophils. They represent the group of true eosinophils in bird's blood. The granules are spherical and relatively large. Their color is brilliant red as compared to the dull red of the heterophil when stained with Wright's stain. The cytoplasm has a faint, yet distinct bluish gray tint. The nucleus is often bilobed and is of a richer blue than that of the heterophil.

Some believe that the heterophil and eosinophil represent modified forms of the same group, but Olson (1937 and 1948) thinks that these cells have different lineages.

Basophils. Polymorphonuclear basophilic granulocytes are about the same size and shape as the heterophils. The nucleus is weakly basophilic in reaction and round or oval in shape; at times it may be lobulated. The cytoplasm is abundant and contains large, deeply staining basophilic granules.

Lymphocytes. The lymphocytes constitute the majority of the leucocytes in the blood of the fowl. There is a wide range in the size and shape of these cells. The cytoplasm is usually weakly basophilic. It may consist of a narrow rim bordering one side of the nucleus, as in the case of the smaller lymphocytes, or it may constitute the major portion of the cell, as in the larger lymphocytes. The nucleus is usually round and may have a small indentation. There is usually a fairly coarse pattern of chromatin. In some instances, however, the chromatin is fine and is not distinctly separated by the parachromatin. Sometimes a few nonspecific azure granules are seen in the cytoplasm.

Monocytes. The monocytes in the blood of the fowl are sometimes difficult to identify and to distinguish from large lymphocytes because there are transitional forms from one to the other. In general, the monocytes are large cells with relatively more cytoplasm than the large lymphocytes. The cytoplasm of these cells has a blue-gray tint. The nucleus is usually irregular in outline. The nuclear pattern in the monocyte is of a more delicate composition than in the lymphocyte. Chromatin appears in monocytes in strands rather than in blocks.

Number of Leucocytes

Counts of leucocytes and thrombocytes for different species of birds are shown in Table 4. In most cases, the smears for the differential counts were stained with Wright's stain. Twisselmann (1939) showed that the supravital technique is more reliable for the

Table 4. Number of leucocytes and thrombocytes in bird blood

Species, Age, and Sex	Numbers in thousands		Differential count (percent)					Author
	Leuco-cytes	Thrombo-cytes	Lympho-cytes	Hetero-phils	Eosino-phils	Baso-phils	Mono-cytes	
Chicken, adult male	19.8	25.4	59.1	27.2	1.9	1.7	10.2	Olson (1937)
Chicken, (nonlaying) female	19.8	26.5	64.6	22.8	1.9	1.7	8.9	
Chicken, young, 2–21 weeks, males and females	29.4	32.7	66.0	20.9	1.9	3.1	8.1	
Chicken, White Leghorn, 6 weeks to maturity, males and females —*supravital*	32.6	—	40.9	35.6	2.7	4.3	16.5	Twisselmann (1939)
Wright's	—	—	54.0	27.8	1.5	2.7	13.7	
Chicken, average, all ages	30.4	—	73.3	15.1		2.7	6.3	Cook (1937)
Chicken, 5–10 weeks, males	—	—	69.5	20.4	1.3	3.3	3.7	Goff et al. (1953)
Ostrich, males and females	21.05	10.5	26.8	59.1	6.3	4.7	3.0	De Villiers (1938)
Turkey, adult	—	—	50.6	43.4	0.9	3.2	1.9	Johnson & Lange (1933)
Duck	23.4	30.7	61.7	24.3	2.1	1.5	10.8	Magath & Higgins (1934)
Pigeon A.M.	13.0	—	65.6	23.0	2.2	2.6	6.6	Shaw (1933)
P.M.	18.5	—	47.8	42.8	1.9	2.4	5.1	

reasons already given and that the number of lymphocytes is higher and heterophils lower with Wright's stain. The variation between species for total leucocyte count appears to be no greater than that reported within species (chicken). In all species except the ostrich, the percentage of lymphocytes is higher than for any other cell type, comprising from 40 to 70 percent of the total count, and the heterophils are the second most numerous group. In the ostrich the reverse is true, with the heterophils comprising 60 percent and the lymphocytes 27 percent of the total count. The significance of this difference is not known (De Villiers).

Some of the workers found no differences attributable to sex, and their figures are grouped. Olson (1937) did find differences due to sex. The mean percentage of lymphocytes for adult females (chicken) was significantly higher than for males, but the number of heterophils was higher for the male. The mean percentage for the monocytes was slightly higher for the male, but of borderline significance. The adult females were not laying.

Effects of age. In young chickens, Olson (1937) found no sex or age differences in the counts, and neither did Twisselmann (1939). Cook (1937), studying White Leghorn chickens from 26 to 183 days of age, indicated that there is little variation due to age or sex.

Table 5. Effect of riboflavin deficiency on the differential leucocyte count of White Leghorn cockerels, 52 to 66 days of age (Goff, Russell, and Taylor, 1953)

Cell types	Percent			
	Group 1	Group 2	Group 3	Group 4
Heterophils	36.7	36.7	19.8	20.4
Eosinophils	1.7	0.6	0.8	1.3
Basophils	4.1	4.2	4.9	3.3
Myelocytes	0.3	0.0	0.4	0.0
Lymphocytes	52.3	53.0	69.3	69.5
Monocytes	3.2	4.5	2.8	3.7

Groups 1 and 2, deficient in riboflavin ($\frac{1}{3}$ and $\frac{1}{2}$ minimum requirements). Groups 3 and 4, adequate riboflavin.

Effects of diet. While the work of Cook suggested that diet influences the leucocyte count, the data are not conclusive. Recent work by Goff, Russell, and Taylor (1953) shows conclusively how a specific nutrient of the diet, namely riboflavin, influences the differential count of chickens. Their results are shown in Table 5. The data demonstrate conclusively that a deficiency of riboflavin increases significantly the heterophils and decreases the lymphocytes.

Lance and Hogan (1948) showed that turkey poults fed a diet deficient in folic acid were anemic and had decreased leucocyte counts, including a decrease in lymphocytes, heterophils, basophils, monocytes, and thrombocytes. When the diet was deficient in inositol, the total leucocyte count was also decreased.

Effects of environment. Very little experimental work has been conducted with regard to the effects upon leucocyte count of changes in management exclusive of ration. Olson's studies indicate that more work should be conducted along these lines. He showed that when adult birds were reared in batteries within a building, where there was little or no exposure to the elements, their total leucocyte counts were lower than for chickens reared outside. For the birds raised indoors, the leucocyte count was 17,000, and for those raised outside, 23,600. He states, however, that there was no difference with regard to percentage of lymphocytes, heterophils, eosinophils, or basophils. The percentage of monocytes for the birds raised outdoors (11.9 percent) was higher than for those raised indoors (7.6 percent). This difference, however, does not account for the differences observed in total counts.

Effects of hormones, drugs, and X-rays. It is known that epinephrine, adrenal cortical extract (ACE), and adrenocorticotrophic hormone (ACTH) and some other substances when injected into certain mammals may cause a decrease in the number of lymphocytes (lymphopenia) and eosinophils (eosinopenia) in the circulating blood. Shapiro and Schechtman (1949) reported that a single injection of ACE in the adult fowl causes a transient lymphopenia and leucocytosis. The increase was mainly in the heterophils. Weller and Schechtman (1949) also found that when ACE (0.2 to 0.6 cc.) is injected in chick embryos at 13 to 15 days of incubation, the number of lymphocytes is not changed significantly, but there is a marked increase (about 3 times) in the number of poly-morphonuclear cells. There was no effect upon the red cells.

Stamler, Bolene, Katz, Harris, and Pick (1950) injected ACTH for a 5-day period into chicks and reported no effect upon the number of eosinophils.

Denning, Meschan, Keith, and Day (1950) demonstrated that X-radiation decreased the leucocyte count in hens from 29,500 to 13,000. When urethane was injected, the count dropped to 9,400. The X-ray treatments reduced respiration, choline oxidase, and succinoxidase in the bone marrow.

Leucocytosis and Disease

Various diseases in man and animals produce an increase in leucocytes of the blood. In the chicken, the disease leukemia results in an increase in the number of leucocytes (leucocytosis). The increase is mainly in the number of lymphocytes and immature cells of the lymphocyte series. Pullorum and typhoid also produce leucocytosis (see Olson, 1948). Jungherr (1948) has demonstrated in blue comb, or pullet disease of chickens, that there is a moderate increase in total leucocytes and a relative and absolute increase in the number of monocytes. Since there is considerable variation in the blood picture of the normal fowl, caution should be exercised before attributing changes in the blood picture to disease.

COAGULATION AND PHYSICAL CHARACTERISTICS OF BLOOD

Bainbridge and Menzies (1919) stated that the blood of birds contains no platelets and will not clot if it is drawn directly from a blood vessel without contact with the tissues. De Villiers (1938) found also that the coagulation time of ostrich blood was prolonged and sometimes failed to clot. Chicken blood contains no platelets, but it clots readily. According to Dukes (1947), the coagulation time is $4\frac{1}{2}$ minutes, and Johnson and Connor (1933) found it to vary from 1 to 14 minutes, with an average of 6 minutes. Calcium is necessary for the coagulation of bird's blood, as it is for the mammal, but little else is known about the clotting mechanism in birds. It is thought by some that the thrombocyte figures in the process in birds, but this has not been proven.

Osmotic Pressure

The osmotic pressure of bird's blood is approximately the same as that of mammals. In terms of equivalent concentrations of NaCl, chicken blood has an osmotic pressure of 0.93 (Korr, 1939; see Chapter 13), and ostrich blood, about 0.90 (De Villiers). The pressure exerted by the colloids of chicken blood (mainly by plasma proteins) ranges from 11 to 12 mm. Hg.

Table 6. Specific gravity of blood of birds

Species	Whole blood	Plasma	Serum	Author
Chicken	1.064	—	—	Reichert & Brown (1909)
Chicken (adult female)	1.050	1.0190	—	Sturkie (1947)
Chicken	1.054	—	1.023	Wirth (1931)
Goose	1.050	—	1.021	"
Duck	1.056	—	1.020	"
Guinea Fowl	1.057	—	1.021	"
Ostrich	1.063	1.022	—	De Villiers (1938)

Viscosity and Specific Gravity

Wirth (1931), quoting Kruger, stated that the viscosity of chicken serum is 1.4 and that of duck serum 1.24, but he gave no figures for plasma or whole blood. The figure for the ostrich (whole blood) is 4.5 (De Villiers).

The specific gravity of bird blood is shown in Table 6.

REFERENCES

Bainbridge, F. A., and J. A. Menzies 1919 Essentials of Physiology. 3d ed., p. 187. Longmans, Green and Co., London.

Bankowski, R. A. 1942 Studies of the hemoglobin content of chicken blood and evaluation of methods for its determination. Am. J. Vet. Res. 3:373.

Barcroft, J. 1925 The significance of hemoglobin in sub-mammalian forms of life. Physiol. Rev. 5:596.

Blount, W. P. 1939 Thrombocyte formation in the domestic hen. Vet. J. 95:195.

Common, R. H., W. A. Rutledge, and W. Bolton 1947 The influence of gonadal hormones on the serum riboflavin and certain other properties of blood and tissues in the domestic fowl. J. Endocrinol. 5:121.

Cook, S. F. 1937 A study of the blood picture of poultry and its diagnostic significance. Poultry Sci. 16:291.

Davis, J. E., A. W. McCullough, and R. H. Rigdon 1945 Polycythemia produced by cobalt in the duck: A hematologic and pathologic study. J. Lab. & Clin. Med. 30:327.

Denning, J. S., I. Meschan, C. K. Keith, and P. L. Day 1950 Effects of X-irradiation and urethane treatment on chicken bone marrow. Proc. Soc. Exp. Biol. & Med. 74:776.

De Villiers, O. T. 1938 Blood of ostrich. Onderstepoort J. Vet. Sci. 11:419.

Domm, L. V., and E. Taber 1946 Endocrine factors controlling erythrocyte concentration in the blood of the domestic fowl. Physiol. Zool. 19:258.

Dukes, H. H. 1947 The Physiology of Domestic Animals. 6th ed. Comstock Publishing Co., Ithaca, N.Y.

Dukes, H. H., and L. H. Schwarte 1931 The hemoglobin content of the blood of fowls. Am. J. Physiol. 96:89.

Goff, S., W. C. Russell, and M. W. Taylor 1953 Hematology of the chick in vitamin deficiencies. I: Riboflavin. Poultry Sci. 32:54.

Groebbels, F. 1932 Der Vogel. Erster Band: Atmungswelt und Nahrungswelt. Verlag von Gebrüder Borntraeger, Berlin.

Harmon, I. W. 1936 Hemoglobin regulation in chickens. Poultry Sci. 15:53.

Harmon, I. W., E. Ogden, and S. F. Cook 1932 The reservoir function of the spleen in fowls. Am. J. Physiol. 100:99.

Hart, E. B., C. A. Elvehjem, and A. R. Kemmerer 1930 Does the practical chick ration need iron and copper additions to insure normal hemoglobin building? Poultry Sci. 9:92.

Hevesy, G., and J. Ottesen 1945 Life-cycle of the red corpuscles of the hen. Nature (London) 156:534.

Holmes, A. D., M. G. Pigott, and P. A. Campbell 1933 The hemoglobin content of chicken blood. J. Biol. Chem. 103:657.

Hunter, F. R., L. D. Stringer, and H. D. Weiss 1940 Partial retention of hemoglobin by chicken erythrocytes. J. Cell. & Comp. Physiol. 16:123.

Johnson, E. P., and B. V. Connor 1933 Blood studies of fowls with various forms of lymphomatosis. J. Am. Vet. Med. Assoc. 83:325.

Johnson, E. P., and C. J. Lange   1939   Blood alterations and typhlo-hepatitis of turkeys with notes on the disease. J. Parasit. 25:157.

Jordan, H. E.   1939   The lymphocytes in relation to erythrocyte production. Anat. Record 73:227.

Juhn, M., and L. V. Domm   1930   The relation of gonadal condition to erythrocyte number in fowls. Am. J. Physiol. 94:656.

Jungherr, E.   1948   Avian monocytosis, Chapter 29 in Biester and Schwarte, Diseases of Poultry. 2d ed. Iowa State College Press, Ames.

Klemperer, P.   1938   Handbook of Hematology. III. Paul B. Hoeber, Inc., New York.

Krumbhaar, E. B.   1928   The erythrocyte. Cowdry's Special Cytology 1:275. Paul B. Hoeber, Inc., New York.

Lance, B. G., and A. G. Hogan   1948   Inositol and nicotinic acid in the nutrition of the turkey. J. Nutrition 36:369.

Magath, T. B., and G. M. Higgins   1934   The blood of the normal duck. Folia Haematol. 51:230.

Maughan, G. H.   1935   Hemoglobin studies in chickens. Am. J. Physiol. 113:96.

Melampy, R. M.   1948   Cytochemical studies on the chicken erythrocyte. I: Amino acid content and distribution. J. Biol. Chem. 175:589.

Newell, G. W., and C. S. Shaffner   1950   Blood volume determinations in chickens. Poultry Sci. 29:78.

Olson, C.   1937   Variations in the cells and hemoglobin content in the blood of the normal domestic chicken. Cornell Vet. 27:235.

Olson, C.   1948   Avian hematology, Chapter 4 in Biester and Schwarte, Diseases of Poultry. 2d ed. Iowa State College Press, Ames.

Reichert, E. T., and A. P. Brown   1909   The Crystallography of the Hemoglobins. Carnegie Institution of Washington, Publication 116.

Riddle, O., and P. F. Braucher   1934   Hemoglobin and erythrocyte differences according to sex and season in doves and pigeons. Am. J. Physiol. 108:554.

Rostorfer, H. H.   1949   Comparison of methods of measurement of avian hemoglobins. J. Biol. Chem. 180:90.

Schultze, M. O., and C. A. Elvehjem   1934   An improved method for the determination of hemoglobin in chicken blood. J. Biol. Chem. 105:253.

Schultze, M. O., C. A. Elvehjem, E. B. Hart, and J. G. Halpin   1936   The hemoglobin content of blood of laying hens on practical poultry rations. Poultry Sci. 15:9.

Shapiro, A. B., and A. M. Schechtman   1949   Effect of adrenal cortical extract on the blood picture and serum proteins of fowl. Proc. Soc. Exp. Biol. & Med. 70:440.

Shaw, A. F. B. 1933 The leucocytes of pigeons with special reference to diurnal rhythm. J. Path. & Bacteriol. 37:411.

Stamler, J., C. Bolene, L. N. Katz, R. Harris, and R. Pick 1950 Influence of pancreatectomy on lipid metabolism and atherogenesis in the chicken. Fed. Proc. 9:121.

Sturkie, P. D. 1943 Reputed reservoir function of the spleen of the domestic fowl. Am. J. Physiol. 138:599.

Sturkie, P. D. 1947 Effects of hypothermia upon the specific gravity and proteins of the blood of chickens. Am. J. Physiol. 148:610.

Sturkie, P. D., and H. J. Newman 1951 Plasma proteins of chickens as influenced by time of laying, ovulation, number of blood samples taken, and plasma volume. Poultry Sci. 30:240.

Twisselmann, N. M. 1939 A study of the cell content of blood of normal chickens with supra-vital stains. Poultry Sci. 18:151.

Weller, E. M., and A. M. Schechtman 1949 Effect of adrenal cortex extract on blood cells of the embryonic chick. Proc. Soc. Exp. Biol. & Med. 72:370.

Winters, A. R. 1936 Influence of egg production and other factors on iron content of chicken blood. Poultry Sci. 15:252.

Wirth, D. 1931 Grundlage einer klinischen Haematologie der Haustiere. Urban & Schwarzenberg, Berlin.

Wolterink, L. F., J. A. Davidson, and E. P. Reineke 1947 Hemoglobin levels in the blood of Beltsville small white poults. Poultry Sci. 26:559 (Abs.)

CHAPTER 2

Chemical Constituents
of the Blood

Normal Values

THERE is considerable variation in the values reported by different workers for the various constituents of the blood of birds. Shimer (1937), who studied the blood chemical constituents of normal and paralytic chickens, also compiled the values reported by a number of investigators. This compilation includes glucose, nonprotein nitrogen, urea nitrogen, uric acid, creatine and creatinine, calcium, phosphorus, chlorides, potassium, and alkali reserve. The conditions under which the determinations were made are given in some cases. In most cases this information is lacking. Shimer's table has been modified slightly by omitting determinations made on four or less birds, and some values of other workers have been added.

Inspection of Table 7 indicates that no well-defined limits have as yet been established for some of the constituents of the blood of healthy, normal adult chickens. The wide range noted for most of the constituents seems to be dependent upon a number of factors that have not been taken into account by most workers. Among these factors are (1) age, (2) sex, (3) state of health, (4) state of egg production, (5) type of food consumed, (6) time of last feeding, and (7) method of determinations. The data given in the table pertain to the female in most cases, but the ages of the birds were not always indicated, nor their state of egg production.

Table 7. Chemical constituents of chicken blood as reported in the literature (from Shimer, 1937, with omissions and additions), expressed as milligrams per 100 ml. of whole blood unless otherwise stated

Glucose	Nitrogen		Uric acid	Creatine	Total calcium serum		Phosphorus		NaCl	K	Author
	Non-protein	Urea			Non-laying	Laying	Total plasma	Inorganic serum		a—whole blood b—serum	
	61.6		2.78	1.85							Thompson & Powers
213.2	39.1		4.49	1.45							Thompson & Carr
259.4	18.4		5.31	1.01				3.43	429.6		Horvath
280.4	32.0		4.80	1.23				4.81			Horvath (serum)
139.1	28.8	5.38	2.47	1.10	9.9			3.96	487.6		Hayden
173.0	44.0	5.60	6.39	1.21					461.0		Braucher*
157.0	36.0		4.20	1.30			13.0	4.60	563.0	164a; 22b	Dyer & Roe†
161.6	16.9	1.96	5.20								Gonzago
179.2‡	25.8‡	3.23‡	2.84‡	0.83‡		23.9‡		8.05‡	471.3‡		Hayden & Sampson
	32.0	8.00	4.90								Folin & Denis
171 & 177	38.5 & 36.2	19.6 & 19.1									Hermann (serum) young and old birds
					11.8	21.5					Taylor & Russell
					12.0	25.1					Correll & Hughes
		.5, .7, 1.2‡									Howell
					12.0	24.0	15.3	3.85			Heller et al.
192.9	41.8	7.01	8.08	1.29	17.1				479.0		Shimer§, ‖
	35.0	2.40	3.20	0.90					376.0		Heller & Pursell
										3.9b#	Hunter

* Creatine and creatinine, 4.02.
† Alkali reserve 42.0, pH 7.36.
‡ Laying.
§ Alkali reserve 58.6, pH 7.52.
‖ Creatine and creatinine, 4.91.
Milliequivalents.

Effects of Age and Laying on Chemical Constituents

Significant changes in blood calcium, in lipids, and in certain phosphorus fractions occur preceding and during ovulation of birds. These changes are due principally to the action of estrogen and are discussed further in Chapters 18 and 20.

Calcium, phosphorus. The total calcium of the blood includes a fraction that is filterable or diffusible and a nonfilterable or nondiffusible fraction. The filterable fraction is mainly inorganic calcium. The nonfilterable fraction includes an adsorbable fraction, probably colloidal calcium phosphate, and a nonadsorbable calcium bound to protein, according to those workers using the $BaSO_4$ adsorption technique (Benjamin and Hess, 1933; Heller, Paul, and Thompson, 1934; and others). These workers also reported an adsorbable filterable calcium phosphate fraction. The validity of the $BaSO_4$ technique has been questioned, however, by other investigators. Greenberg and Larson (1935) doubt the true existence of the filterable adsorbable calcium phosphate, and McDonald and Riddle (1945) state that it is impossible to distinguish between the protein-bound and the nonfilterable adsorbable fraction because there is a partial adsorption with $BaSO_4$ of the nonfilterable fraction rather than a complete adsorption of one or more specific fractions (see also Laskowski, 1935; Riddle, 1942; Gardner and Pfeiffer, 1943).

The increase in blood calcium just prior to and coincident with ovulation and laying is mainly in the nondiffusible or bound fraction, there being little or no change in diffusible or inorganic fraction (Heller, Paul, and Thompson, 1934; Greenberg, Larson, Pearson, and Burmester, 1936; McDonald and Riddle, 1945). The changes with age and laying in the calcium fractions of the blood of the chicken are shown in Figure 2. Similar results were obtained in the pigeon by MacDonald and Riddle, except that after ovulation of the second egg of the clutch there was a slight drop in these fractions, which had shown a marked increase subsequent to and during ovulation of the first egg of the clutch.

Coincident with laying there is also an increase in the protein-bound phosphorus, lipid phosphorus, and colloidal calcium phosphate of the blood, but no appreciable change in inorganic phosphorus in the pigeon (McDonald and Riddle, 1945) or in the

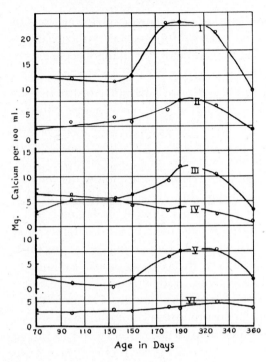

Figure 2. Changes with age and laying in calcium fractions in chicken serum.

I, total calcium; II, protein-bound calcium; III, adsorbable (includes IV and V); IV, adsorbable, filterable; V, adsorbable, nonfilterable; VI, ionized remainder (inorganic). The sharp rises in the curves precede slightly or coincide with ovulation and laying, and the drops, with cessation of laying or molting. (Modified from Heller, Paul, and Thompson, *J. Biol. Chem.*, 1934.)

chicken (Heller, Paul, and Thompson, 1934). See Figure 3. Greenberg, Larson, Pearson, and Burmester (1936), however, claimed there is a drop in inorganic phosphorus with laying.

Rochlina (1934), who made blood calcium determinations on the same laying birds three times per day, indicated that calcium tended to increase at noon and decrease in the afternoon. Since it

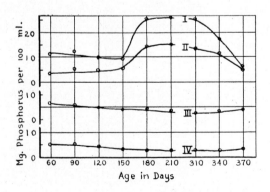

Figure 3. Phosphorus fractions in chicken serum.

I, total phosphorus; II, lipid phosphorus; III, inorganic; IV, acid soluble phosphorus. The sharp rises in the curves coincide with laying, and the drops, with cessation of laying or molting. (Modified from Heller, Paul, and Thompson, *J. Biol. Chem.*, 1934.)

has been demonstrated by Sturkie and Newman (1951) that an increase in blood volume and hemodilution occurs with successive blood sampling, it is possible that some of the changes reported by Rochlina are due to this factor.

Blood lipids. The blood lipids comprise a number of fractions—cholesterol, phospholipids, neutral fat, and fatty acids. Most of these are much higher in the blood of laying females than in that of nonlaying females or males, and the higher levels are due to the release of estrogen from the ovary of the laying bird (see Chapter 18). The lipid fractions of mature males and nonlaying females are of about the same magnitude, but the total lipids and total fatty acids of laying birds are 3 to 5 times those of nonlaying females or males (Table 8). The phospholipids are 2 to 3 times higher, and the residual fatty acids, 7 to 11 times higher in the laying bird. Neutral fat also increases greatly with laying (Lorenz, Entenman, and Chaikoff, 1938; Walker, Taylor, and Russell, 1951). Cholesterol changes little with age and egg production. The correlation between the individual lipid constituents and total lipids is shown in Figure 4. Phospholipids and neutral fat of the blood of laying hens constitute approximately 30 and 62 percent of the total lipids respectively, and total cholesterol averages 7 percent of the total lipids (Walker, Taylor, and Russell, 1951).

The dietary level of fat has little or no influence on most of the lipid constituents. Hermann (1946a) reported figures for total

Table 8. Blood lipids of the fowl in milligrams per 100 ml. of whole blood (Lorenz *et al.*, 1938) and plasma (Walker *et al.*, 1951)

Sex	Cholesterol			Total fatty acids	Phospho-lipids	Total lipids	Residual fatty acids	Neu-tral fat
	Total	Free	Ester or com-bined					
Males	114	92	22	314	299	428	99	15
Females, immature	117	83	35	329	282	446	115	47
Females, laying	125	109	16	1564	642	1689	1122	922
	101.4*	82	18.7	989	363	1253	—	767

* Plasma. Figures in this line from Walker *et al.*

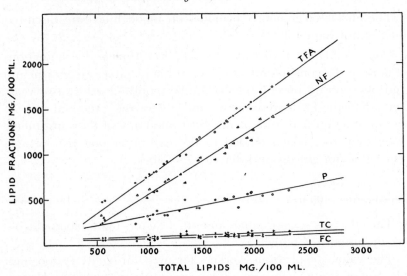

Figure 4. Correlation between individual lipid constituents and total lipids of the serum of the laying hen.

TFA, total fatty acids; NF, neutral fat; P, phospholipids; TC, total cholesterol; FC, free cholesterol. (Modified from Walker, Taylor, and Russell, *Poultry Sci.*, 1951.)

cholesterol of 217 and 248 mg./100 ml. for the serum of immature chickens and old hens. These figures are somewhat higher than those reported by others. When the chickens were fed 0.5 gram of choline daily, in addition to a complete ration, for 4 to 10 weeks, total cholesterol decreased to 179 mg./100 ml. in the blood and also decreased in the tissues, particularly in the aorta, heart, and liver.

Similar increases in the blood lipids of ducks and pigeons have been reported. The relationship of lipid level to reproductive cycle in the pigeon follows (Riddle, 1942):

	Neutral fat *mg./100 ml.* *serum*
Resting stage (more than 108 hours before ovulation)	470
Preovulation (108 hours before ovulation)	800
Preovulation (48 hours before ovulation)	2950
Ovulation	2200
Postovulation (65 hours)	570

The effects of gonadal hormones on blood lipids are discussed further in Chapter 17.

Other constituents. Heller and Pursell (1937) made determinations of most of the constituents shown in Shimer's table, except calcium and phosphorus, on chickens from one month of age to two years and when the birds were laying and not laying. Age and state of egg production had little or no effect upon any of the constituents except glucose, which tended to decrease after one year of age. The values for glucose at different ages follow:

Age in months	1	3	6	9	12	15	18
Glucose (mg./100 ml.)	231	235	211	227	196	186	183

The effects of sex hormones and other factors upon blood glucose are discussed in Chapter 12.

The values of previous workers for urea nitrogen are too high because of faulty techniques of determination, according to Howell (1939), whose values are shown in Table 7. Birds suffering from paralysis, tumors, parasites, and respiratory disorders have increased amounts of urea nitrogen in the blood (Howell).

Effects of Diet, Breed, and Disease

Shimer (1937) reported no difference in nonprotein nitrogen and uric acid of the blood of chickens fed high and low protein diets, and Hermann (1946b) found no difference in these constituents between young birds and old hens. Fritz, according to Shimer, studied the effects of time of feeding and starvation on nonprotein nitrogen of the blood and found that these factors accounted for little of the variation observed. Shimer showed no difference in the chemical constituents of blood of normal birds and those afflicted with paralysis and cannibalism and no difference among the different breeds which he studied, namely White Leghorn, Barred Plymouth Rock, New Hampshire, and crossbreds.

Chickens suffering from blue comb or pullet disease have higher than average amounts of nonprotein nitrogen (26.8 mg. percent) and uric acid (18.9 mg.) in the blood, according to Jungherr (1948). The values for phosphorus, magnesium, and glucose were normal. The values for calcium and chlorides were low. In birds severely affected, serum potassium was subnormal, but the amount in whole blood was high.

BLOOD PROTEINS

Whole blood contains albumin, globulin, and fibrinogen. These constituents may be separated or fractionated by appropriate chemical techniques. The albumins and globulins comprise a number of fractions which can be differentiated by electrophoretic analysis. Plasma contains albumin, globulin, and fibrinogen, but serum lacks fibrinogen.

Electrophoretic Analysis of Blood Proteins

The ions of the different fractions of albumin and globulin have different mobilities, and the lighter, more highly charged ions migrate faster; after a period of time the various protein ions present will be distributed in proportion to their mobilities. By suitable optical methods the patterns of distribution can be photographed

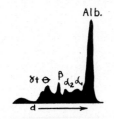

Figure 5. Electrophoretic pattern (descending, d) of chicken plasma.

Alb., albumin; α_1 and α_2, alpha$_1$ and alpha$_2$ globulins; β, beta globulin; θ, fibrinogen; γ, gamma globulin. (Modified from Sanders, Huddleson, and Schaible, *J. Biol. Chem.*, 1944.)

and the areas determined (see Hawk, Oser, and Summerson, 1947). Figure 5 is an electrophoretic pattern of chicken blood.

Deutsch and Goodloe (1945), who also studied electrophoretic patterns of chicken blood, stated that males and females exhibit slightly different patterns. In the male, alpha globulin appears as a more distinct entity than in the female. According to Brandt, Clegg, and Andrews (1951), laying birds exhibit a component not shown by nonlaying females or males, namely a fast-moving one, which moves ahead of the albumin. Fibrinogen could not consistently be detected or separated in electrophoretic patterns by Deutsch and Goodloe or by Sanders, Huddleson, and Schaible (1944).

Normal Values

A number of investigators have reported total plasma proteins, but fewer have studied the individual components—albumin, globulin, and fibrinogen. Howe (1925) in his review stated that much of

Table 9. Serum and plasma proteins of avian blood in grams per 100 ml.

Species, age, sex, and condition	Total proteins	Albumin	Globulin	A/G	Investigator
Chicken (2 birds)	3.60	1.82	1.78	1.02	Howe (1925)
Chicken	4.83	1.95	2.86	0.68	Chorine (1938)
Hens	3.28*	1.48	1.83	0.80	Dyer & Roe (1934)
Hens, White Leghorn (laying 50–70%)	4.64*	2.15	2.48	0.86	Sturkie & Newman (1951)
Hens (laying)	5.18*	2.50	2.67	0.93	"
Hens (laying)	5.32*	2.53	2.79	0.90	"
Hens (nonlaying for 2 mos.)	5.34*	2.00	3.34	0.60	"
Cocks, White Leghorn, 18 mos.	4.00	1.66	2.33	0.71	"
Cocks	5.00	—	—	—	Rochlina (1934)
Hens (laying)	5.60	—	—	—	"
Hens, White Leghorn	5.30–6.10	—	—	—	Hermann (1946a)
Hens (laying)	4.20	—	—	—	Greenberg et al. (1936)
Hens (nonlaying)	3.80	—	—	—	"
Numida meleagris (guinea hen)	2.82	—	—	—	Defalco (1942)
Anser anser (goose)	3.94	—	—	—	"
Turkey	3.95	—	—	—	"
Anas platyrhynchos (duck)	3.50	—	—	—	"
Phasianus colchicus (pheasant)	2.80	—	—	—	"
Turkey buzzard	2.94	—	—	—	"
Pelican	3.20	—	—	—	"
Pigeon	2.30	1.38	0.95	1.50	Mandel et al. (1947a)
Pigeon	2.75–3.62*	—	—	—	McDonald & Riddle (1945)

* Plasma proteins.

the earlier work on proteins of chicken blood is unreliable because of faulty techniques. Table 9 represents a compilation of later data on the blood proteins of birds. Methods used include the Kjeldahl method, calculation of total proteins from refractive index, specific gravity, and the biuret method. Dyer and Roe (1934), Howe (1925), Chorine (1938), and Defalco (1942) used the Kjeldahl method, admittedly the most reliable for nitrogen determination. Sturkie and Newman (1951) used the biuret method and found it quite reliable when compared with the Kjeldahl. The agreement between the two methods was within 0.1 gram percent. Obviously the methods of determination do not account for all of the observed variation in values reported.

Factors Causing Variation in Plasma Proteins

The plasma proteins of males are lower than those of females (Rochlina, 1934; Sturkie and Newman, 1951; Brandt, Clegg, and Andrews, 1951), and this suggests that gonadal hormones are involved. Experiments designed to test the effects of the male sex hormone (androgen) on plasma proteins in the fowl have not been made. Brandt, Clegg, and Andrews fractionated the proteins by the salting-out method and reported that total serum proteins of chickens increase with age and that the increase is in the alpha and gamma globulin fractions, with little change in the albumin. Thus the A/G (albumin-globulin) ratio decreased from 0.96 for the chicks to 0.52 for laying hens. This ratio for hens is much lower than that of previous workers. The mean for total proteins of 4-month-old nonlaying hens was 4.49 grams percent, and for the layers 5.40. The means were based on a small number of observations, and the variation was great.

The data of Greenberg, Larson, Pearson, and Burmester (1936), based upon a small number of hens, indicate that total proteins are slightly higher in laying females, but the difference is of questionable significance. Rochlina (1934) reported that plasma proteins are 25 to 60 percent lower on the day that hens lay, suggesting a relationship between mobilization of albumin for egg formation and level of protein in the blood.

Sturkie and Newman (1951) were unable to confirm the results of Rochlina, nor did they find a significant difference in the plasma proteins of laying and nonlaying adult females. They determined plasma proteins of birds on the day that the birds laid only, laid and ovulated, ovulated only, and neither laid nor ovulated. The differences in all cases were not significant. Considerable variation existed between the different groups of laying birds. The plasma proteins of some of these were as high as the nonlayers, which were out of production for about two months. Moreover, plasma proteins were determined on the laying birds about the time of ovulation for most birds (9 A.M.), at the time the albumin is being secreted (11 A.M. to 12 noon), and at approximately the time the egg had reached the uterus (3 to 4 P.M.). There were no differences that could be related to time of ovulation or laying, but there was a progressive decrease in plasma proteins with successive blood samples, as was shown by Rochlina (1934), who believed that this indicated a diurnal rhythm in the formation of blood proteins. When the first blood samples were taken in the afternoon and the second samples the following morning, there was also a significant decrease in proteins (Sturkie and Newman). It was shown later that the changes were due to changes in blood volume rather than to changes in rate of formation or destruction of proteins. (See Chapter 3.)

It thus appears that the amount of estrogen normally present in the blood of adult sexually mature female chickens either laying or nonlaying does not affect the protein content of the blood appreciably. Sturkie (1951) has shown that massive doses of estrogen must be administered to hens before the plasma proteins are altered, as follows:

	Total proteins			Albumin			Globulin		
	Control birds	Dienestrol		Control birds	Dienestrol		Control birds	Dienestrol	
		0.02	0.04		0.02	0.04		0.02	0.04
Mean	5.13	5.50	8.39	1.94	2.10	3.20	3.20	3.39	5.20

The estrogen (dienestrol), given at the 0.02 percent level in the feed for 5 weeks, increased the constituents, but not significantly; at the 0.04 percent level, however, the proteins were increased about 60 percent, and the increase was highly significant. The A/G ratios were not changed by the estrogen. Large doses of diethylstilbestrol also increase plasma proteins of male chickens (Clegg *et al.*, 1951).

Mandel, Clavert, and Mandel (1947a) have shown similar increases in pigeon blood when estrogen was administered, but the increase was mainly in the albumin fraction. The level of circulating estrogen in the pigeon, which increases with ovulation, does appear to affect plasma proteins, according to McDonald and Riddle (1945), as follows:

	Days before ovulation			*Days after ovulation*		
	6–5	*2*	*0*	*2*	*12*	*20*
Total plasma proteins Grams percent	2.75	3.62	3.50	3.25	3.03	2.93

The ratio of albumin to globulin (A/G) in chickens is usually less than 1, and in pigeons, over 1. Some of the protein of the blood is bound to phosphorus, and this fraction increases with laying. Indirect evidence presented by Laskowski in 1944 (see McDonald and Riddle, 1945) suggests that the amount of globulin other than that bound with phosphorus is less than the amount of albumin.

Formation of Plasma Proteins

The liver is usually considered a site of formation of plasma proteins in mammals, at least for albumin. Recently, Mandel, Clavert, and Mandel (1947b) presented evidence that albumin is formed by the liver of birds. They ligated the hepatic blood vessels of the pigeon and found that globulins were increased relatively and albumins decreased. The effects on the plasma proteins, in grams percent, follow:

	Globulin	*Albumin*	*Total protein*
Normal pigeons	0.95	1.38	2.32
Pigeons with ligated hepatic blood vessels	1.08–1.33	0.70–1.17	2.03–2.25
Pigeons following estrogen treatment	0.92	3.46	4.38
Estrogen-treated and ligated hepatic vessel	1.76–2.50	1.03–2.26	3.65

They found that estrogen increases albumin considerably in the normal bird, but after ligation of the hepatic blood vessels, albumin decreases significantly.

Hormones other than estrogen also play a role in the regulation and maintenance of the albumin and globulin levels in the blood. Estrogen administered at high levels increases the proteins of blood and liver and causes hypertrophy of the liver in the chicken and pigeon. These effects can be counteracted or prevented by administration of thyroxine (Fleischmann and Fried, 1945; McDonald and Riddle, 1945; Common, Rutledge, and Bolton, 1947; Common, Bolton, and Rutledge, 1948; Sturkie, 1951). Thus, it has been suggested that excess thyroxine either inhibits the synthesis of plasma proteins in the liver or increases the oxidative destruction of them.

This, however, fails to explain the recent results obtained with thiouracil (an antithyroid drug) by Common, Keefe, and Maw (1950), who reported that thiouracil also prevents or inhibits the hyperproteinemia induced by estrogen in the fowl, but does not prevent liver hypertrophy or an increase in liver protein as does thyroxine. Actually, thiouracil enhanced the liver hypertrophy and the increase in protein. These data, however, are based on a small number of observations, and the experiments need to be repeated.

The work of Levin and Leathem (1942) and of Levin, Leathem, and Crafts (1942) suggests that estrogen increases the albumin level of the cat and rat by way of the adrenals (estrogen enlarged the adrenals), by stimulating the release of cortical hormones. They further showed that adrenalectomy decreases significantly serum albumin, but not globulin, and that the level of the former can be restored to normal with cortical extracts. These investigators and also Leathem (1945) revealed that the level of serum globulin in the rat and cat is influenced by activity of the thyroid gland. Thyroidectomy and administered goitrogens increased serum globulin in these species, but had no appreciable effect on albumin. Thyroxine prevented the rise in globulin resulting from hypophysectomy or thyroidectomy. Large doses of thyroxine depress both albumin and globulin levels in chicken blood (Sturkie, 1951). The effects of thyroidectomy, goitrogens, and hypophysectomy or of adrenalectomy and cortical extracts on the albumin and globulin levels of bird's blood have not been determined.

It is interesting to note that the plasma protein level of laying hens remains fairly constant and is not related to time of ovulation, formation of albumen in the egg, or laying. Yet the amount of protein which must be mobilized and stored in the yolk and albumen of a single egg (approximately 6 grams) is equivalent to the total circulating plasma proteins of the hen. This suggests that rate of formation and turnover of plasma proteins is indeed rapid in the fowl. Studies of this nature and also upon the effects of the various hormones on the plasma proteins are needed.

Functions of Plasma Proteins

Fibrinogen in mammals when converted into fibrin constitutes the main part of the blood clot. Presumably it has a similar function in the chicken; however, the thrombocytes instead of the platelets are believed by some to initiate the clotting process.

One of the chief functions of the plasma proteins is the maintenance of normal blood volume and water content in the tissues. The molecules of the proteins are of such dimensions that they do not normally diffuse through the wall of the blood vessel as do crystalloids. Hence, they exert a colloidal osmotic pressure which tends to hold a certain volume of water in the blood. Any upset in this mechanism may upset the normal water balance between the blood and the tissues. Albumin in mammalian blood accounts for about 80 percent of the total osmotic pressure of the plasma proteins, because such blood contains more albumin than globulin and because the albumin molecule is smaller than that of globulin. In avian blood, which contains more globulin than albumin, the osmotic pressure exerted by the proteins is considerably less than that for mammals. Changes in body temperature and other factors may upset the balance of water between the blood and tissues so that more than normal amounts of fluid diffuse from the blood into the tissues, thus concentrating the plasma proteins, or from the tissues to the blood, causing hemodilution. This has been demonstrated in mammals and by Sturkie (1947 and 1951) in chickens.

Globulins are associated with the production of antibodies. In mammalian blood the antibodies can be salted out with the globulins. Chickens are known to be good producers of antibodies, and this could be associated with the fact that chicken blood contains a higher ratio of globulins to albumin than mammalian blood.

Sanders, Huddleson, and Schaible (1944) have shown that in chickens suffering from leucosis there is a decrease of approximately 8 percent in the plasma albumin and an increase of 7 percent in the alpha globulins. The beta and gamma globulins were not changed. The A/G ratio was changed from a normal of 0.87 to 0.46. The proteins of the blood of the diseased birds also exhibited a new electrophoretic component, designated L. The authors believed that the new component was closely related to gamma globulin.

REFERENCES

Benjamin, H. R., and A. F. Hess 1933 The forms of calcium and inorganic phosphorus in human and animal sera. J. Biol. Chem. 103:629.

Brandt, L. W., R. E. Clegg, and A. C. Andrews   1951   The effect of age
    and degree of maturity on the serum proteins of the chicken. J. Biol.
    Chem. 191:105.

Chorine, V.   1938   Les protéides du sérum des poules. Comp. Rend. Soc.
    Biol. 127:170.

Clegg, R. E., P. E. Sanford, R. E. Hein, A. C. Andrews, J. S. Hughes,
    and C. D. Mueller   1951   Electrophoretic comparison of the serum
    proteins of normal and diethylstilbestrol-treated cockerels. Science
    114:437.

Common, R. H., W. A. Rutledge, and W. Bolton   1947   The influence
    of gonadal hormones on serum riboflavin and certain other properties
    of blood and tissues of the domestic fowl. J. Endocrinol. 5:121.

Common, R. H., W. Bolton, and W. A. Rutledge   1948   The influence
    of gonadal hormones on the composition of the blood and liver of the
    domestic fowl. J. Endocrinol. 5:263.

Common, R. H., T. J. Keefe, and W. A. Maw   1950   Some biochemical
    effects of thiouracil on the response of the immature pullet to estro-
    gen. Canadian J. Res., D. 28:272.

Defalco, R. J.   1942   A serological study of some avian relationships.
    Biol. Bull. 83:205.

Deutsch, H. F., and M. B. Goodloe   1945   An electrophoretic survey of
    various animal plasmas. J. Biol. Chem. 161:1.

Dyer, H. M., and J. H. Roe   1934   The chemistry of the blood of nor-
    mal chickens. J. Nutrition 7:623.

Fleischmann, W., and I. A. Fried   1945   Studies on the mechanism of
    the hypercholesterolemia and hypercalcemia induced by estrogen in
    immature chicks. Endocrinol. 36:406.

Gardner, W. U., and C. A. Pfeiffer   1943   Influence of estrogens and
    androgens on the skeletal system. Physiol. Rev. 23:139.

Greenberg, D. M., and C. E. Larson   1935   Evidence of adsorption
    experiments on the forms of calcium and inorganic phosphorus in
    blood serum. J. Biol. Chem. 109:105.

Greenberg, D. M., C. E. Larson, P. B. Pearson, and B. R. Burmester
    1936   The state and partition of the calcium and inorganic phos-
    phorus in the serum of the fowl: Effect of growth and ovulation.
    Poultry Sci. 15:483.

Hawk, P. B., B. L. Oser, and W. H. Summerson   1947   Practical Physi-
    ological Chemistry. 12th ed. Blakiston Co., Philadelphia.

Heller, V. G., H. Paul, and R. B. Thompson   1934   Changes in the
    blood calcium and phosphorus partition during the life cycle of the
    chicken. J. Biol. Chem. 106:357.

Heller, V. G., and L. Pursell   1937   Chemical composition of the blood of the hen during its life cycle. J. Biol. Chem. 118:549.

Hermann, G. R.   1946a   Effect of choline on blood and tissues with especial reference to cholesterol in old hens. Proc. Soc. Exp. Biol. & Med. 61:302.

Hermann, G. R.   1946b   Blood and tissue chemical studies in fowl. Proc. Soc. Exp. Biol. & Med. 61:229.

Howe, P. E.   1925   The function of the plasma proteins. Physiol. Rev. 5:439.

Howell, S. F.   1939   The determination of urea in chicken blood. J. Biol. Chem. 128:573.

Hunter, F. R.   1951   Observations on the use of the flame photometer for analysis of blood. J. Biol. Chem. 192:701.

Jungherr, E.   1948   Avian monocytosis, Chapter 29 in H. E. Biester and L. H. Schwarte, Diseases of Poultry. 2d ed. Iowa State College Press, Ames.

Laskowski, M.   1935   Über die Phosphorverbindungen im Blutplasma der Legehenne. Biochem. Z. 279:293.

Leathem, J. H.   1945   Influence of thiourea on plasma proteins and organ weights in the rat. Endocrinol. 36:98.

Levin, L., and J. H. Leathem   1942   The relation of the pituitary, thyroid, and adrenal glands to the maintenance of normal serum albumin and globulin levels. Am. J. Physiol. 136:306.

Levin, L., J. H. Leathem, and R. C. Crafts   1942   The effects of adrenalectomy and replacement therapy on the serum protein levels of the cat. Am. J. Physiol. 136:776.

Lorenz, F. W., C. Entenman, and I. L. Chaikoff   1938   The influence of age, sex, and ovarian activity on the blood lipids of the domestic fowl. J. Biol. Chem. 122:619.

McDonald, M. R., and O. Riddle   1945   The effect of reproduction and estrogen administration on the partition of calcium, phosphorus, and nitrogen in pigeon plasma. J. Biol. Chem. 159:445.

Mandel, P., J. Clavert, and L. Mandel   1947a   Effets de la folliculine sur les diverses fractions protéiques du plasma chez le pigeon. Comp. Rend. Soc. Biol. 141:678.

Mandel, P., J. Clavert, and L. Mandel   1947b   Modifications des protéines du sérum après ligature des vaisseaux hépatiques chez le pigeon soumis à l'action de la folliculine. Comp. Rend. Soc. Biol. 141:913.

Riddle, O.   1942   Cyclic changes in blood calcium, phosphorus, and fat in relation to egg laying and estrogen production. Endocrinol. 31:498.

Rochlina, M.   1934   Les protéines du sang et la ponte des poules. Bull. Soc. de Chimie Biol. 16:1645.

Sanders, E., I. F. Huddleson, and P. J. Schaible   1944   An electrophoretic study of serum and plasma from normal and leucosis-affected chickens. J. Biol. Chem. 155:469.

Shimer, S. R.   1937   Chemical studies on chicken blood. Univ. New Hampshire Tech. Bull. 69.

Sturkie, P. D.   1947   Effects of hypothermia upon the specific gravity and proteins of the blood of chickens. Am. J. Physiol. 148:610.

Sturkie, P. D.   1951   The effects of estrogen and thyroxine upon plasma proteins and blood volume in the fowl. Endocrinol. 49:565.

Sturkie, P. D., and H. J. Newman   1951   Plasma proteins of chickens as influenced by time of laying, ovulation, number of blood samples taken, and plasma volume. Poultry Sci. 30:240.

Walker, H. A., M. W. Taylor, and W. C. Russell   1951   The level and interrelationship of the plasma lipids of the laying hen. Poultry Sci. 30:525.

CHAPTER 3

Circulation, Blood Pressure, and Blood Volume

CIRCULATION

DURING ventricular contraction (systole) oxygenated blood from the left ventricle is forced through the aortic valve into the aorta and to the branches of the arterial system, and venous blood is forced from the right ventricle through the pulmonary valve into the pulmonary artery, which carries blood to the lungs where it is oxygenated (see Figure 6 and Chapter 4). Oxygenated blood leaves the lungs via the pulmonary veins and enters the left atrium. Venous blood from the systemic circulation enters the right atrium through the venae cavae. After the blood is ejected, the pressure in the ventricles drops below that in the aorta, pulmonary arteries, and the atria, and the valves of these arteries close and the atrioventricular valves open. Blood then flows from the atria into the ventricles (diastole and diastasis).

Circulation Time

The time required for the blood to make a complete circuit is considered the circulation time. It is determined, for example, by injecting dye or other substances in a blood vessel in one limb and measuring the time required for one of these to reach the corresponding vessel in the opposite limb. The injected substance may also be one, such as acetylcholine, which causes a drop in blood pressure and slowing of the heart. The time required for the drug to reach the heart does not represent complete circulation time, but

41

the latter may be estimated from it. Acetylcholine has been used to determine the time required for the drug to cause a drop in blood pressure when injected in the femoral vein of the chicken (Rodbard and Fink, 1948). The average time reported by Rodbard and Fink for White Leghorn chickens (sex and age not given) was 2.8 seconds.

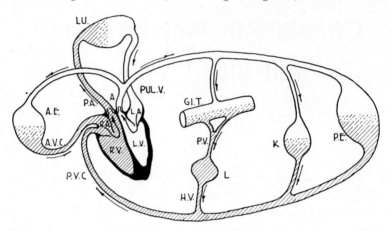

Figure 6. Schematic representation of the blood circulation in mammals and birds.

R.A., right atrium; R.V., right ventricle; L.A., left atrium; L.V., left ventricle; GI.T., gastrointestinal tract; K, kidney; P.E., posterior extremities; P.V., portal vein; L, liver; H.V., hepatic veins; P.V.C., posterior vena cava; A.E., anterior extremities; A.V.C., anterior vena cava; P.A., pulmonary artery; Lu, lungs; Pul.V., pulmonary veins. (From Dukes, *Physiology of Domestic Animals*, Comstock Publishing Co., Ithaca, N.Y., 1947.)

A 1 mg. dose of acetylcholine injected intravenously in the fowl causes a momentary arrest or slowing of the heart, which can be detected with the electrocardiogram (Sturkie, unpublished). When this dose was administered in the brachial vein of adult White Leghorn hens (four), the time required for it to reach the heart averaged 2.5 seconds.

BLOOD PRESSURE

The pressure in the heart and arteries reaches its peak during systole (systolic pressure) and its minimum during diastole (diastolic pressure). The difference between these two pressures is known as the pulse pressure. Mean blood pressure is equal roughly to systolic plus diastolic pressure divided by two. The pulse pressure decreases in the small arteries and disappears in the arterioles. In the large arteries of man, for example, mean pressure may be 100, and in the arterioles, as low as 30 mm. Hg. In the venules the pressure may drop to 12 mm. Hg; it continues to fall in the veins and may become negative in the large central veins, due to the negative pressure in the thorax (Wiggers, 1949). The positive pressure at the peripheral end and the negative pressure at the central end of the venous system plus muscular activity force the venous blood to the heart.

Changes in heart rate, output of the heart, and elasticity and resistance of the arteries influence blood pressure. Any factor which increases or decreases the distention of the system will cause changes in blood pressure. An increase in stroke volume or output ordinarily increases blood pressure, and this may be influenced by the amount of blood returned to the heart from the veins. If the heart rate is increased, this also may increase pressure, provided the output of the heart is not decreased. It is possible to have a decreased output with an increased rate, with no change in blood pressure.

As the blood flows through the arteries it meets resistance, particularly in the small arteries and arterioles, due to the friction exerted by the blood. Constriction of these vessels resulting from the stimulation of vasoconstrictor nerves and from the action of certain chemicals and drugs (adrenaline) increases blood pressure. Dilatation occurring from stimulation of vasodilator nerves and from the action of certain chemicals (acetylcholine, histamine) decreases blood pressure.

The elasticity of the blood vessels tends to decrease the work of the heart and to provide for a continuous flow of blood. It dampens blood pressure and thereby protects the capillaries from sudden fluctuations in pressure. Decreased elasticity resulting from arteriosclerosis may also increase blood pressure.

Methods of Determining Blood Pressure

The methods may be classified as direct and indirect. The most direct method is to insert a glass tube into the vessel and observe the height to which the blood flows in the vertical tube (method of Stephen Hales). This is a cumbersome method and is not ordinarily employed. In all of the commonly used direct methods, a cannula or needle is inserted in the artery or vein and pressure of the blood is exerted against a tube of liquid (containing an anticoagulant), which is attached to the manometer. In the case of the mercury manometer, the liquid is in contact with the mercury, which rises and falls in the U tube with heartbeat. (For details, see Wiggers, 1949.)

Because of the inertia of mercury, systolic and diastolic pressures are not recorded accurately. At slow heart rates the mercury over-shoots, and systolic pressure is recorded too high and diastolic pressure too low. At very rapid heart rates, full systolic and diastolic pressures are not reached, and systolic pressures are therefore recorded too low and diastolic pressures too high. If the mercury system can be so damped that only minute oscillations occur, a reasonable approximation of mean pressure may be obtained (Wiggers).

The membrane manometer is more sensitive than the mercury manometer and records sudden pressure changes more accurately.

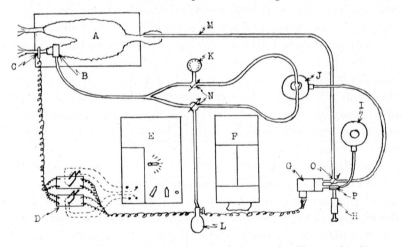

Figure 7. Apparatus for determining blood pressure by direct and indirect methods on the bird.

A, chicken and holder; B, cuff; C, strain gage pulse detector; D, double throw switches; E, strain gage analyzer; F, oscillograph; G, strain gage; H, syringe; I, stock bottle; J, calibration bottle; K, pressure gage; L, pressure bulb; M, cannula tube; N, two-way valves; O, three-way valve; P, bi-valve. (From Weiss and Sturkie, *Poultry Sci.*, 1951.)

Here the pressure, exerted against the tube of liquid, is transmitted to a thin rubber membrane. The membrane moves up and down with changes in pressure, and these movements can be made to activate a recording lever.

There are other types of manometers in which the pressure is exerted against a relatively rigid membrane. These are more sensitive than the membrane or mercury manometers. Examples of these are the Hamilton manometer, in which the recording is done optically, and various types of strain gage manometers. With the strain gage, the blood pressure and pressure pulses can be recorded by a direct writing electrocardiograph, an oscillograph, and other recording devices (Grundfest, Hay, and Feitelberg, 1945; Braunstein, Brosene, Ablendi, Green, Strauss, Hauenstein, and Kersten, 1947). Weiss and Sturkie (1951) used a Statham strain gage (Model P23-156-255; see G, Figure 7) for determining blood pressure in the chicken. The gage is attached to rigid plastic tubing (M) which is filled with an anticoagulant. A hypodermic needle, attached to the end of the tubing, is inserted into the blood vessel. Changes in pressure create an electrical imbalance in the gage or Wheatstone bridge, and this is picked up and amplified (E of Figure 7) and then recorded by the oscillograph (F), as in Figure 8.

Indirect methods. An apparatus which is commonly used clinically for measuring blood pressure is the sphygmomanometer. It consists essentially of a compressing cuff, a manometer, and an air-inflating bulb. The cuff is applied to the upper arm and is inflated enough to obliterate the pulse. Then the cuff is deflated slowly, and when the pulse reappears, as may be determined by auscultation or palpation, the reading of the pressure of the manometer is taken. Indirect methods have been used on some species of animals, notably the horse, cow, dog, and rat. In the rat, the pressure cuff is applied to the tail (see Sobin, 1946, for details). Olmsted, Corcoran, Glasser, and Page (1948) have reported an indirect method of taking blood pressure in the rat, which involves the use of a miniature cuff and an inelastic cloth band attached to the foot. The cloth contains an electric displacement unit (strain gage), which records electrically the changes in volume of blood in the foot before and after inflation of the cuff.

An indirect method for chickens has been developed by Weiss and

Sturkie (1951). This consists of a Statham strain gage (Model G1-1.5-315), which picks up the pulse in the shank, and a direct-writing oscillograph, which records it (Figures 7 and 9). A cuff, one inch in diameter for adult chickens, made to fit the lower part of the thigh, is inflated to the point where the pulse disappears. It is then deflated, and the point of reappearance of the pulse, or the return

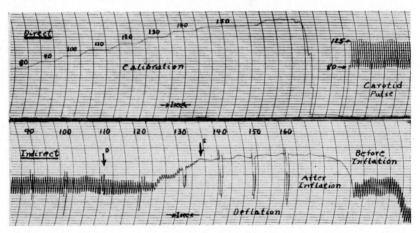

Figure 8. Direct (upper) and indirect (lower) blood pressure recordings from White Leghorn hens, taken with a Statham strain gage pickup and amplified and recorded with Brush equipment.

Systolic and diastolic pressures in upper tracing, 125 and 80 respectively, and in lower tracing, 135 and 110 mm. Hg. Read from right to left. (From Weiss and Sturkie, *Poultry Sci.,* 1951.)

of blood to the leg, is detected with the electrical pickup. See Figure 8 for blood pressure tracings. A simpler modification of the electrical pickup is the use of a carbon granule microphone attached to the shank and the null point galvanometer (Figures 7 and 9). The change in blood volume in the leg as a result of constriction or re-appearance of pulse causes a deflection of the galvanometer needle. This method is fairly accurate for determining systolic pressure, but less so than the strain gage pickup.

Systolic pressures determined by the gage direct and indirect methods on chickens agree, on the average, within 4 mm. Hg. Diastolic pressure can be estimated with a fair degree of accuracy in some birds which have good pulse records, but not in birds with poor pulse tracings.

Normal Values for Birds

Values for normal arterial blood pressure of the chicken are shown in Table 10. It is observed that determinations have been made on relatively few birds, and considerable variation exists. The values obtained with the more reliable direct methods (Hamilton manometer, strain gage, etc.) range from 130 to 142 mm. Hg for

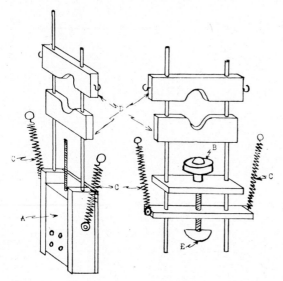

Figure 9. Strain gage and microphone pulse detectors for determining blood pressure indirectly in the chicken.

The shank is placed through the clamps (D), which come in contact with the upright rod from the strain gage (A) or the carbon granule (B). The pressure pulse is transmitted to the clamps and to the gage or microphone pickup. See Figure 7. (From Weiss and Sturkie, *Poultry Sci.*, 1951.)

systolic pressure and from 85 to 117 for diastolic. The difference, or pulse pressure, ranges from 15 to 45 mm. Hg.

The pressure in the male is significantly higher than that in the female (Stubel, 1910; Sturkie, Weiss, and Ringer, 1953), and pressure tends to increase with age after maturity, particularly in the female. Actually, the pressures recorded for older chickens may not be representative, because by the time that the chicken reaches three years of age approximately two-thirds of the original birds have died and only records of the survivors are available. Some of the original birds may have died from hypertension. Serial studies on the same birds over a period of years may provide a clearer picture of changes in pressure due to age and may show whether or not

Table 10. Normal arterial blood pressure of the chicken in mm. Hg

Investigator	Year	No. of birds	Age	Av. body weight gm.	Sex	Breed	Blood pressure Mean	Blood pressure Sys./Dias.	Method	Anesthetic	Blood vessel
Riddle & Matthews	1907	3	?	?	M	?	117	—	Hg man.	Ether	Carotid and innominate
Stubel	1910	17	?	?	F	?	170	180/160	Membrane man.	None	Carotid
"	"	10	?	2190	M	?	196	—	Hg man.	"	"
"	"	19	?	1770	F	?	164	—			
Kaupp	1924	4	?	?	M	?	104	—	Hg man.	Ether	Femoral
"	"	13	?	?	M	?	135	—	"	None	"
Woodbury & Abreu	1944	7	?		?	varied	108	130/85	Hamilton man.	Barbital, ether, morphine	Ischiatic
Rodbard & Tolpin	1948	22	6–10 wks.	?	?	W. Wyan. W. Leg.	128	135/120	Hamilton man.	None	Ischiatic
Lenel et al.	1948	8	6 wks.	?	?	W. Leg.	125	132/117	Hamilton man.	None	Ischiatic
Weiss & Sturkie	1951	9	1½–2 yrs.	?	F	W. Leg.	130	142/117	Strain gage man.	Barbital	Carotid
"	1951	9	"	?	F	W. Leg.	—	139	Indirect	None	1" cuff on thigh
Sturkie et al.	1953	80	mos. 10–14	?	F	W. Leg.	—	131	Indirect	None	1" cuff on thigh
"	"	62	19–26	?	F	"	—	139	"	"	"
"	"	54	30–38	?	F	"	—	155	"	"	"
"	"	21	42–54	?	F	"	—	163	"	"	"
"	"	33	10–14	?	M	"	—	164	"	"	"
"	"	42	22–54	?	M	"	—	189	"	"	"

hypertension contributes to the excessive adult mortality in chickens.

It is known that the incidence of arteriosclerosis in chickens is very high (Dauber, 1944; Paterson, Slinger, Gartley, Mitchell, Wallace, and Cottral, 1949). In a study of the blood vessels of chickens, Dauber showed that about 45 percent of male and female chickens over one year of age showed macroscopic lesions of the aorta. The lesions were found most frequently in the abdominal aorta and were characterized by fatty plaques of the intima of the vessels (atherosclerosis). He showed also that 28 percent of the young males between five and nine months of age exhibited the lesions. The incidence of the lesions may also be increased by administration of cholesterol (Dauber and Katz, 1943) and estrogen (Chaikoff, Lindsay, Lorenz, and Entenman, 1948).

Milch (1952) reported that the severity of atherosclerotic lesions of the aorta which develop spontaneously in two-year-old hens could be decreased by administering adenosine-5-monophosphate. This treatment also depressed blood cholesterol, but elevated the phospholipids. Whether or not atherosclerosis in the fowl causes hypertension has not been determined.

Blood pressure values for other species of birds are shown in Table 11. In general, the blood pressure of birds, particularly that in the male, appears to be higher than that for many of the mammals.

Comparisons of the heart rates and blood pressures of the different bird species suggest that normally heart rate plays a minor role in the control of blood pressure. For example, the male chicken has a lower pulse rate and higher blood pressure than the female. Moreover, birds exhibiting the highest heart rates do not have higher blood pressures than birds with lower pulse rates. The heart rate of normal chickens may vary from about 250 to 400 without causing appreciable changes in blood pressure (Weiss and Sturkie, unpublished).

Effects of Anesthesia, Drugs, and Hormones

Anesthesia may lower blood pressure in birds, as in mammals, depending upon the type, dose, and time after administration. Pentobarbital sodium (25 to 30 mg. per kilogram), injected intra-

Table 11. Blood pressure of birds other than the chicken. Determinations were made with mercury manometer (Stubel, 1910) and Hamilton manometer with local anesthesia, from the ventricles (V), carotid arteries (C), and brachial arteries (B) (Woodbury and Hamilton, 1937)

Species	No.	Age or weight (gm.)	Blood pressure			Author
			Mean	Systolic	Diastolic	
Turkey (male)	— C	8750	193	—	—	Stubel
Duck	— C	2304	162	—	—	"
Pigeon	4 B	adult	—	135	105	Woodbury & Hamilton
Starling	2 C	adult	—	180	130	"
Robin	2 V	adult	—	118	80	"
Canary	2 C	adult	—	130	—	"
	4 V	adult	—	220	154	"
Sparrow	1 C	adult	—	180	140	"
	3 V	Very young	—	108	—	"

venously in the chicken, depresses blood pressure from a normal of 144.4 mm. Hg to 110 within 2 to 5 minutes after injection. Within one-half to one hour after injection, however, blood pressure returns to approximately the preinjection level (Weiss and Sturkie, 1951).

The oxytocic fraction of posterior pituitary preparations (0.1 oxytocic unit per kilogram of body weight) depresses blood pressure in the fowl from 130/85 to 80/40 within a few seconds (Woodbury and Abreu, 1944). Twenty to ninety seconds later the values return to normal. The drop in pressure is not due to cardiac weakness or changes in heart rate, as has been observed in certain mammals, but to vasodilatation. Similar effects are produced in the duck (Paton and Watson, 1912; Morash and Gibbs, 1929).

Thompson and Coon (1948) demonstrated that pressor substances, such as epinephrine, benzedrine, ephedrine, and neo-synephrine, increase blood pressure in the fowl. Dibenamine, an adrenergic blocking agent, does not block the pressor response in chickens, even in large doses (20 mg./kg., intravenously), but it protects the bird from the toxic effects of epinephrine. The chicken is very resistant, however, to the toxic effects of epinephrine. Priscol, another adrenergic blocker, diminishes the pressor response to epinephrine. One milligram of epinephrine injected intravenously in chicks elevates systolic blood pressure 70 mm. Hg and diastolic pressure 55 mm. Hg (Rodbard and Tolpin, 1947). The increased pressure resulting from pressor substances is due mainly to vasoconstriction, because blood pressure may remain elevated long after heart rate becomes normal (Sturkie, unpublished).

Acetylcholine and histamine, which cause vasodilatation, depress blood pressure in the fowl. A dose of 0.2 mg. of acetylcholine administered to 6 to 12-week-old chicks reduces blood pressure 40 to 60 mm. Hg within three seconds (Rodbard and Fink, 1948; see also Morash and Gibbs, 1929). Intramuscular injections of 5 mg. to adult fowls decrease blood pressure similarly and decrease momentarily heart rate, which then increases (Weiss and Sturkie, 1951). The induced hypotension is in large part attributable to peripheral vasodilatation, because blood pressure remains depressed long after heart rate returns to normal or, as in most cases, is increased.

Respiratory Influence

Blood pressure in the fowl, as in mammals, changes with respiration. Mean pressure usually falls in inspiration and rises on expiration. The explanations for these changes are numerous and complicated (see Wiggers, 1949). The differences are usually exaggerated when the mercury manometer is used. Blood pressure changes in the bird during normal inspiration and expiration range from 1 to 10 mm. Hg in most cases when the mercury manometer is used (Stubel, 1910). In the slow-breathing, bilaterally vagotomized bird, the fluctuations in blood pressure are also associated with the respiratory phases, according to Stubel. Some birds show an increase and others no change in pressure after vagotomy, depending apparently upon the degree of vagal release and consequent heart rate.

Body Temperature and Blood Pressure

Hypothermia depresses blood pressure and heart rate in the bird and mammal. The decrease in the bird is proportional to the degree of hypothermia (Rodbard and Tolpin, 1947). Rewarming of the fowl causes an immediate rise in pressure and body temperature, until normal body temperature is reached; then with further warming and hyperthermia there is a drop in blood pressure, resulting apparently from extreme vasodilatation induced by the heat. The hypotension occurs in spite of a continued increase in heart rate with hyperthermia, and Rodbard and Tolpin stated that this is evi-

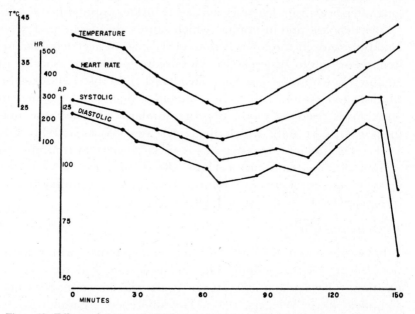

Figure 10. Effects of changes in body temperature on blood pressure and heart rate in the chicken. (From Rodbard and Tolpin, *Am. J. Physiol.*, 1947.)

dence that heart rate plays a minor role in the control of blood pressure (Figure 10). Other investigators on the fowl (see Chapter 8) report that heart rate does not continue to rise in hyperthermia. The hyperthermic and hypothermic fowls respond normally to epinephrine and acetylcholine, indicating, according to Rodbard and Tolpin, that contractability of the blood vessels is not impaired.

Nervous Control of Blood Pressure

Rodbard and co-workers believe that there is a direct central control of blood pressure in the chicken, as they reported in the turtle. The center in the turtle is at the level of the third ventricle. They reasoned that as the metabolic needs of the body change with changing body temperature, an active adjustment, operating through the nervous system, is made in the head of pressure driving the blood through the vascular system.

The body of evidence suggests that the vasomotor center in mammals is located in the medulla (Wiggers, 1949). Less is known about this center in birds, but there is some evidence which suggests that it is in the thalamus, according to Dijk (1932), who showed that stimulation of this area produces changes in blood pressure.

The vasomotor center of mammals influences blood pressure through the vasoconstrictor and vasodilator nerves, which are sympathetic and parasympathetic respectively in origin. The constrictors cause contraction of the muscular elements of arterioles by liberating adrenergic substances. The vasodilators produce their effect by releasing an acetylcholine-like substance and are said to be cholinergic. Although these nerve fibers are present in birds, little is known about their effect on blood pressure.

Cardioinhibitor and accelerator nerves. The effects of the accelerator nerves on blood pressure of birds have not been reported, but the vagus nerve, a cardioinhibitor, influences blood pressure much the same as it does in mammals. Bilateral vagotomy decreases heart rate only slightly in most birds and less so when the heart rate is normally rapid (see Chapter 4), and therefore has little effect on blood pressure. Stimulation of the peripheral end of the vagus slows heart rate one-half to one-third of normal and decreases blood pressure from 150 to 100 mm. Hg (Stubel, 1910). The effects of stimulation of the central end of the vagus are inconsistent. Some chickens exhibit a slight increase, some no change, and some a slight decrease in blood pressure.

Reflex stimulation of blood pressure. The vasomotor centers may be stimulated reflexly. Most afferent nerves contain fibers which, when stimulated, cause an increase in blood pressure by activating the vasoconstrictor center. Strong stimulation of the central end of the sciatic or brachial nerves increases blood pressure in the fowl as it does in mammals. The increase following stimulation of the brachial nerve in the fowl averages 47.9 percent (Porter and Richardson, 1908).

Venous and Pulmonary Pressures

Few determinations have been made on venous and pulmonary pressures. Rodbard and Tolpin (1947) reported the pressure in the pulmonary artery of the fowl to be 20/8 mm. Hg, which is about the same as in some mammals. Venous pressure in the right and left brachial veins of the duck, taken at a distance of 3 cm. from the distal end of the humerus, ranges from 3.5 to 6.5 mm. Hg (Riddle and Matthews, 1907).

Experimental Hypertension

Hypertension can be produced in mammals by ligation or constriction of the renal arteries (Goldblatt, 1937 and later; Katz, Friedman, Rodbard, and Weinstein, 1939; and others). Attempts in preliminary experiments to produce persistent hypertension in the chicken by the above means or by occluding the ureters failed, according to a statement made by Lenel, Katz, and Rodbard (1948).

Salt hypertension has been produced in the chicken (Krakower and Heino, 1947; Lenel *et al.*, 1948). Lenel *et al.* induced it by adding sodium chloride to the drinking water (0.9 and 1.2 percent) of 6-week-old chickens. At the 0.9 percent level, blood pressure increased in most cases within 4 days from 122/112 to 165/155; at the 1.2 percent level, it increased to 182/154 within 20 to 30 days. Removal of salt from the drinking water caused a prompt drop in blood pressure, which approached normal levels within one week. The mechanism for the production of salt hypertension is not known.

BLOOD VOLUME

Blood volume may be determined directly or indirectly. In the direct or exsanguination method, the animal is bled and the blood collected, but since some of the blood is retained in the vessels, the latter must be washed out and the washings included in the determination.

There are a number of indirect methods, including the dye technique, CO-inhalation method, and tagging of red cells with radioactive isotopes. (See Wiggers, 1949, for a discussion of methods.) The most commonly used method consists of measuring the dilution

in the blood of a known amount of dye and calculating the amount
of blood from the dilution.

Details of Dye Technique

A known amount of dye (Evans blue or T-1824) is injected intravenously and allowed to mix completely with the blood. Then a
blood sample is drawn, and the amount of dye in the sample is determined in comparison to a standard of known dilution. The concentration of the dye in the blood, or its dilution, is a measure of the
total volume of the blood and can be determined colorimetrically or
spectrophotometrically. The whole blood (see Benditt, Straube, and
Humphreys, 1946) or plasma may be used. If plasma is used, then
total plasma volume is determined and total blood volume calculated by adding to the plasma volume the volume of corpuscles
(hematocrit in percent).

$$\text{Blood volume} = \frac{\text{Plasma volume} \times 100}{\text{Percent plasma}}$$

Thus, if the plasma volume of a chicken is 100 cc. and the hematocrit is 30 percent, then total blood volume equals approximately
142 cc. Since the heart rate and circulation time in the bird are
more rapid than in larger mammals, the time required for the dye
to become adequately mixed in the blood is much less and amounts
to 2 to 3 minutes (Pino, Weiss, Sturkie, and DeFalco, 1951). The
rate of disappearance of the dye from the blood is also more rapid
in the bird, averaging approximately 1 percent per minute. Thus,
if the blood sample following dye injection is taken after 3 minutes,
then the concentration of dye decreases and this causes the calculated volumes to be too high.

The accuracy of the dye method has been compared with a number of other methods and more recently with the antigen-antibody
technique in mammals (Gregersen, Boyden, and Allison, 1950 and
earlier) and in chickens (Pino *et al.*, 1951). The principle of the
latter method is as follows. A known amount of an antitoxoid is
injected and allowed to mix with the blood. After mixing, a sample
of blood is taken, and the plasma is allowed to react with a known
amount of toxoid (antigen). In addition the toxoid is allowed to
react with a given amount of antitoxoid in a test tube (standard).

The reaction consists of flocculation, and the degree of reaction depends upon the optimum proportions of toxoid and antitoxoid (concentrations). Thus, the flocculation in the blood sample is proportional to the concentration or dilution of the antitoxoid in the blood, and from this dilution and the reaction of the standard, blood volume can be determined. The rate of disappearance for the antibody from the blood of the chicken up to 20 minutes is slower than for the dye. The average rate is 0.26 percent per minute. Comparison of this method with the dye technique for blood volume showed agreement within about 2 percent.

Blood Volume of Birds

Crude blood volume (bleeding out, but not washing out of blood vessels) has been determined in the chicken by Common, Bolton,

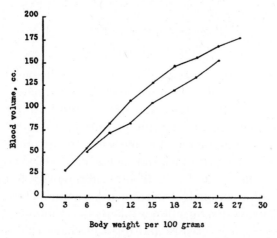

Figure 11. The relationship between total blood volume and body weight of normal New Hampshire (upper curve) and White Leghorn females.

Upper curve represents data from Newell and Shaffner, *Poultry Sci.*, (1950), and lower curve, data from Pino *et al.*, *Proc. Ninth World's Poultry Congr.* (1951).

and Rutledge (1948), Turner (1948), and others. The crude volumes, which average about 4 percent of body weight, are approximately one-half those obtained with the dye technique. Earlier work on birds by Welcher and Brandt (1903) and others who used the exsanguination technique showed blood volumes of about the same order, suggesting that they measured only the amount of blood drained out, but not washed out.

The dye technique has been used by Pappenheimer, Goettsch, and Jungherr (1939), Newell and Shaffner (1950), Pino *et al.* (1951), and Sturkie and Newman (1951). Pappenheimer *et al.* reported that blood volume of chicks 1 to 6 weeks of age is approximately 9 percent of body weight. Their mixing time was 5 minutes. Newell and Shaffner (1950) determined blood volumes on New Hampshire chickens ranging in age from 6 weeks to maturity. The relationship of blood volume to body weight is shown in Figure 11. Blood vol-

Table 12. Blood volume of New Hampshire (Newell and Shaffner, 1950) and White Leghorn (Pino) *et al.*, 1951) chickens

Body weight gm.	New Hampshire				White Leghorn		Percent difference in volume 1 and 2
	Male		Female (1)		Female (2)		
	Blood volume cc.	Percent body weight	Blood volume cc.	Percent body weight	Blood volume cc.	Percent body weight	
300			27	9.0			
400	40	10.0					
600			56	9.3	53	8.8	5.6
800	80	10.0					
900			82	9.1	71	7.9	15.4
1200	120	10.0	106	8.8	84	7.0	26.1
1500			127	8.4	105	7.0	20.9
1600	155	9.7					
1800			145	8.0	119	6.6	21.9
2000	190	9.5					
2100			158	7.5	137	6.5	15.3
2400	230	9.6	168	7.0	151	6.3	11.2
2700			176	6.9			
2800	260	9.2					
3200	300	9.4					
3600	330	9.2					
4000	370	9.2					

ume of females, according to Newell and Shaffner, increases in an almost straight-line fashion with body weight, between 400 and 1200 grams. In percent of body weight, this is approximately 9 percent (see Table 12). Above 1200 grams of weight the relationship is no longer linear. The blood volumes in percentage of body weights at 1800, 2400, and 2700 grams are 8.0, 7.0, and 6.93 respectively. The relationship of body weight and blood volume for the males is almost linear throughout, and in percent of body weight the volume ranges from 9 to 10 percent (Table 12).

The difference in sexes is believed to be due to the fact that the females have more body fat, which contains less blood than non-fatty tissue. However, part of the increase in blood volume of males over females is attributable to the higher corpuscular volume of males, beginning at about sexual maturity. Up to body weights of about 1800 grams, this volume for both sexes is the same and averages slightly less than 30 percent.

Blood volume in the White Leghorn female, as reported by Pino *et al.*, is lower than for New Hampshires (Figure 11 and Table 12). The values ranged from 5 to 26 percent lower for the same ages of birds. Part of this difference may be attributed to breeds, but most of it appears to be due to differences in mixing time, which for Newell and Shaffner was 10 minutes, and this made their values too high.

Sturkie and Newman (1951), using the dye technique, with a mixing time of 3 minutes, reported the following blood volumes for 15 laying White Leghorn females, ranging in weight from 1.7 to 2 kg.:

Plasma volume ml.	Cell volume gm./100 ml.	Blood volume ml.
93.5	28.5	130.8

Effects of hormones and other factors. Common, Bolton, and Rutledge (1948) reported that estrogen administered to chickens increases greatly the crude blood volume, but Sturkie (1951), using the dye technique, found no change in the blood volume following administration of massive doses of estrogen or thyroxine. Estrogen causes extreme dilation of the blood vessels which may account for the increased "bleeding out" reported by Common *et al.*

The act of taking a blood sample from the heart may cause a 10 percent increase in blood volume and a decrease in cell volume within 12 hours after sampling (Sturkie and Newman, 1951). It appears that handling and sampling set in motion a shift of water from the tissues to the blood (hemodilution), but the effects of the shift are not appreciable until after 5 or 6 hours. The amount of blood taken appears not to be the main factor involved, since the withdrawing of as little as 2 cc. results in hemodilution.

REFERENCES

Benditt, E. P., R. L. Straube, and E. M. Humphreys 1946 The determination of total circulating serum proteins and erythrocyte volumes in normal and protein-depleted rats. Proc. Soc. Exp. Biol. & Med. 62:189.

Braunstein, J. R., W. G. Brosene, Jr., F. Ablendi, R. S. Green, V. Strauss, V. Hauenstein, and H. J. Kersten 1947 A new method of recording arterial blood pressure. Science 105:267.

Chaikoff, I. L., S. Lindsay, F. W. Lorenz, and C. Entenman 1948 Production of atheromatosis in the aorta of the bird by administration of diethylstilbestrol. J. Exp. Med. 88:373.

Common, R. H., W. Bolton, and W. A. Rutledge 1948 The influence of gonadal hormones on the composition of the blood and liver of the domestic fowl. J. Endocrinol. 5:263.

Dauber, D. V. 1944 Spontaneous arteriosclerosis in chickens. Arch. Path. 38:46.

Dauber, D. V., and L. N. Katz 1943 Experimental atherosclerosis in the chick. Arch. Path. 36:473.

Dijk, J. A. 1932 Arch. Néerl. Physiol. 17:495. Cited from Chapter 23, Nervous system, in Prosser, Brown, Bishop, Jahn, and Wulff, Comparative Animal Physiology, 1950. W. B. Saunders Co., Philadelphia.

Dukes, H. H. 1947 The Physiology of Domestic Animals. 6th ed. Comstock Publishing Co., Inc., Ithaca, N.Y.

Goldblatt, H. 1937 Studies on experimental hypertension. V: The pathogenesis of experimental hypertension due to renal ischemia. Ann. Int. Med. 11:69.

Gregersen, M. I., A. A. Boyden, and J. B. Allison 1950 Direct comparison in dogs of plasma volume measured with T-1824 and with antigens. Am. J. Physiol. 163:517.

Grundfest, H. J., J. Hay, and S. Feitelberg 1945 A strain gage recorder for physiological volume, pressure, and deformation measurements. Science 101:255.

Katz, L. N., M. Friedman, S. Rodbard, and W. Weinstein 1939 Observations on the genesis of renal hypertension. Am. Heart J. 17:334.

Kaupp, B. F. 1924 Physiology of blood pressure in the domestic fowl. Poultry Sci. 3:96.

Krakower, C. A., and H. E. Heino 1947 Relationship of growth and nutrition to cardiorenal changes induced in birds by a high salt intake. Arch. Path. 44:143.

Lenel, R., L. N. Katz, and S. Rodbard 1948 Arterial hypertension in the chicken. Am. J. Physiol. 152:557.

Milch, L. J. 1952 Serum and aortal lipid changes in atherosclerotic hens treated with adenosine-5-monophosphate. Fed. Proc. 11:487.

Morash, R., and O. S. Gibbs 1929 The effect of pituitary on the bird. J. Pharm. & Exp. Thera. 37:475.

Newell, G. W., and C. S. Shaffner 1950 Blood volume determinations in chickens. Poultry Sci. 29:78.

Olmsted, F., A. C. Corcoran, O. Glasser, and I. H. Page 1948 Systolic pressure in intact unanesthetized rat. Fed. Proc. 7:88.

Pappenheimer, A. M., M. Goettsch, and E. Jungherr 1939 Nutritional encephalomalacia in chicks and certain related disorders of domestic birds. Storrs Agric. Exp. Sta. Bull. 229.

Paterson, J. C., S. J. Slinger, K. M. Gartley, C. A. Mitchell, A. C. Wallace, and G. E. Cottral 1949 Coronary sclerosis in chickens. Poultry Sci. 28:779 (Abs.)

Paton, N., and A. Watson 1912 The actions of pituitrin, adrenaline, and barium on the circulation of the bird. J. Physiol. 44:413.

Pino, J. A., H. S. Weiss, P. D. Sturkie, and R. J. DeFalco 1951 Blood volume determinations in the fowl using diphtheria antitoxoid. Proc. Ninth World's Poultry Congr. 3:102.

Porter, W. T., and R. Richardson 1908 A comparative study of vasomotor reflexes. Am. J. Physiol. 21:15 (Proc.).

Riddle, O., and S. A. Matthews 1907 The blood pressure of birds and their modification by drugs. Am. J. Physiol. 19:108.

Rodbard, S., and A. Fink 1948 Effect of body temperature change on the circulation time in the chicken. Am. J. Physiol. 152:383.

Rodbard, S., and M. Tolpin 1947 A relationship between the body temperature and blood pressure in the chicken. Am. J. Physiol. 151:509.

Sobin, S. S. 1946 Accuracy of indirect determinations of blood pressure in the rat: Relation of temperature of plethysmograph and width of cuff. Am. J. Physiol. 146:179.

Stubel, H. S. 1910 Beiträge zur Kenntnis der Physiologie des Blutkreislaufes der verschiedenen Vogelarten. Arch. ges. Physiol. (Pflügers) 135:249.

Sturkie, P. D. 1951 The effects of estrogen and thyroxine upon plasma proteins and blood volume of chickens. Endocrinol. 49:565.

Sturkie, P. D., and H. J. Newman 1951 Plasma proteins of chickens as influenced by time of laying, ovulation, number of blood samples taken, and plasma volume. Poultry Sci. 30:240.

Sturkie, P. D., H. S. Weiss, and R. K. Ringer 1953 The effects of age on blood pressure in the fowl. Am. J. Physiol. 174:405.

Thompson, R. M., and J. M. Coon 1948 Effect of adrenolytic agents on the response to pressor substances in the domestic fowl. Fed. Proc. 7:259.

Turner, C. W. 1948 Effect of thyroprotein-feeding on the gland and organ weights of two-year-old White Leghorn hens. Poultry Sci. 27:155.

Weiss, H. S., and P. D. Sturkie 1951 An indirect method for measuring blood pressure in the fowl. Poultry Sci. 30:587.

Welcher, H., and A. Brandt 1903 Gewichtswerte der Körperorgane bei dem Menschen und den Tieren. Arch. für Anthropologie 28:1.

Wiggers, C. J. 1949 Physiology in Health and Disease. 5th ed. Lea and Febiger, Philadelphia.

Woodbury, R. A., and B. E. Abreu 1944 Influence of oxytocin (pitocin) upon the heart and blood pressure of the chicken, rabbit, cat, dog, and turtle. Am. J. Physiol. 142:114.

Woodbury, R. A., and W. F. Hamilton 1937 Blood pressure studies in small animals. Am. J. Physiol. 119:663.

CHAPTER 4

Contraction and Conduction
in the Heart

ANATOMY OF THE HEART AND CONDUCTING SYSTEM

THE heart of birds is located in or slightly to the left of the median line of the thoracic cavity and is ventral to the lungs, with the apex resting in the median fissure of the liver (Kaupp, 1918). The heart of the chicken is almost parallel to the long axis of the body except that the apex may be bent to the right, according to Lewis (1915). In most of the chicken hearts studied by Kisch (1951), the long axis was directed toward the right wing, while the duck heart was more nearly in and parallel to the median line. The heart is surrounded by the pericardial sac, which contains serous fluid.

The bird heart, like that of mammals, has four chambers—two atria and two ventricles. The right atrium of the chicken heart is larger than the left. The mass of the left ventricle is three times that of the right ventricle (Lewis). The atria have openings into the ventricles which are closed by the atrio-ventricular valves. The left valve is thin and membranous like that of mammals, but the right valve is simply a muscular flap. The valves of the aorta and pulmonary arteries are like those in mammals.

The interior of the heart is lined by a thin serous membrane, the endocardium. The main mass of the heart wall, the myocardium, consists of cardiac muscle like that in mammals. The muscle is thickest in the ventricles, particularly the left one. The outer surface of the heart is termed the epicardium.

The heart muscle is supplied with arterial blood through the coronary arteries, and venous blood is returned to the venous circulation through the coronary veins, which course through the heart wall near the surface. Most birds have two main coronary arteries, but some may have three or four. Petren (1926) showed that among the chicken and pigeon hearts studied, 28 and 38 percent respectively had three coronary arteries.

The right coronary artery is larger than the left in chickens and is located on the ventral surface of the heart. It branches from the ventral side of the aorta at the point where the latter enters the heart. The left coronary artery originates from the dorsal side of the aorta and courses mainly over the dorsal surface of the heart. The ends and branches of the right and left coronary arteries anastomose freely, and many of these are located deep in the myocardium.

The size or weight of the bird heart varies considerably with body size. In proportion to body weight, smaller birds usually have larger hearts. The heart and body weights of some bird species are as follows (see Groebbels, 1932):

Species	Body weight gm.	Heart weight in gm./kg. of body weight
Goose	4405	8.00
Duck	1685	7.44
Chicken	3120	4.40
Pigeon	297	13.80

Specialized Conducting System

The existence of a specialized conducting system in bird hearts was doubted for a number of years. Earlier work by Mackenzie indicated that sinoatrial nodal tissue was absent. Work by Aschoff, however, indicated the presence of a S-A node. See Eyster and Meek (1921) for review.

Later work by Drennan (1927) on the ostrich and by Davies (1930) leaves little doubt as to the existence of a specialized conducting system in the heart of birds. Davies, who worked with swans and pigeons, made detailed histochemical studies on the hearts of these species. A diagram of the system as described by him is shown in Figure 12.

The system consists of the sinoatrial node, the atrioventricular node and branches, and the right A-V ring of Purkinje fibers. The S-A node is located in the right atrium between the posterior and right anterior venae cavae.

The A-V node (pigeon) is embedded in connective tissue in the lower and posterior part of the atrial septum, a short distance in front and to the left of the opening of the left superior vena cava, a position similar to that occupied by the mammalian node. It is ovoid in shape, and its lower and anterior parts narrow into the commencement of the A-V bundle. The lower part of the node consists of cells which are larger than the atrial myocardial cells proper and are frequently multinucleated, the nuclei being rounded in shape and central in position.

The A-V bundle begins as a narrow, rounded bundle continuous with the lower and anterior end of the A-V node. It soon broadens out and runs forward and to the left in the ventricular septum. It then passes downward, forward, and to the left, to a point slightly below and to the right of the anterior septal attachment of the muscular right A-V valve. This site is about one-quarter of the distance from the base to the apex of the ventricular septum, and here the bundle divides into the right and left limbs.

The right limb runs downward and slightly forward. It passes in front of and close to the main septal artery, but no fibers appear to pass directly from the right limb to the collection of Purkinje fibers around the artery. The limb then reaches the subendocardial connective tissue on the right side of the septum, where it spreads out and becomes continuous with the subendocardial network of Purkinje fibers. The cells of the limbs are like those of the bundle.

The right limb also gives off a branch which runs up and around the right A-V valve. It suggests, according to Davies (1930), that the right valve actively contracts early in the ventricular systole, so allowing exit for the blood from the right ventricle through the pulmonary artery alone during the greater part of systole. This, he believed, represents an example of adaptation of structure to function.

The left limb branches at the point where the right limb branches; it passes posteriorly and to the left, in the manner described for the right limb. The left branch, at its beginning, gives rise to another

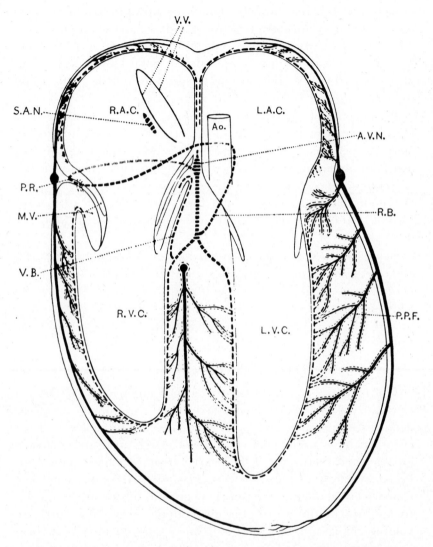

Figure 12. Diagram of the conducting system in the avian heart (pigeon).
Ao., aorta; A.V.N., atrioventricular node; L.A.C., left atrial cavity; M.V., muscular right A-V valve; P.P.F., periarterial Purkinje fibers; P.R., ring of Purkinje fibers about right A-V orifice; R.A.C., right atrial cavity; R.V.C., right ventricle cavity; R.B., left recurrent branch of A-V bundle; S.A.N., sinoatrial node; V.B., branch of right limb of A-V bundle to muscular valve; V.V., venous valves, right and left. (From Davies, *J. Anat.*, 1930.)

branch, the recurrent branch, which runs upward, forward, and to the left in the ventricular septum. Finally, it passes backward in the connective tissue on the left side of the root of the aorta and ends by joining the aortic end of the bundle of Purkinje fibers, which passes from the A-V node around the right A-V orifice behind the root of the aorta.

The absence of a fibrous sheath around the A-V bundle of birds is correlated with the rapidity of the heart rate (according to Davies). No nerve cells were observed in the A-V node with the stain used, but abundant nerve fibers penetrate the connective tissue surrounding the node. Similarly, no nerve fibers were observed in the S-A node, but small ganglia and fibers were plentiful in the epicardial tissue in the region of the node, and these could be traced to the node.

Davies believed that the A-V node is a derivative of the S-A ring and not the A-V ring and that the right vagus and right sympathetic nerves are associated experimentally with the S-A node, and the left vagus and left sympathetic with the A-V node. This remains to be proved. He believed that both nodes are derivatives of the S-A ring.

THE CARDIAC CYCLE

The sequence of events occurring in a complete heart beat, a cardiac cycle, has been determined in the mammalian heart (for details, see any good textbook on mammalian physiology). These events include mechanical contraction of the atria and ventricles (systole) and relaxation of the heart muscle (diastole). This is followed by filling of the ventricles (diastasis). Accompanying these changes are changes in volume and pressure in the atria and ventricles. Apparently no measurements upon intracardiac pressure, volume changes, and output as related to the heartbeat in birds have been made.

Kisch (1951 and 1953), who made records of the heart sounds of birds (phonocardiograms), reported that usually two sounds can be registered per cycle when the heart rates are below 500 per minute. (See Figure 17.)

INITIATION OF THE HEARTBEAT

The wave of contraction originates in the sinoatrial (S-A) node and spreads through the atria, thence to the atrioventricular (A-V) node, the A-V bundle, and its branches to all parts of the heart. The rhythm and initiation of the heartbeat are normally controlled by the S-A node (the pacemaker), but under certain conditions, for example when the S-A node is discharging abnormally, the A-V node or ventricles may initiate the beat (ectopic impulses) and may continue to do so (ectopic rhythm). This may occur in S-A block, where the impulse does not leave the S-A node, or when the S-A node discharges very slowly or arrhythmically, and it may occur in A-V block, where the impulse does not pass through the A-V node or bundles. These conditions have been reported in the bird and will be described later (Chapter 5). Complete atrioventricular block has been produced in the chicken by ligating the heart in the A-V groove and also by transecting both right and left bundles. Cutting either right or left bundle alone does not produce complete block (Mangold and Kato, 1914).

FACTORS AFFECTING HEART RATE

Most birds have higher heart rates than mammals of the same size. The smaller birds and mammals usually have higher heart rates than larger ones. The high heart rate of birds cannot be accurately counted without resorting to electrical pickup and recording equipment. It may be accurately counted by the electrocardiograph, electrocardiotachometer, and other electrical devices.

The heart rates of adult birds, presumably at rest, are shown in Table 13. It is known that the rate varies considerably with excitement. Rates below 220 and above 400 in the adult chicken may be considered abnormally low (bradycardia) and high (tachycardia) respectively. Heart rate is somewhat higher in the female than in the male chicken. The relationship of sex to rate in other species apparently has not been determined.

The heart of the chick embryo exhibits rhythmic contractions at about the 30th hour of incubation (Barry, 1940), but the complete vascular circuit is not established until the 40th hour (Patten and

Table 13. Heart rate of adult birds at rest

Species, age, and sex	Body weight gm.	Average heart rate	Author
Chicken, male	2190	286	Stubel (1910)
Rhode Island Red, male	2743	243	McNally (1941)
White Leghorn, male	2095	273	"
White Leghorn, female	1733	341	"
Rhode Island Red, female	2178	279	"
Chicken, female	1980	312	Stubel
Duck	2270	217	Kisch (1951)
Duck	2304	212	Stubel
Turkey	8750	93	"
Pigeon	240	192	Buchanan (1909)
Pigeon	237	244	Stubel
Pigeon	adult	221	Woodbury & Hamilton (1937)
Robin	adult	570	"
Canary	adult	795	"
Canary	20	1000	Tigerstedt (1921)

Kramer, 1933). The heart rate at 40 hours of incubation is 90 to 100 per minute and increases gradually; it reaches a peak of 220 on the eighth or ninth day (Romanoff, 1944) and then decreases to 200 per minute just before hatching.

Nervous Control of the Heart

The heart of birds is supplied by sympathetic and parasympathetic nerve fibers. According to Kaupp (1918) and others, sympathetic fibers originate from the large inferior cervical ganglion, near the entrance to the thorax, and run to the heart. The peripheral branches of these may be fused with the vagus nerve, which also sends preganglionic fibers to the heart. The atrium receives sympathetic fibers from thoracic nerves 1 to 4, according to Clark (1927), Paton (1912), and Stubel (1910). Sympathetic nerve fibers reach the heart of the chick by the fifth day of age. (See Clark.)

The vagus, a parasympathetic nerve, sends preganglionic fibers to the heart, and from ganglia located on the heart the short postganglionic fibers emerge. The sympathetic nerves in mammals have an accelerator effect, and the parasympathetic nerves, a cardio-inhibitory effect, and this is also the case in birds.

Stimulation of accelerator nerves (thoracic nerves 1 to 4 and cervical nerves) increases heart rate in the duck and buzzard (Paton, 1912; Stubel, 1910) and augments the amplitude of contraction of the atria, but not the ventricles (Paton). This is evidence that the accelerator nerves innervate only the atria, according to Paton. His belief that the vagus may also contain accelerator fibers was based upon increased, rather than decreased, ventricular contraction which he observed in some cases after vagal stimulation.

The vagi in mammals and birds exert a tonic effect on the heart. The degree of vagal control varies considerably with the species and size of the bird. Stubel (1910) found that in all birds with large hearts in relation to body size (pigeon, duck, sea gull, and hawk) the vagus had a powerful cardio-inhibitory effect, whereas in birds such as the chicken, rook, and jackdaw it exerted little control on heart rate. For example, when both vagi were sectioned in pigeons and chickens, the following results were obtained:

	Heart rate, nerves intact	Heart rate, vagi sectioned
Pigeon	120	300
Chicken	288	312

The degree of vagal control on the heart appears to be influenced by respiration, according to Paton (1912) and Jurgens (1909), who demonstrated that vagotomy in the duck does not increase heart rate if artificial respiration is applied. Stimulation of the peripheral end of the vagus of the pigeon, chicken, and duck slows the heart and may arrest it momentarily in the pigeon and chicken and for a longer period in the duck (Jurgens, Paton). It also diminishes the amplitude of contraction of the atria (see Clark, 1927) and sometimes that of the ventricles (Jurgens, Paton).

Effects of Drugs

Sympathetic nerves, when stimulated, release sympathin or an adrenaline-like substance; stimulated parasympathetic nerves release acetylcholine. These substances account for the effects observed after stimulation of these nerves. The former are known as adrenergic and the latter as cholinergic nerves. Sympathomimetic drugs are those which mimic the effects of sympathetic nerve stimulation. Adrenaline or epinephrine, ephedrine, and neosynephrine are examples of some of these. Some of the parasympathomimetic drugs are acetylcholine, pilocarpine, and arecoline. The effects of such drugs on the chicken heart have received little attention. According to the meager data available, the effects appear to be the same as in the mammal. Epinephrine in smaller doses increases, while larger doses (1 mg. or more, intravenously) may slow, the heart rate (Sturkie, unpublished). Epinephrine at the higher level of dosage, when injected intravenously into hens weighing 2 kg., not only slowed the heart, but also produced premature systoles and other cardiac arrhythmias. Rodbard and Tolpin (1948), who injected 1 mg. of epinephrine intravenously into immature chickens, reported increased heart rate.

Acetylcholine (0.2 to 1 mg. or more injected intravenously) in chickens causes a momentary slowing of the heart, after which the rate increases rapidly (Sturkie, unpublished).

Atropine is a drug which blocks parasympathetic nerves and releases the heart from vagal control. When injected into birds, heart rate may increase, depending upon the degree of vagal control and release (Clark, 1927). The heart rate of chicks on a potassium-deficient diet usually slows, and the rate reverts to normal when atropine sulfate is injected (Sturkie, 1950).

That body temperature influences heart rate is discussed elsewhere.

REFERENCES

Barry, A. 1940 Age changes in the pulsation frequency of the embryonic chick heart. J. Exp. Zool. 85:157.

Buchanan, F. 1909 The frequency of the heart beat and the form of the ECG in birds. J. Physiol. 38:62.

Clark, A. J. 1927 Comparative Physiology of the Heart. Macmillan Co., New York.

Davies, F. 1930 The conducting system of the bird's heart. J. Anat. 64:9.

Drennan, M. R. 1927 The auriculo-ventricular bundle in the bird's heart. Brit. Med. J. Part 1:321.

Eyster, J. A. E., and W. J. Meek   1921   The origin and conduction of the heart beat. Physiol. Rev. 1:1.

Groebbels, F.   1932   Der Vogel. Erster Band: Atmungswelt und Nahrungswelt. Verlag von Gebrüder Borntraeger, Berlin.

Jurgens, H.   1909   Über die Wirkung des Nervus Vagus auf das Herz der Vögel. Arch. ges. Physiol. (Pflügers) 129:506.

Kaupp, B. F.   1918   The Anatomy of the Domestic Fowl. W. B. Saunders Co., Philadelphia.

Kisch, B.   1951   The electrocardiogram of birds (chicken, duck, pigeon). Exp. Med. & Surg. 9:103.

Kisch, B.   1953   Heart sounds in tachycardia. Trans. Am. College of Cardiology II.

Lewis, T.   1915   The spread of the excitatory process in the vertebrate heart. V: The bird's heart. Phil. Trans. Roy. Soc. London 207:298.

Mangold, E., and T. Kato   1914   Zur vergleichenden Physiologie des His'schen Bundels. III: Mitteilung: Die atrioventrikulare Erregungsleitung im Vogelherzen. Arch. ges. Physiol. (Pflügers) 160:91.

McNally, E. H.   1941   Heart rate of the domestic fowl. Poultry Sci. 20:266.

Paton, N. D.   1912   On the extrinsic nerves of the heart of the bird. J. Physiol. 45:106.

Patten, B. M., and T. C. Kramer   1933   The initiation of contraction in the embryonic chick heart. Am. J. Anat. 53:349.

Petren, T.   1926   Die Coronararterien des Vogelherzens. Morph. Jahrb. 56:239.

Rodbard, S., and M. Tolpin   1948   A relationship between the body temperature and the blood pressure in the chicken. Am. J. Physiol. 151:509.

Romanoff, A. L.   1944   The heart beat of avian embryos. Anat. Rec. 89:313.

Stubel, H. S.   1910   Beiträge zur Kenntnis der Physiologie des Blutkreislaufes bei verschiedenen Vogelarten. Arch. ges. Physiol. (Pflügers) 135:249.

Sturkie, P. D.   1950   Abnormal electrocardiograms of chickens produced by potassium deficiency and effects of certain drugs on the abnormalities. Am. J. Physiol. 162:538.

Tigerstedt, R.   1921   Physiologie des Kreislaufes. Vol. II. Berlin and Leipzig.

Woodbury, R. A., and W. F. Hamilton   1937   Blood pressure studies in small animals. Am. J. Physiol. 119:663.

CHAPTER 5

Electrocardiography

DIPHASIC ACTION POTENTIALS

ACTIVE muscle or nerve exhibits electrical activity. If two electrodes, A and B, are attached, some distance apart, to a strip of muscle and the muscle is stimulated, it depolarizes or becomes electrically negative at the electrode nearest the point of stimulation, for example at A. Muscle B is still in the resting stage, and a difference in potential is produced between the electrodes. When the electrodes are attached to a suitable recording instrument (galvanometer) the potential difference is registered as an initial upward deflection. As the excitation wave spreads to electrode B, the difference in potential decreases and finally reaches zero, and the curve returns to the base, or isoelectric line. (See Wiggers, 1949, for further details.)

The muscle which depolarized first at A now begins recovery or repolarization ahead of the muscle at B, and there is now a new potential difference but in the opposite direction. The curve is now downward, and as the repolarization process passes to B, the potential difference continues to decrease and the curve returns to the isoelectric line. The upward and downward (positive and negative) deflections constitute a diphasic record.

SPREAD OF THE ELECTRICAL EXCITATION WAVE
IN THE BIRD HEART

The electrical excitation wave precedes mechanical contraction slightly and spreads from the S-A node through the other branches of the conducting system. The paths and speed of conduction of this

72

wave may be determined by placing electrodes at different areas of the heart and determining the change in potential at the electrodes (method of relative negativity).

Lewis (1915), Mangold (1919), and Kisch (1949 and 1951) used this method on the bird heart. Lewis and Mangold used bipolar leads. Lewis placed the exploring electrode on the heart and the other on the chest wall; Mangold placed both electrodes on the heart. Kisch used, for the most part, unipolar leads (chest, direct, and endocavity leads). Mangold and Lewis reported that the impulse started in the region of the S-A node and spread to the left side of the right atrium, thence to the left atrium and then to the septum.

The order of depolarization in the different areas of the ventricles (chicken) is according to Lewis, Mangold, and Kisch as follows:

Kisch 1951	Lewis 1915	Mangold 1919	Region of Heart
1	1	1	Apex of right ventricle
3	3	2	Base of left ventricle
2	4	3	Base of right ventricle
4	2	4	Apex of left ventricle

The time required for the impulse to spread from the region of the septum to other parts of the ventricle's surface, according to Lewis, is shown in Figure 13. Lewis found that the rate of conduction across the surfaces of the right and left ventricles was of the same magnitude but variable, averaging 1119 and 1087 mm. per second respectively. The rate across the septum was much lower, 740 mm. per second.

Based upon the distribution of surface potentials and studies of electro-

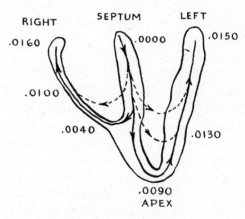

Figure 13. Diagram of spread of impulse or excitation wave in ventricles of bird heart.

Coronal section; time in seconds. (Modified slightly from Lewis, *Phil. Trans. Roy. Soc. London,* B, 1915.)

cardiograms, Lewis' conclusion was that the impulse spreads (see Figure 13) downward through the septum and later upward through the septum and later upward through the free walls, almost in line with the latter rather than at right angles to them. The very rapid spread of the impulse downward (electrical axis, $+90°$; see Figure 14) corresponds to the small upright R wave of the electrocardiogram. The depolarization wave then shifts abruptly upwards (electrical axis approximately $-90°$), and its duration is relatively long (Figure 13). This produces the S wave of the electrocardiogram (Lewis, 1915).

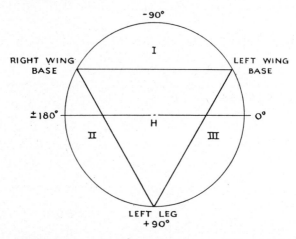

Figure 14. Limb leads for the ECG of the bird, with heart in center (H).

Neither Mangold nor Lewis determined which of the endocardial and epicardial surfaces was activated first. Kisch (1951) made such studies on the bird heart, using direct leads with the electrodes placed respectively in the interior and on the exterior surfaces of the atria or ventricles. The leads were taken simultaneously. He showed that the epicardial surface of the ventricles is activated or depolarized before the endocardial surface in the chicken, pigeon, duck, and sea gull. Depolarization on the surface of the right ventricle of the chicken heart begins about 0.02 to 0.03 seconds earlier than inside the right ventricle, but on the left ventricle it starts about 0.01 second earlier than on the inside. Depolarization in the interior of the left and right ventricles occurs at approximately the same time. When the exploring electrode was placed on the ventricular surface (right or left), the resulting electrogram (EG) resembled the normal electrocardiogram (ECG). Leads from the interior of the ventricle produce EG's with the configuration of waves in the opposite direction, similar to the normal ECG of man and dog, in which the endocardial surfaces are depolarized before the epicardial.

THE ELECTROCARDIOGRAM

The electrocardiogram (ECG) is a record of the electrical activity of the heart, picked up from electrodes attached to parts of the body other than the heart itself (leads). For details concerning the essentials and methods of taking and recording electrocardiograms, consult textbooks by Wiggers (1949), Burch and Winsor (1946), and Katz (1947). Leads taken directly from the heart produce records termed electrograms (EG's). Records from any two electrodes constitute a lead. The standard limb leads for man are: lead I, right arm and left arm; lead II, right arm and left leg; and III, left arm and left leg. The limb leads for the bird heart are the same as for man, except that the electrodes (usually needles) are attached to, or inserted in, the bases of the wings (Figure 14). The three limb leads form roughly an equilateral triangle with the heart located near the center. This is more nearly true for the bird heart than for man.

The ECG may be recorded optically or directly. When current flows through a string galvanometer, the string deflects and casts a shadow which can be enlarged by mirrors or lenses and projected upon a moving strip of photosensitive paper and photographed. The deflection may also be amplified and made to activate a direct writer. The frequency response of direct writing instruments is less than optical ones.

The standard speed for the paper of the electrocardiograph is 25 mm. per second. The vertical lines 1 mm. apart on the paper represent time lines (0.04 second), at standard speeds. The horizontal lines, also 1 mm. apart, represent amplitude or voltage. For work with humans, the instrument is usually standardized at 1 millivolt. When 1 millivolt is impressed upon the instrument, it causes a deflection of 10 mm. Since the heart rate of the chicken is considerably faster than that of humans, the standard chart speed is, in some cases, not fast enough to record all waves faithfully. Usually, if the heart rate is 300 per minute or above, the P and T waves may be fused together, and the P wave is not always discernible (particularly in leads II and III). However, the P wave of the chicken may not, in some cases, be discernible even when the chart speed is increased to 50 or 75 mm. per second (Sturkie, 1948 and 1949; Kisch, 1951) and when the frequency response of the instrument is increased to 500 cycles per second, which is more than adequate (Sturkie, 1953, unpublished). It appears that the P and T waves are fused because the auricles begin depolarizing before the ventricles are completely repolarized.

Normal Electrocardiogram of the Bird

The normal ECG of man shows P, Q, R, S, and T waves. The bird ECG exhibits P, S, and T waves and usually a small abortive R in some leads, but no Q wave (see Figures 15, 16, and 17). The

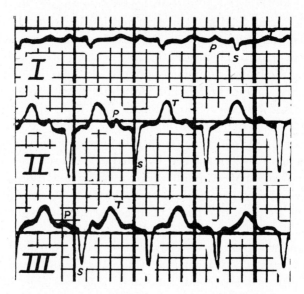

Figure 15. Leads I, II, and III of a normal electro-cardiogram of the chicken.

Standardization, 1 millivolt equals 1 cm.; chart speed, 25 mm. per second. Tracings taken with direct writing instrument. Some of the time and amplitude lines were blocked out before the charts were photographed. (From Sturkie, *Am. J. Vet. Res.*, 1949.)

A   B

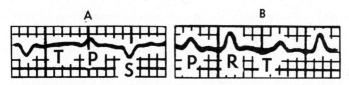

Figure 16. Electrocardiogram of lead I of chicken exhibiting two
types of configurations.
   In A, there is an S but no R wave, and the T is slightly positive.
In B, there is no S, but an R wave is evident, and the T is slightly
negative. Standardization is 1 millivolt equals 1.6 cm., and the
chart speed is approximately 60 mm. per second. (From Sturkie,
Am. J. Vet. Res., 1949.)

P wave, as in man, represents the depolarization or electrical discharge of the atrial muscle and corresponds roughly to, or precedes
slightly, atrial contraction. There is no recognizable wave of repolarization. R and S waves represent the depolarization of the
ventricular muscle which signals the onset of ventricular systole.
The T wave represents repolarization of the ventricles and, presumably as in man, the end of systole.

The P wave when observed is usually upright (positive) in all
leads in the chicken, duck, and pigeon (Sturkie, Kisch), but usually
negative in lead III of the sea gull (Kisch). It is observed more often
in lead I, even though the amplitude may be lower, because the T
wave is almost isoelectric. In leads II and III, T is positive. A small
upright R is usually (Sturkie, 1949) or always (Kisch, 1951) present
in lead II of the chicken and pigeon respectively, but is rarely pres-

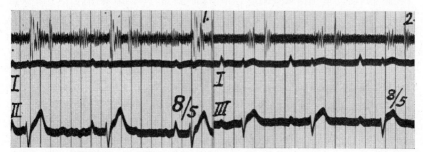

Figure 17. Phonocardiogram (upper tracing) and electrocardiogram of pigeon
(leads I, II, and III).
   Standardization, 1 millivolt equals 1.6 cm.; chart speed, 75 mm. per second.
Photographic method of recording. (From Kisch, *Exp. Med. & Surg.*, 1951.)

ent in III. Occasionally the R wave is prominent in II and III of the duck ECG (Kisch).

Lead I is the most variable of the limb leads. In most cases the height or amplitude of all the complexes, except P, is low, and in some cases some of the waves may be isoelectric. With respect to the configuration of R, S, and T in lead I, there are three main types described as follows (Sturkie, 1948 and 1949):

(a) A relatively prominent S and no R or a very small R. The T is usually isoelectric or slightly positive (Figure 16).

(b) A relatively prominent R and no S or a small S. The T wave is usually isoelectric or slightly negative.

(c) R's and S's of about equal prominence.

In a study involving 205 ECG's from 72 adult chickens, the percentage of the records (lead I) exhibiting these types were: a, 13; b, 63; and c, 24.

Intervals. The duration in seconds of the different waves or complexes has been determined in ECG's by Sturkie (1949) and in EG's by Kisch (1951). Durations of P, S, and T and intervals from the beginning of P to the start of S and from the beginning of S to the end of T have been determined for leads II and III in the chicken. The R wave in II and III is usually small or absent, and when present, its starting point is difficult to locate. For this reason the P-S, instead of the P-R, interval is determined. In many cases there is no S-T segment. T usually begins where S ends, and that point is used as the starting point for T. S-T represents the interval from the beginning of S to the end of T, or the time required for depolarization and repolarization of the ventricles.

The P-S interval is the time required for the impulse, beginning in the right atrium, to reach the ventricles. The intervals presented in Table 14 are based upon studies of selected ECG's in which the beginning and end of all waves were discernible.

In general, as heart rate increases, the intervals for all complexes except S decrease, and this was demonstrated also by Kisch in the chicken, pigeon, duck, and sea gull with direct leads. The intervals determined with direct leads on the chicken by Kisch (1951) are in close agreement with those determined with limb leads by Sturkie, except that for the ventricular complex. The duration of this interval is 0.037 second according to Kisch and 0.024 according to

Table 14. Intervals of the chicken electrocardiogram in seconds. Chart speed is 25 mm. per second (Sturkie, 1949)

		Heart rates	221 240	241 260	261 280	281 300	301 340
P	Mean		0.0408	0.0429	0.0421	0.0410	0.0374
	Minimal		0.0350	0.0390	0.0400	0.0350	0.0310
	Maximal		0.0480	0.0450	0.0450	0.0470	0.0440
S	Mean		0.0242	0.0247	0.0234	0.0233	0.0235
	Minimal		0.0210	0.0200	0.0200	0.0200	0.0200
	Maximal		0.0260	0.0290	0.0310	0.0270	0.0280
T	Mean		0.1161	0.1095	0.1048	0.1043	0.0925
	Minimal		0.1230	0.1220	0.1210	0.1180	0.1110
	Maximal		0.1710	0.1590	0.1550	0.1330	0.1250
P-S	Mean		0.0812	0.0847	0.0849	0.0790	0.0723
	Minimal		0.0760	0.0720	0.0760	0.0720	0.0670
	Maximal		0.0900	0.0910	0.0940	0.0860	0.0820
S-T	Mean		0.1402	0.1342	0.1281	0.1270	0.1164
	Minimal		0.1230	0.1220	0.1210	0.1180	0.1110
	Maximal		0.1710	0.1590	0.1550	0.1330	0.1250
	No. of ECG's		7–9	9–12	16	14–16	12–14

Sturkie. Lewis (1915), who determined the S interval of the ECG on five anesthetized chickens (heart rates below 200 for most of them), reported values from 0.027 to 0.037 seconds. Intervals of EG's (in seconds) of birds are according to Kisch (1951) as follows:

Species	No. of birds	Average heart rate	S or QRS	P−Q or P−S	Q−T or S−T
Duck	9	182	0.028	0.090	0.110
Pigeon	13	227	0.021	0.069	0.100
Chicken	10	335	0.027	0.061	0.132
Sea gull	5	447	0.026	0.048	0.116

Amplitude. The amplitude of all waves of the bird ECG is relatively low and is considerably less than that of the human ECG. It is so low in lead I that it is difficult or impossible to get accurate measurements with the usual standardization. An estimate of average amplitude in I can be deduced from the differences in mean amplitude for the various waves in leads II and III, in accordance with Einthoven's law, which states that the amplitude of a given wave in I and III should equal that in II. This is true provided that the three leads are run simultaneously or, if not, that there is no appreciable change in heart rate and amplitude. Thus, the amplitude in millivolts of S in lead I and S in III (added algebraically; see Figure 15) should equal that in S II, and does. In this figure, where S in I is the main ventricular wave (type a, lead I), S II is greater than S III. When R is predominant in I, then the amplitude of S II is less than S III. If S II and S III are equal, then R or S waves are absent in I.

The amplitudes of P, R, S, and T for leads II and III of the chicken are shown in Table 15. These figures were derived from selected records, but they are subject to error because of the limitations of the instrument used, whose sensitivity to low voltages and response to high frequencies were not optimum for the bird heart. The P and T waves were not always clearly delineated, and the values for these, particularly for P, represent rough estimates. Chickens have ECG's of lower voltage than pigeons, swans, or ducks (Lewis, Kisch; see also Lepeschkin, 1951).

Table 15. Amplitude in millivolts of P, R, S, and T in leads II and III
(Sturkie, 1949)

	ECG's (No.)	II Mean	Stand. error	ECG's (No.)	III Mean	Stand. error	Difference between II and III
P	40	0.0602	0.0026	40	0.0421	0.0016	*
R	56	0.0346	0.0021	56	0.0221	0.0013	*
S (S in lead I)	18	0.2193	0.0135	18	0.1787*	0.0150	—
S (R in lead I)	43	0.1241	0.0067	44	0.1430*	0.0071	—
T (II>III)	46	0.1095	0.0056	46	0.0900	0.0050	*
T (II<III)	15	0.0716	0.0036	15	0.0901	0.0062	*

* Difference statistically significant.

The relative amplitude of the waves in the limb leads is dependent upon the direction and magnitude of the electromotive force (electrical axis) in the heart in relation to the electrodes and also upon the degree to which this force is conducted to the limbs of the body. It is known that certain organs of the body are good and some are poor conductors of this force. If the heart of the bird is exposed by removing the sternum, sternal ribs, coracoids, and clavicle and the tissues attached thereto, the amplitude of all waves in the limb leads is increased twofold to threefold (Sturkie, 1948; Figure 18).

Electrical axis. The electrical axis represents the mean or average electromotive force (magnitude) of depolarization and repolarization acting in an average direction during the period of electrical activity of the heart. It is a vector quantity in that it has direction, magnitude, and sense. Axes for any of the waves may be determined by measuring the amplitude of complexes in any two of the limb leads and plotting these values (for details, see Burch and Winsor, 1946; Wiggers, 1949). Leads I and III are usually used in human ECG's, and II and III for the chicken, because in the latter the

Table 16. Electrical axes of chicken hearts in relationship to type of lead I (Sturkie, 1949)

Type of ECG in I	No. of birds	ECG'S No.	ECG'S Percent	RS axes in degrees Range	RS axes in degrees Average
S present	15	17	25.8	−91 to −120	−102.11
R present	30	46⎱	74.2	−26 to −103*	− 74.04
	2	3⎰		+10 to + 30	

* Only one ECG above −90 degrees.

Direction of T wave in I	No. of birds	ECG's No.	ECG's Percent	T axes in degrees Range	T axes in degrees Average
Positive	34	43	70.49	+68 to + 89	+ 81.8
Negative	10	12	19.67	+95 to +115	+100.3
Isoelectric	6	6	9.83	+88 to + 91	+ 89.6

amplitude for all waves in I is too low for accurate measurement. Electrical axes for chicken ECG's are shown in Table 16. An RS axis of $-90°$ (see Figure 14) means that the mean electromotive force is directed upward and parallel to the long axis of the body. This would mean that the amplitude of R and the amplitude of S were equal in leads II and III and zero in I. It is observed from the table that 74 percent of the chickens studied had RS axes averaging $-74.04°$. Thus, the axis is directed anteriorly and to the left of the long axis of the body (almost halfway between 12 and 1 o'clock). In these ECG's the amplitude of S III exceeds S II, and the amplitude of R in I exceeds S or S is absent. Twenty-six percent had RS axes

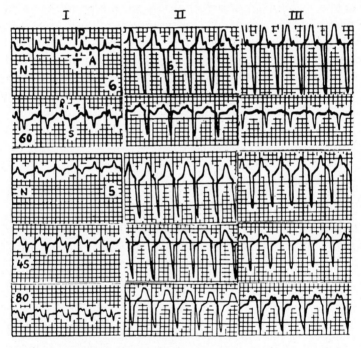

Figure 18. Effects on the electrocardiogram of rotation of the heart on its anterio-posterior axis to the left.

Leads I, II, and III for chickens No. 5 and 6 before rotation (N) and after different degrees of rotation. The degrees of rotation, 60, 45, and 80, are indicated on the left side. The bird was opened and the heart exposed. After rotation, there was a pronounced decrease in amplitude of S and T in lead III. Standardization, 1 millivolt; chart speed, 25 mm. per second. (From Sturkie, *Am. J. Physiol.*, 1948.)

averaging $-102.11°$ (between 11 and 12 o'clock). Thus, S II is greater than S III, and S I exceeds R I or R is absent. The normal RS axis in birds differs markedly from that in normal humans (which ranges from 0 to $+90°$) and in a number of other animals.

The electrical axes for T are grouped according to the direction of T in lead I (Table 16). In 70 percent of the ECG's studied, T I was positive and the axis averaged $+81.8°$ (axis directed posteriorly between 5 and 6 o'clock). In 20 percent, with negative T I's, the axis was $+100.3°$; in those remaining, with isoelectric T waves, the axes averaged $89.6°$, or approximately $90°$, as expected in accordance with Einthoven's law. Thus, the more nearly the electrical axis parallels a given lead line, the higher the amplitude of the waves, and when it runs almost perpendicular to the lead line (as in lead I of the chicken), the amplitude is low. This can be demonstrated experimentally by rotating the heart on its anterio-posterior axis to the left or right (Sturkie, 1948). When the heart is rotated to the left, so that the apex of the left ventricle is directed perpendicularly to the lead III line and more nearly parallel to lead I (see Figure 18), there is a pronounced decrease in amplitude of all the ventricular complexes in III, a slight decrease in II, and a great increase in lead I, and the change is proportional to the degree of rotation. There is, moreover, a change in direction or configuration of the waves in I. Normally, if an R and an inverted T are present in lead I, the R may be replaced after rotation to the left by an S, and the T wave becomes positive. If an S is normally present in I, its amplitude is decreased relatively, and an R wave appears after rotation to the left. Thus, the RS electrical axis for all birds increases after rotation, from an average normal of $-87°$ to $-98.7°$ after rotation to the left.

Conversely, when the heart is rotated to the right, there is a significant decrease in amplitude of all ventricular waves in II, a slight decrease in III, and a great increase in I. The RS electrical axis decreases from a normal of $-87°$ to $-68.6°$. Rotation to the right increases the height of R in lead I and the negativity of the T waves. When an S wave is normally present in I, it is replaced by an R after rotation.

Chest, extremity, and direct leads. If one electrode (exploring) is attached to the chest wall near the apex of the left ventricle and the other electrode attached to the right wing (lead IV R), the resulting ECG resembles that recorded from limb leads II and III except that R is usually more prominent. This is also the case with unipolar chest leads (V) in which the Wilson central terminal constitutes the indifferent electrode (Kisch, 1951). If, however, the exploring electrode is attached to the upper chest wall near the atria, the record shows an R wave, no S, and an inverted T wave. Similar results are obtained in endocavity leads in which the exploring electrode (direct V lead) is placed in the ventricular cavity, except that the amplitude is much higher than in the chest leads. EG's recorded from the surface of the ventricles show opposite configuration, like the normal ECG from limb leads.

Unipolar extremity leads VR, VL, and VF represent leads taken with the exploring electrode at right arm, left arm, and left leg respectively, with the indifferent electrode as the Wilson central terminal. ECG's from these leads have been recorded in the pigeon, duck, and chicken by Kisch (1951). In leads VR and VL of the chicken and pigeon, there is a prominent R, no S, and an inverted T, like the endocavity leads, but in the duck, these leads show an S, a QS, or a small R and prominent S, unlike the endocavity leads. Kisch attributes this difference to the position of the heart, which is more vertical in the duck, according to him. In VF of all birds studied by Kisch there was a QS or a small R and a prominent S.

Electrograms of Explanted Hearts

Electrograms of embryonic chicken hearts explanted and grown *in vitro* show two or three components or complexes, depending on the type and amount of heart tissue present (Szepsenwol, 1946; Von Bonsdorff, 1950). If portions of both atria and ventricles are explanted, P, QRS, and T waves are recorded. If only the atrium is explanted, two main complexes, a QRS (mainly positive) and a T wave, are recorded. Similar complexes are recorded in ventricular explants. The heart rate in ventricular explants is about one-half or less that of the atrial and compound explants (atrial and ventricular tissue). The rate is higher in the atrial explants when more S-A nodal tissue is present. The rate is highest when both atrial and ventricular tissues are present.

ABNORMAL ELECTROCARDIOGRAMS

Heart disorders as revealed by the electrocardiogram appear to cause few deaths in chickens during the first year of life. Serial ECG's were made on 72 adult females (White Leghorns) from 5 months (maturity) to 18 months of age (Sturkie, 1949). Although 27 of the birds died during this period, only 5 percent of these exhibited heart abnormalities which may have caused death. In

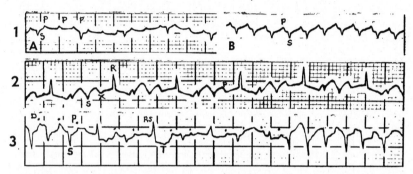

Figure 19. Partial and complete atrioventricular block in the chicken, produced by potassium deficiency in the diet.

1-A, three atrial beats (P's) to 1 ventricular beat (S), or two blocked ventricular beats. The ventricular and auricular rates are approximately 125 and 375 per minute respectively. 1-B, normal ECG of same bird. P and T are fused in these records.

2, one blocked ventricular beat (X) followed by an ectopic beat (R), initiated by the A-V node or ventricules.

3, complete A-V block with idioventricular rhythm. The atria and ventricles are beating independently at rates of approximately 300 and 200 per minute respectively. Since all of the impulses originating in the S-A node do not pass through the A-V node, the ectopic beats from the ventricle constitute a protective mechanism. Black dots indicate P waves. Chart speed, 25 mm. per second. (From Sturkie, *Am. J. Physiol.*, 1950.)

studies involving approximately 1000 ECG's of normal chickens of various ages, very few irregularities were observed. Four cases revealed inverted T waves in leads II or III, but these changes were transient. A few cases of premature systoles were also observed. Respiratory diseases, such as Newcastle and coryza, have no effect on the ECG. Phasic sinus arrhythmia, a variation in the discharge of the S-A node associated with respiration, has been reported in the

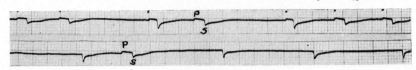

Figure 20. Partial (upper tracing) and complete sinoatrial (S-A) block (lower) with slow heart rate (100 per minute) and mild sinus arrhythmia.

Upper tracing shows examples of normal beats (P's and S's) followed by long pauses, with almost doubled P-P interval, indicating dropped atrial and ventricular beats. Lower tracing shows one normal P and S, followed by no P's and three ectopic beats (complete S-A block). The bird died shortly thereafter. (From Sturkie, *Poultry Sci.*, 1952.)

pigeon (Kisch, 1951), but has not been observed in the normal chicken (Sturkie).

Effects of Mineral and Vitamin Deficiencies on the ECG

Acute potassium deficiency in growing chicks produces a high percentage of abnormal ECG's (70 percent) and 100 percent mortality within two to four weeks (Sturkie, 1950 and 1952). Most of these disorders are concerned with the rhythm and conduction of the heartbeat. They include partial and complete atrioventricular block, partial and complete sinoatrial block, sinus arrhythmia and marked sinus slowing, premature nodal and ventricular systoles, and others. Examples of some of these are shown in Figures 19–22. For further details concerning the physiology of such abnormalities, consult textbooks on electrocardiography.

Pathological lesions in the A-V node or bundle or in the S-A node

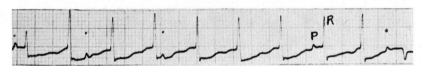

Figure 21. Nodal rhythm and A-V dissociation in the chicken, produced by potassium deficiency in the diet.

The atrial rate (P waves) is very slow (75) and fairly regular; and the nodal rate (R waves) is faster (120). Thus, the S-A node is discharging so slowly that the A-V node initiates its own rhythm, and the two rhythms are independent. Some of the P waves precede, some follow, and the fourth P (not seen) merges with the nodal beats. The sinus impulses reach the A-V junction when the latter is in a refractory state and are not conducted to the ventricles. The last sinus impulse (P) is conducted to the ventricles. (From Sturkie, *Poultry Sci.*, 1952.)

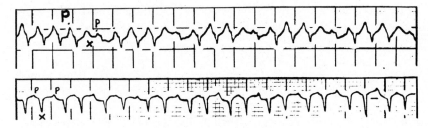

Figure 22 (upper), represents a type of sinus arrhythmia characterized by marked slowing (X) or discharge of the impulse from the S-A node on every fourth or fifth beat. The P-P interval is about $1\frac{1}{2}$ times the normal P-P. P and T are fused.

The lower record represents a case of premature nodal systoles, with alternate premature and long (fully compensated) beats, or bigeminal rhythm. The S-A node initiates the impulses normally (P waves), but the A-V node initiates the premature ventricular beat (X). (From Sturkie, *Am. J. Physiol.*, 1950.)

may cause A-V and S-A block. Gross lesions were not observed in the hearts of potassium-deficient chickens, and it appears that the blocks result from a functional rather than a pathological disturbance in conduction. For example, functional A-V block in mammals may result from increased vagal action or tone. In such cases it may be abolished by administration of atropine, a cholinergic blocker. In potassium-deficient chicks, whose ECG's exhibited A-V block and premature systoles, atropine and also diethylaminoethanol were effective in reverting the ECG's to normal. That the ions of potassium and calcium are concerned in the irritability and activity of cardiac muscle is well known. The requirement of potassium for the bird heart may be higher than for mammals, since, according to Clark (1927), the blood of birds contains three times as much potassium as that of mammals.

Acute thiamine deficiency in pigeons results in sinus arrhythmia, bradycardia, and A-V block (Carter and Drury, 1929), but chronic deficiency of the vitamin rarely produces heart abnormalities (Swank and Bessey, 1941). Sectioning of the vagi or administration of atropine abolishes the disorders, according to Carter and Drury. These and other abnormalities have been observed in thiamine-deficient animals (Hundley, Ashburn, and Sebrell, 1945, and others).

Deficiencies of niacin, riboflavin, and vitamins A and D have no effect upon the ECG of the chicken (Sturkie, unpublished).

REFERENCES

Bonsdorff, R. von 1950 The electrogram of embryonic heart muscle cultivated _in vitro_ and its relation to the electrocardiogram of the embryonic heart. Acta Physiol. Scand. 22 (supp. 75).

Burch, G., and T. Winsor 1946 A Primer of Electrocardiography. Lea & Febiger, Philadelphia.

Carter, C. W., and A. N. Drury 1929 Heart blocks in rice-fed pigeons. J. Physiol. 68:1 (Proc.).

Hundley, J. H., L. L. Ashburn, and W. H. Sebrell 1945 The electrocardiogram in chronic thiamine deficiency in rats. Am. J. Physiol. 144:404.

Katz, L. N. 1947 Electrocardiography. Lea & Febiger, Philadelphia.

Kisch, B. 1949 Electrocardiographic studies in sea-gulls. Exp. Med. & Surg. 7:345.

Kisch, B. 1951 The electrocardiogram of birds (chicken, duck, pigeon). Exp. Med. & Surg. 9:103.

Lepeschkin, E. 1951 Modern Electrocardiography, Vol. I. Williams and Wilkins Co., Baltimore.

Lewis, T. 1915 The spread of the excitatory process in the vertebrate heart. V: The bird's heart. Phil. Trans. Roy. Soc. London 207:298.

Mangold, E. 1919 Elektrographische Untersuchungen des Erregungsverlaufes im Vogelherzen. Arch. ges. Physiol. (Pflügers) 175:327.

Odum, E. P. 1945 The heart rate of small birds. Science 101:153.

Sturkie, P. D. 1948 Effects of changes in position of the heart of the chicken on the electrocardiogram. Am. J. Physiol. 154:251.

Sturkie, P. D. 1949 The electrocardiogram of the chicken. Am. J. Vet Res. 10:168.

Sturkie, P. D. 1950 Abnormal electrocardiograms of chickens produced by potassium deficiency and effects of certain drugs on the abnormalities. Am. J. Physiol. 162:538.

Sturkie, P. D. 1952 Further studies of potassium deficiency in the chicken. Poultry Sci. 31:648.

Swank, R. L., and O. A. Bessey 1941 Avian thiamine deficiency: Characteristic symptoms and their pathogenesis. J. Nutrition 22:77.

Szepsenwol, J. 1946 A comparison of growth, differentiation, activity, and action currents of heart and skeletal muscle in tissue culture. Anat. Rec. 95:125.

Wiggers, C. J. 1949 Physiology in Health and Disease. 5th ed. Lea & Febiger, Philadelphia.

CHAPTER 6

Respiration

ANATOMY OF THE RESPIRATORY APPARATUS

THE respiratory apparatus of birds consists of the lungs and the air passages leading to and from them. The air passages comprise the nasal cavities, pharynx, trachea, syrinx, bronchi and ramifications, and also the air sacs and certain of the bones of the body which are pneumatic.

The lungs are small and attached to the ribs of the thorax and by some are considered purely passive in action, capable of dilating and contracting only when the ribs and pulmonary diaphragm contract. Others consider them capable of active movements independent of other movements. It is sufficient here to state that the lungs of birds are not capable of the elastic recoil characteristic of mammals.

The diaphragm of birds is likewise different from that of mammals. According to Soum (1896), McLeod and Wagers (1939), and others, there are two diaphragms in the bird, the pulmonary and the thoracio-abdominal. The pulmonary diaphragm has the shape of an isosceles triangle with its apex directed anteriorly and attached to the inferior surface of the lung. It is a horizontal sheet which divides the thoracic cavity into dorsal and ventral parts and is perforated by the openings for the air sacs and bronchi. The thoracio-abdominal diaphragm is a large fibrous membrane which is connected to the pericardium and passes between the liver and the intrathoracic sacs and attaches to the wall of the abdomen. It is an incomplete structure and is perforated by the connections of the abdominal air sacs.

Structure of Lungs and Air-Sac System

A great number of workers have reported on the structure of the lungs and the air-sac system. For a review of the early work, see the monograph of Soum (1896), and for later reviews and contributions, consult reports by Locy and Larsell (1916), Dotterweich (1930 and 1936), McLeod and Wagers (1939), Gilbert (1939), and Hazelhoff (1951).

The trachea bifurcates to form the mesobronchi, or primary bronchi, each of which runs through each lung. From these arise secondary bronchi (ecto- and entobronchi, or dorso- and ventro-bronchi according to some workers; also lateral bronchi) and from these, in turn, tertiary bronchi (parabronchi) which branch and anastomose freely (Figures 23 and 25). Thus, the parabronchi are continuous, forming a network of air capillaries, the bronchial circuit, in which course the blood capillaries. Such an arrangement (Figure 26) forms a hexagonal column of almost perfect geometrical design.

The air sacs are connected to the lungs by way of the mesobronchi and secondary bronchi. Other connections to the lungs are provided by the recurrent bronchi, which bud off from the proximal ends of all of the sacs (except the cervicals) in variable numbers and extend back to the lungs, where they anastomose with the parabronchi. The sacs are thus to be thought of as expanded reservoirs on the course of the bronchial circuits, rather than as terminal sacs (Locy and Larsell, 1916).

It is generally agreed that there are nine air sacs, plus their diverticula, which communicate with the lung. They are known by various names. McLeod and Wagers (1939) have listed four different terminologies, including one of their own, which have been used in the literature. There are still other variations (Soum, 1896, and others).

Only the interclavicular sac is not paired. The paired sacs are the cervicals, the thoracic sacs, and the abdominals, or extrathoracic sacs. There are two pairs of thoracic sacs, described by some as the anterior and posterior thoracics. Other terminologies are anterior and posterior intermediates and diaphragmatics. McLeod and Wagers (1939) refer to the posterior intermediate sacs as the lesser

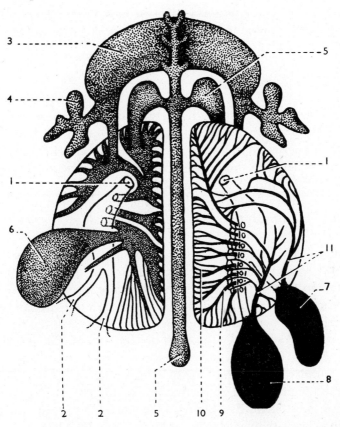

Figure 23. Diagram of lungs, bronchi, and air-sac system of the bird.
Left side, ventral view; right side, dorsal view. Black represents the system involved in inspiration, and stippling, that in expiration. 1, mesobronchi; 2, opening of mesobronchi into air sacs; 3, interclavicular sac; 4, diverticula of interclavicular sac; 5, cervical sac; 6, anterior thoracic sac; 7, posterior thoracic sac; 8, abdominal sac; 9, dorsobronchi; 10, parabronchi; 11, recurrent bronchi. (From Portmann, in *Traité de Zoologie*, edited by P. P. Grassé, Tome XV, Figure 200, Masson & Co., Paris, 1950, after Brandes and Hirsch.)

abdominals and to the true abdominal sacs as the greater abdominals.

Numerous diverticula arise from the interclavicular sac, including, in certain species, the axillare, suprahumeral, sternale, and subscapulare. The suprahumeral is the most prominent of these and is responsible for the marked pneumaticity of the humerus of some species of birds (Figure 23).

Pneumatic Bones of the Body

Hunter, who in 1843 described the air sacs and their communications with the bones of the body, stated that for the most part all birds except nonflying ones had the following pneumatic bones: femur, humerus, sternum, and vertebral column. He even thought that air penetrated the bones of the shank and feet of some birds. A number of workers before and since have held the same views. Baer (1897) stated that the bones of the cranium are not pneumatic and are no different from those of the mammal except that they are more developed.

Kaupp (1918) states that the abdominal air sacs communicate with the sacrum, the coccygeal vertebrae, the iliac bones, and the femurs. In fact, he says, the bones that are always aerated in all birds are the cervical and dorsal vertebrae, the sterna, and the humeri. Those aerated in some species only are the furculum, vertebral and sternal ribs, the sacrum, the coccyx, and the femur.

Groebbels (1932), who reviews this subject thoroughly, states that considerable variation exists between species of birds with respect to the number of bones that are pneumatic. He states that, in general, most small flying birds have few or no pneumatic bones, but that large flying birds have many pneumatic bones. It would appear, therefore, that whether or not the bones are pneumatic has little to do with flying ability. The humerus is pneumatic in most species, and markedly so in the chicken, according to Groebbels (1932). The femur is pneumatic in some species, but not in the chicken (McLeod and Wagers, 1939).

Many of the bones have air spaces and are considered pneumatic by anatomists, but this does not mean that these air spaces are important physiologically. Many species of birds are able to respire through the humerus, if the latter is broken and the opening exposed, even though the trachea is occluded. This is not true for the femur and some other bones which have been considered pneumatic.

MECHANICS OF RESPIRATION

A number of workers have described the movements undergone by the thorax and abdomen during respiration. A diagram of the movements of the sternum and ribs on inspiration and expiration is shown in Figure 24.

On inspiration (dotted lines), the sternum, coracoid, furcula, and the sternal ribs move forward and down. The vertebral ribs are pulled forward and inward. Thus, on inspiration, the vertical diameter of the thorax increases greatly and the transverse diameter decreases slightly. The lungs are thus expanded on inspiration by the pull of the ribs and sternum, mainly the latter, according to Soum (1896). He studied the effects of sectioning of the inspiratory and expiratory muscles of the pigeon and found that most of these muscles are not necessary for respiration.

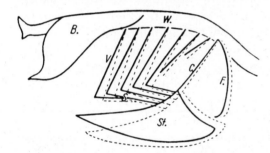

Figure 24. Lateral view of movements of ribs, sternum, coracoids, and furcula in respiration of bird.

Solid lines represent expiration; dotted lines, inspiration. (From Zimmer, *Zoologica*, 1935.)

Physiologically, the costoscapular muscles are unimportant and the elevators of little importance, but the triangular muscle is of greatest importance. Paralyzing the anterior and posterior elevators by sectioning of the spinal cord at the proper level was found not to arrest respiration, even though amplitude was diminished. Sectioning of the spinal cord at the point of the second thoracic vertebra completely paralyzed the triangular muscle and caused death of the bird (pigeon).

A number of workers, mainly on anatomical grounds, have considered the abdominal and the internal intercostals to be expiratory muscles. After sectioning or paralysis of the abdominal muscles, Soum (1896) found that the amplitude of respiration was lessened. This he attributed to the decrease in thoracic movements, which he demonstrated. His experiments showed that the abdominal muscles are not of great importance in respiration. When he paralyzed the abdominal muscles of a pigeon and then placed the bird on the ground with the abdomen and sternum down, respiratory movements were affected slightly. The weight of the bird sufficed to produce expiration in this position. A pigeon was observed to live for eight days after complete circular sectioning of the abdominal muscles.

Since the time of Harvey, many anatomists have considered one or the other of the diaphragms in birds the analogue or homologue of the mammalian diaphragm. The principal function of the pulmonary diaphragm, according to Soum (1896), is to remain tense and stretched over the surface of the lung. This is accomplished by the thin strips of muscles, bordering the periphery of the membrane, which are attached to the ribs. In inspiration, when the lung dilates, the diaphragm expands; in expiration it contracts when the lungs do. However, this membrane is not indispensable to respiration, since respiration continues regularly even after sectioning of the spinal cord at the third thoracic vertebra, which parzlyzes the diaphragm (Soum). This operation, according to Soum, is the same as that of sectioning the nerves which go directly to the musculature of the diaphragm; the latter is a difficult operation.

The thoracio-abdominal diaphragm is capable of compressing the abdominal viscera, according to Sappey, but Soum stated that the musculature of the diaphragm is too poorly developed for this function. It has been sectioned or destroyed by a number of workers without affecting respiration (see Soum, 1896, and Winterstein, 1921). Thus, it has no apparent function.

Duration of the Phases and Respiratory Rate

The following terms are used to designate the types and rates of breathing: (1) eupnea is the state of ordinary quiet breathing; (2) dyspnea represents labored breathing of different degrees; (3) hyperpnea represents a moderate increase in rate and/or amplitude of breathing; and (4) polypnea is characterized by a rapid shallow type of breathing, or panting. In apnea (5), there is a transient cessation of breathing.

The respiratory frequency varies within and between species, de-

Table 17. Respiratory rates of birds (number per minute)

Species	Male	Sex not stated	Female	Author
Canary		96–120		Groebbels (1932)
Pigeon		25–30		Zander (Groebbels)
Domestic duck		60–70		"
"		32		Hepke (Groebbels)
"	42		110	Kaupp (1923)
Domestic goose		13		Loer (Groebbels)
"	20		40	Kaupp
Domestic turkey		13.4		Loer (Groebbels
"	28		49	Kaupp
Chicken	21		37	"
"	12		20	Bert & Heubèl (Bert, 1870)
"	18		31	Stubel (Groebbels)

pending upon body size, excitement, and other factors. Bert (1870) and Groebbels (1932) presented tables upon the respiratory frequencies of many birds. A compilation of data from their tables and other sources is shown in Table 17. In general, the larger the bird the fewer the respirations per minute. The large condor and the small canary, for example, have respiratory frequencies of 6 and 100 respectively. The frequency is higher for females than for males. The effects of air temperature and other factors upon breathing rate are discussed later in this chapter and in Chapter 8.

Duration of inspiration and expiration has been studied by a number of investigators with varying results. Bert (1870) maintained that in the duck there are no true inspiratory or expiratory pauses; the movements follow each other rapidly. He did find, however, that expiration was slightly longer than inspiration. Huxley also found expiration to be longer in the duck (Winterstein, 1921). Baer (1896) on the pigeon, Soum (1896) on the pigeon and duck, and Kaupp (1923) on the duck observed inspiration to be of longer duration than expiration. Soum supposed that these differences were due to a partial closure of the glottis, since after tracheotomy duration of the phases was the same. Kaupp found that in the female chicken the phases are of about equal duration, but that expiration is longer than inspiration in the cock. Expiration is longer than inspiration in both sexes of chickens according to Graham (1940). In turkeys, inspiration is longer in both males and females (Kaupp, 1923). Inspiration in the goose is three times as long as expiration, but in the gander the phases are of the same duration (Kaupp, 1923).

CIRCULATION OF AIR IN LUNGS AND AIR SACS

A number of viewpoints have been expressed in the literature as to the manner in which air circulates through the lungs and air sacs and the influence of the latter on pulmonary ventilation. Shortly after Harvey described the air sacs in 1651, Perrault elaborated the antagonism theory, which holds that the thoracic sacs expand on inspiration, while the interclavicular, cervical, and abdominal sacs contract in inspiration. A tenet of this theory is that the lungs are ventilated with fresh air in both inspiration and expiration, thus providing for a more efficient exchange of gases. Mery in 1869, and others since, claimed to have demonstrated this so-called antagonism (see Soum, 1896). By placing a bird on its back and arranging recording tambours on the thorax and the abdomen, tracings of these movements were observed to run in opposite directions. Since these movements supposedly represented pressure changes within, it was concluded that the air sacs in these areas also behaved antagonistically. Soum demonstrated conclusively that the movements of the sternum and abdomen are not antagonistic normally. The apparent antagonism reported by earlier workers was based upon records taken on birds lying always on their backs, stated Soum. He showed that when the records were taken on birds in the normal position, standing or prone, the so-called antagonism disappeared. In accordance with the antagonism theory, if the abdominal sacs are destroyed or their action suppressed, this should not affect the volume of air traversing the trachea and lungs on inspiration, since such sacs are considered expiratory. However, a destruction of these sacs in the duck and pigeon by Soum actually decreased volume of inspired air by approximately 20 percent. Further evidence against the antagonism theory is the fact that pressure changes in the lungs and air sacs are synchronous.

Direction of Air Movement

The direction of air movement in lungs, in air sacs, and in the primary, secondary, and tertiary bronchi (parabronchi) on inspiration and expiration has been studied in a number of ways. Some have studied the O_2 and CO_2 content of the various sacs and have inferred from these studies how the air moves in the system on inspiration and expiration. Others have used colored material, which upon inhalation was carried through the system, and the paths traversed by it could be determined upon autopsy. Still others have used radiopaque material as the inhalant and have studied its movement with radiophotographs, while some have made glass models of the lung and air-sac system and have attempted to simulate normal respiration.

The subject is reviewed most recently by Hazelhoff (1943 and 1951), who also presents the results of his own experiments. Dotterweich (1930) studied the movement of lampblack in the lung and air-sac system of birds and concluded that during inspiration and expiration a current of air flows through the dorsobronchi to the

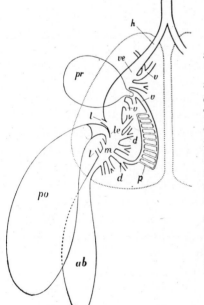

Figure 25. Diagram of the right lung of a bird (ventral aspect).

The outline of the lung is indicated by a dotted line. Of the anterior air sacs, only the anterior thoracic sac is shown. The recurrent bronchi are not reproduced. Only the parabronchi arising from one ventrobronchus and one dorsobronchus are shown as a series of connected, parallel tubes. h, primary bronchus; ve, vestibulum; m, mesobronchus; v, ventrobronchi; p, parabronchi; d, dorsobronchi; l, laterobronchi; pr, prethoracic or anterior sac; po, postthoracic sac; ab, abdominal sac; le, "guiding dam." (From Hazelhoff, *Poultry Sci.,* 1951.)

parabronchi and to the ventrobronchi (the d-p-v system; see Figure 25). During inspiration the anterior sacs suck air through the lungs, and during expiration the posterior sacs force air through the lungs. Dotterweich postulated the existence of valves, some of which closed on inspiration and expiration.

Vos (1934) injected powdered charcoal into the air sacs of live ducks and permitted other ducks to inhale it. He concluded that air passes through the d-p-v system only during expiration, mainly as a result of contraction of the large posterior sacs. During inspiration, air passes directly through the mesobronchus to the posterior sacs. Between the points where the dorsobronchi and ventrobronchi lead off, there must be valves which close during expiration (Vos).

Dotterweich (1936) conducted experiments with a glass model of a lung and air sacs without valves. By inflating and deflating the air sacs in the model he reportedly simulated normal respiratory movements. Movement of the air was followed by introducing ammonia and acid in the system; this caused a clouding of the air in the direction in which it moved. He concluded, contrary to the results of Vos, that the parabronchi receive air on inspiration, but not during expiration. On inspiration, fresh air enters the mesobronchi and is distributed to the dorsobronchi, ventrobronchi, and laterobronchi. Some of it goes direct from the mesobronchi to the abdominal air sacs, while the posterior thoracic sacs receive fresh air from the dorsobronchi.

The anterior sacs are also filled on inspiration; but part of this air is vitiated air which comes from the ventrobronchi and parabronchi, and part of it is fresh air which comes via the mesobronchus to the ventrobronchi and the sacs. On expiration, all of the air sacs contract and empty their air to the mesobronchi. At this time the air going from the air sacs to the mesobronchi is under pressure, and because of the aerodynamic principle involved, the air in the parabronchi, recurrent bronchi, and some of the dorso- and ventrobronchi is static. This arrangement provides for adequate ventilation of the entire lung, and presumably most of the gaseous exchange in the parabronchi occurs on expiration, according to Dotterweich. He also studied the effects of inflating only one or some of the air sacs at a time on air movement in the system (glass model). If the posterior sacs were inflated while the anterior sacs were inactive (equivalent to destroying the latter sacs), the posterior part of the lungs was ventilated adequately, but not the anterior part. When only the anterior sacs were inflated, opposite results were obtained.

Hazelhoff (1951) stated that Dotterweich offered no proof that the air movement in his model simulated normal conditions. He studied air movement in the bird lung (crow, chicken, pigeon, heron) by injecting charcoal in the air sacs and later tracing the substance. In other experiments, he injected a liquid containing starch granules into the trachea, lungs, and air sacs of a dead bird. The skin was removed at the point where the large dorsobronchi run beneath the surface of the intercostal muscles. A pump was then attached to the trachea, and inspiration and expiration were induced. By suitable magnification of the dorsobronchi, he was able to observe the movements of the starch granules in inspiration and expiration. In inspiration and expiration the starch granules moved in the same direction, toward the parabronchi (d-p-v system, Figure 25). Hazelhoff assumed that the volume changes in the various air sacs of the dead bird were approximately the same as in the live animal.

Based upon these and other experiments with a glass model of the lung, Hazelhoff concluded that during expiration air is forced out of the posterior sacs (which have recurrent bronchi) into the dorsobronchi and from there to the parabronchi, ventrobronchi, vestibulum, primary bronchi, and trachea. He explains that it is possible for the air to pass in the same direction in both phases of respiration without the operation of valves (which have not been demonstrated) because of the peculiar structure and arrangement of the bronchi of the lungs. The guiding dam (see *le* of Figure 25) during expiration directs the air from the posterior thoracic sacs (and presumably from the abdominal sacs, although they are not mentioned) toward the dorsobronchi. During inspiration, the other side of the dam directs the air toward the dorsobronchi. The correctness of this assumption was confirmed by experiments with a simplified glass model, according to the author.

Most investigators are agreed that on inspiration the anterior air sacs receive vitiated air that has passed through the d-p-v system, but the posterior sacs receive most of their air directly through the mesobronchi (pure air) and, according to Hazelhoff, some through the d-p-v system. This explains why the CO_2 content of the anterior sacs is greater than in the posterior sacs, and why the CO_2 content of the latter sacs is only slightly higher than in atmospheric air.

DIFFUSION OF AIR IN PARABRONCHIAL CAPILLARIES

Hazelhoff (1951) believed that the renewal of air in the capillaries of the parabronchi takes place exclusively by diffusion. He made measurements and calculations to support this assumption. His discussion follows:

If we look at a 1 mm. segment of a parabronchus 0.5 mm. wide, and its air capillaries [Figure 26], it is clear that the average diffusion distance amounts to 0.3 to 0.4 mm. The total surface of the air capillaries growing

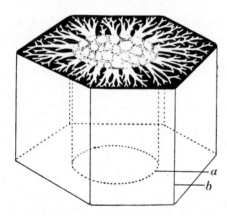

Figure 26. Diagram of a segment of a parabronchus with the air capillaries growing out of it.

The parabronchus (a) and surrounding area are always in the shape of an irregular, five- or six-sided prism (b). The stippled network in the section of the parabronchus represents the ingression of the air capillaries. (From Hazeloff, *Poultry Sci.*, 1951.)

out of the segment of the parabronchus is approximately equal to the inner surface of cylinder *a*. If the radius of *a* is 0.25 mm. and that of *b* (which for the sake of simplicity, we can think of as a cylinder) is 0.5 mm., then for each mm. length of parabronchus, that is of each 0.25 mm.³ of lung volume, there is a system of air capillaries with a total surface of 0.5 mm.² and a diffusion area of 2 mm.² per mm.³ of lung volume.

If we estimate the volume of a crow's lungs at 10 cc. and the average diffusion area at 2 mm.² per mm.³ of lung volume, the total diffusion area is then 200 cm.². We further assume that the diffusion distance is 0.25 mm. According to Krogh's diffusion coefficient (1941), at a pressure difference of 1 atm. per cm., 11 cc. of O_2 per minute diffuses through a surface of 200 cm.².

This is about the pressure difference prevailing in the parabronchi, according to Hazelhoff. Assuming an O_2 tension of 15 percent in the parabronchi, he calculates that 2,200 cc. per minute of oxygen are supplied to the parabronchial capillaries of the crow by diffusion.

RESPIRATION DURING FLIGHT

Hazelhoff (1951) concluded that the supply of oxygen in the lungs as well as its rate of diffusion is ample for the requirements of the bird in sustained flight. Krogh (1941), in discussing the heat production of birds in flight, stated that a higher rate of ventilation appears to be necessary to eliminate the extra heat generated rather than to obtain necessary oxygen. This statement is based upon a consideration of the data and calculations of Zeuten, which Krogh discusses. Zeuten calculated that the heat production of a pigeon flying at the rate of 43.5 miles per hour would be approximately 27 times as great as heat production at rest and that 14.8 Calories would be expended in overcoming the resistance of the air. These calculations have not been verified by actual experiments. Krogh further states that a number of authors have assumed that ventilation of the lungs is synchronized with wing movements in flight and that the downstroke of the wings corresponds with expiration, but Zimmer (1935) reported that the upstroke of the wings corresponded to expiration.

PRESSURE CHANGES IN THE RESPIRATORY APPARATUS

In the mammal, the thoracic and abdominal cavities are distinctly separated, and the pressures in them are different. The pressure in the thoracic cavity is ordinarily negative, due to the elastic recoil of the lungs. In the bird, the lungs are fixed and there is no analogous thoracic cavity; the thoracic and abdominal cavities are not distinctly separated, but are continuous. Thus, the pressure changes in them should be the same and are. The respiratory apparatus, including the lungs, bronchi, air sacs, and pneumatic bones are intercommunicable; hence we speak not of intrathoracic pressure in the bird, but only of pressure in the lungs and air passages, or intrapulmonic pressure.

Evidence from Baer (1896), Soum (1896), Francois-Franck

(1906), and Victorow (1909) demonstrates conclusively that pressure changes in the air passages are synchronous in the duck, pigeon, and crow, and this is true also in the chicken (Sturkie, unpublished). In inspiration, pressures in the trachea, air sacs, and even the humerus become slightly negative, and on expiration, slightly positive. The negative pressure on inspiration ranges from -4 to -6.5 mm. of water for the trachea and thoracic and abdominal sacs of the pigeon, and positive pressure on expiration was of about the same magnitude (Victorow). The pressures in the air passages of the crow were considerably higher.

TIDAL AIR AND VOLUME OF THE LUNGS AND AIR SACS

Tidal air or the amount of air inspired or expired in a normal respiration has been determined in a number of birds (Table 18). It is impossible to determine directly the volume or content of air in the air sacs or lungs in the live bird during a given inspiration or expiration, but such volumes may be estimated in the dead bird by filling the lungs and air sacs with molten paraffin (Vos, 1934), metal (Scharnke, 1938), cocoa butter (Victorow, 1909), and other substances. Vos claims to have inflated the lungs and air sacs of the dead bird to the extent that they are expanded in a normal inspiration. For example, he inflated the lungs and then closed the trachea, following which he froze the bird. He believed that the sacs and lungs were frozen in the normal inspiratory position. He then opened the air sacs and filled them with melted paraffin. It is doubt-

Table 18. Volume of air inspired or expired (in cc.) in one respiration (tidal air) of adult birds

	Duck			Pigeon		Chicken
Author	1	2	3	1	2	4
Bird (standing)	38	35	38	5.2	4.5	45
Bird (on back)	30			4.7		

1, Soum (1896), based on two birds; 2, Scharnke (1938); 3, Vos (1934); 4, Sturkie, unpublished.

Table 19. Volume of air (in cc.) in the lungs and air sacs

	Pigeon			Duck	Chicken
Author	1	2	3	4	5
Cervical sacs	2	2	—	—	24
Interclavicular	15	8	—	53	
Anterior thoracic	} 11	10	5.9	24	25
Posterior thoracic		4	3.6	57	
Abdominal sacs	38	30–40	19.9	145	74
Total	66	54–64	29.4	279	123
Lungs	8	8	—	—	13

1, Roche (see Victorow, 1909); 2, Victorow (1909), sacs and lungs over-expanded; 3, Scharnke (1938), probably overexpanded; 4, Vos (1934), sacs expanded as in normal respiration; 5, Campana, probably overexpanded (see Victorow, 1909).

ful that normal conditions are thus simulated, and his volumes, particularly for the abdominal air sacs, appear high (see Table 19). Victorow (1909) stated that the lungs and air sacs of the pigeons in his experiments were expanded considerably more than they normally would be. He therefore believed that in a normal inspiration the volume of the abdominal sacs would be about half the figure shown in the table. One may observe in the opened live bird that the abdominal sacs are never inflated maximally in a normal inspiration, and the pressure in them is usually low. The remaining sacs are probably expanded relatively more on normal inspiration than are the abdominal sacs. The volume of the anterior thoracic sacs is greater than the posterior thoracic sacs in the pigeon, but is less in the duck and probably in the chicken. More volume studies should be conducted, particularly on the chicken and duck.

The volume of air inspired or expired in the pigeon (tidal air) is approximately 10 percent of the volume as determined for all the sacs (Tables 18 and 19). This figure is greater for the duck (12 to 15 percent). If these volumes are accepted as normal, then it is apparent that on expiration or inspiration only a small portion of air in the sacs is expired or inspired in a given respiration. To estimate what portion of the tidal air is taken up by the various air sacs on inspiration, Soum (1896) destroyed the various sacs in the pigeon and the duck. He then recorded tidal air minus the volume of air in the destroyed sac.

The volume of inspired air was decreased about 18 percent when the abdominal sacs were destroyed, and 29 percent when the thoracic sacs alone were destroyed. The capacity of the abdominal sacs, as shown in Table 18, is approximately twice that of the thoracic sacs, but these figures indicate that more air is taken up by the thoracic sacs than by the abdominal sacs in inspiration. Destruction of the interclavicular sac decreases tidal air only slightly. When all the sacs (exclusive of cervicals) were destroyed and plugged, tidal air and pulmonary ventilation were decreased by approximately one-half.

Bert (1870) determined what he regarded as the capacity of the air sacs and lungs in chickens and ducks by blowing as much air into the lung through the trachea as possible and measuring the amount expired. The volume expired for the chicken was 820 cc., and for the duck, 843 cc. It is likely that more air was blown into the respiratory apparatus than could be taken in the deepest inspiration, and hence these figures appear to be too high.

ROLE OF THE AIR SACS IN RESPIRATION

That the air sacs increase pulmonary ventilation and the exchange of gases in the lungs has been discussed previously. The sacs, however, are not indispensible structures, because respiration continues after destruction of all of them, but tidal air and pulmonary ventilation are decreased. Various other functions have been ascribed to the air sacs.

Many of the earlier workers believed that the air sacs decrease the specific gravity of the body and thus facilitate flying (see Winterstein, 1921). This view has been discredited by Baer (1897) and Victorow (1909) and others. Victorow states that by increasing the temperature from 15° C. to 40.5° C. the decrease in weight of 100 grams of air would amount to only 0.01 gram, and since the total volume of air sacs of the pigeon is only 50 cc., the decrease in weight of the body would only be 0.005 gram, which obviously would have no effect on flight of the bird.

A belief reported by a number of workers, particularly teleologists, is that the air sacs help regulate body temperature by cooling or warming inspired air. For example, Bert (1870) stated that the ostrich running on the hot arid sands of the Sahara would soon die but for the presence of the air sacs, which cool and moisten the hot, dry air. The trachea and lungs could not do this satisfactorily, according to him.

Cowles and Nordstrom (1946) believed that the abdominal air sacs, which are in contact with the testes, may lower the temperature in the testes and thus facilitate spermatogenesis.

The air sacs do humidify inspired air, as was demonstrated by Soum (1896), who measured the water vapor in the expired air of pigeons and other birds before and after destruction of the air sacs. From 15 to 30 percent less water vapor is exhaled after air-sac destruction, but much of this decrease is due to the decreased intake of air (tidal air) following the operation, and only a small part actually represents decreased humidification of the air sacs, according to Soum.

Soum did not record body temperature after destruction of the air sacs, but Victorow (1909) did. After puncturing and plugging several of the air sacs of the pigeon and after stressing the bird by stimulation of the brachial nerves, he observed a rise in body temperature of 2.6° to 3.2° C., as compared to 0.7° to 0.9° in the control birds. In view of the small number of birds (2 treated and 2 control) and other conditions of the experiment, these results do not appear to be conclusive.

In preliminary, unpublished experiments on adult chickens not subjected to stress, with the air sacs destroyed, Sturkie found no change in body temperature that could be attributed to the operation. Further studies are needed on the effects of air-sac destruction upon body temperature of birds, particularly those in flight.

CONTROL OF RESPIRATION

Relation of Vagus Nerve to Respiration

Most workers agree that unilateral vagotomy results in moderate slowing of breathing momentarily, usually followed by normal breathing. Bilateral vagotomy usually slows respiration in the duck, pigeon, and chicken (Bert, 1870; Grober, 1899; Orr and Watson,

1913; Graham, 1940; Hiestand and Randall, 1942; and others). The rate may drop as low as 4 to 7 per minute in the chicken, pigeon, and duck, but usually increases and may return to normal within 7 to 30 minutes or within 2 to 3 days (Hiestand and Randall, 1942; Couvreur, 1891). This suggests that the respiratory center is stimulated by other receptors as well as those related to the vagi. In some cases, the rate may remain slow and the bird (pigeon) may die in 2 to 3 days following the operation (Knoll, see Winterstein, 1921).

The effects of bilateral vagotomy on the duration of the inspiratory and expiratory phases are inconsistent. Some have reported a pause in inspiration (longer duration), and others a pause in expiration (see Winterstein). It is recalled that the duration of the phases with nerves intact is also highly variable.

Stimulation of the central end of the vagus with a weak to moderate stimulus usually increases respiration in most species (chicken, pigeon, and duck); strong stimulation usually inhibits momentarily respiration in the inspiratory position, but some have reported inhibition in the expiratory position (see Winterstein). The results are highly variable within individuals of the same species. Orr and Watson (1913) were able to produce inhibition in only one bird (duck) by strong central stimulation of the vagus. Strong central stimulation of both vagi may cause death in the duck and hen (Bert, 1870).

Panting in the chicken is abolished by sectioning of the vagi (Hiestand and Randall, 1942), but not in the pigeon (Von Saalfeld, 1936); however, the respiratory rate may be diminished somewhat.

Seifert (see Winterstein, 1921) demonstrated that artificial inflation of the lungs inhibits inspiration and stimulates expiration and that withdrawal of air from the lungs inhibits expiration and stimulates inspiration, but this does not occur after bilateral vagotomy. Graham (1940) stated that deflation of the lung of the bird is without effect on respiration. Distention of the lungs abolishes panting in rabbits, but not in the duck (Hiestand and Randall, 1941 and 1942) except when anesthetized with sodium amytal. Thus, it appears that birds show the Hering-Breuer reflex. There are two kinds of afferent fibers in the vagi which have their receptors in the lungs, and they are stimulated by alternate contraction and expansion of

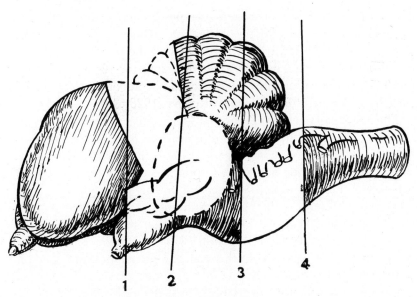

Figure 27. Brain of pigeon showing location of panting and respiratory centers. The panting center (area between 1 and 2) is in the interbrain, and the respiratory center (area between 3 and 4) is in the medulla. (Modified from Von Saalfeld, *Ƶ. vergl. Physiol.*, 1936.)

the lungs and thorax. Expansion stimulates expiratory fibers, and contraction stimulates inspiratory fibers.

Respiratory Center

Little is known concerning this center in birds. There is some evidence that the respiratory center is located in the medulla of birds (pigeon; see Figure 27), as it is in mammals. Von Saalfeld (1936) reported that transection of the medulla in the pigeon inhibited respiration. Fredericq believed also that the respiratory centers of the duck and chicken are located in the medulla, but his experiments were far from conclusive (see Winterstein, 1921).

Von Saalfeld also located a specific panting center in the anterior-dorsal region of the midbrain (interbrain) of the pigeon (Figure 27). Transection of this region abolished panting. Respiration rate (about 500 per minute) dropped to 60 per minute following transection. After panting was abolished by transection of the panting center, it could be induced again by injections of lobeline (a stimulant of the central nervous system), suggesting that the center in the medulla is responding to the stimulant. Thus he concluded that although panting is ordinarily controlled by the panting center this function can be taken over by the true respiratory center. Destruction of the cerebrum of the pigeon does not affect respiration, according to Von Saalfeld and also Rogers (1928).

The respiratory center of mammals is sensitive to changes in temperature, pH of blood, and other stimuli. This has also been demonstrated in the bird, but whether it is the center in the medulla or the panting center or both that respond to these stimuli is not always clear. Further research is needed on this point. In mammals increased CO_2 tension in the blood stimulates the respiratory center, but Orr and Watson (1913) showed that when the duck (*Anas boscas*) breathed CO_2, respiration was inhibited. Dooley and Koppanyi (1929) stated that this was due to the fact that the concentration of CO_2 inspired was so high that it irritated the nasal pathways and therefore probably stimulated inhibitory receptors reflexly. When CO_2 was introduced through the opened humerus or when the nasal pathways were anesthetized, respiration was stimulated. Hiestand and Randall (1941), who studied the effect of CO_2 inhalation in 11 species of birds, found considerable variation in the responses. In some species, CO_2 caused inhibition, in others stimulation, and in many cases the result depended upon whether an anesthetic had been used. When the chicken breathes 10 percent CO_2, respiration is stimulated, but amplitude is increased rather than rate. When the chicken is anesthetized with pentobarbital sodium, CO_2 has no effect, but with ether anesthesia, CO_2 inhibits or slows respiration. Thus, the respiratory center of birds, like mammals, is sensitive to changes in pH of the blood, and the variable responses observed with and without anesthetics indicate that the center is also stimulated or inhibited by anesthetics. Intravenous injections of CO_2 in the duck also increase respiration.

That the respiratory center is also sensitive to postural changes is suggested by the fact that stretching the neck of the duck, experimentally or naturally, as in diving, produces apnea. Emotional disturbances, resulting from sudden noises, produce inspiratory gasps and increase respiration reflexly. That the temperature of the blood flowing to the head and to the respiratory and panting centers affects respiration is discussed in Chapter 8.

REFERENCES

Baer, M. 1896 Beiträge zur Kenntnis der Anatomie und Physiologie der Atemwerkzeuge bei den Vögeln. Z. f. wiss. Zool. 61:420.

Baer, M. 1897 Zur physiologischen Bedeutung des Luftsäcks bei Vögeln. Biol. Zbl. 17:282.

Bert, P. 1870 Leçons sur la Physiologie comparée de la Respiration. Bailliere, Paris.

Brandes, G. 1924 Beobachtungen und Reflexionen über die Atmung der Vögel. Arch. ges. Physiol. (Pflügers) 203:492.

Couvreur, E. 1891 Influence du pneumogastrique sur les phénomènes mécaniques et chimiques de la respiration chez les oiseaux. Ann. Soc. Linn. Lyon 38:33.

Cowles, R. B., and A. Nordstrom 1946 A possible avian analogue of the scrotum. Science 104:586.

Dooley, M. S., and J. Koppanyi 1929 The control of respiration in the domestic duck (Anas boscas). J. Pharm. & Exp. Thera. 36:507.

Dotterweich, H. 1930 Versuch über den Weg der Atemluft in der Vogellunge. Z. vergl. Physiol. 11:271.

Dotterweich, H. 1936 Die Atmung der Vögel. Z. vergl. Physiol. 23:744.

Francois-Franck, M. 1906 Études graphiques et photographiques de mécanique respiratoire comparée. Comp. Rend. Soc. Biol. 2:174.

Gilbert, P. W. 1939 The avian lung and air sac system. Auk 56:57.

Graham, J. D. 1940 Respiratory reflexes in the fowl. J. Physiol. 97:525.

Grober, J. A. 1899 Über die Atmungsinnervation der Vögel. Arch. ges. Physiol. (Pflügers) 76:427.

Groebbels, F. 1932 Der Vogel. Erster Band: Atmungswelt und Nahrungswelt. Verlag von Gebrüder Borntraeger, Berlin.

Hazelhoff, E. H. 1951 Structure and function of the lung of birds. Poultry Sci. 30:3. This is a reprint of material originally published in Verslag van de gewone vergaderingen der Afdeling Natuurkunde van de Nederlanse Akademie van Wetenschappen 52:391–400, 1943.

Hiestand, W. A., and W. C. Randall 1941 Species differentiation in the respiration of birds following carbon dioxide administration and the location of inhibitory receptors in the upper respiratory tract. J. Cell. & Comp. Physiol. 17:333.

Hiestand, W. A., and W. C. Randall 1942 Influence of proprioceptive vagal afferents on panting and accessory panting movements in mammals and birds. Am. J. Physiol. 138:12.

Kaupp, B. F. 1918 The Anatomy of the Domestic Fowl. W. B. Saunders Co., Philadelphia.

Kaupp, B. F. 1923 The respiration of fowls. Vet. Med. 18:36.

Krogh, A.   1941   The Comparative Physiology of Respiratory Mechanisms. University of Pennsylvania Press, Philadelphia.

Ledenfeld, R.   1896   Die physiologische Bedeutung der Lufträume bei den fliegenden Tieren. Biol. Zbl. 16:774.

Locy, W. A., and O. Larsell   1916   The embryology of the bird's lung. II: The air sacs and recurrent bronchi. Am. J. Anat. 20:1.

McLeod, W. M., and R. P. Wagers   1939   The respiratory system of the chicken. J. Am. Vet. Med. Assoc. 95:59.

Orr, J. B., and A. Watson   1913   Study of the respiratory mechanism in the duck. J. Physiol. 46:337.

Rogers, F. R.   1928   Studies on the brain stem. XI: The effects of artificial stimulation and of traumatism of the avian thalamus. Am. J. Physiol. 86:639.

Saalfeld, F. E. von   1936   Untersuchungen über das Hacheln bei Tauben. Z. vergl. Physiol. 23:727.

Scharnke, H.   1938   Experimentelle Beiträge zur Kenntnis der Vogelatmung. Z. vergl. Physiol. 25:548.

Soum, M.   1896   Recherches physiologiques sur l'appareil respiratoire des oiseaux. Ann. Univ. Lyon 28:1.

Victorow, C.   1909   Die kühlende Wirkung der Luftsäcke bei Vögeln. Arch. ges. Physiol. (Pflügers) 126:300.

Vos, H. F.   1934   Über den Weg der Atemluft in der Entenlunge. Z. vergl. Physiol. 21:552.

Winterstein, H.   1921   Handbuch der vergleichenden Physiologie, Vol. I, Part II. Verlag von Gustav Fischer, Jena.

Zimmer, K.   1935   Beiträge zur Mechanik der Atmung bei den Vögeln in Stand und Flug. Zoologica 3:1.

CHAPTER 7

Transport of the Blood Gases

A VERY small quantity of oxygen in the blood (about 2 volumes percent) is in physical solution. The remainder combines with hemoglobin to form oxyhemoglobin:

$$Hb + O_2 \rightleftarrows HbO_2$$

The tissues get oxygen by a drop in partial pressure or tension in the blood, which releases some of the gas in combination with hemoglobin. This will be shown later when oxygen dissociation curves are considered. Very little carbon dioxide is carried by the blood as CO_2. It exists mainly as carbonic acid and sodium bicarbonate. Much depends upon the correct balance between carbonic acid and sodium bicarbonate, if the pH of the blood is maintained within physiological limits.

Our present state of knowledge concerning the exchange of gases between the lungs and blood and between blood and tissues is based upon determinations of oxygen, carbon dioxide, and nitrogen in the air of the lungs and in the blood and tissues. These include analysis of the oxygen and carbon dioxide content, capacity, tension, and percent saturation in arterial and venous blood and some of these on the gases in alveolar air and the tissues.

Capacity represents the amount of O_2 or CO_2 that the blood is capable of holding. *Content* represents the actual amounts of gases present in the blood, air of the lungs, or air sacs at a given tension and temperature. *Saturation* is equal to *content* divided by *capacity*. *Tension* measures the partial pressures of the various gases in mm. Hg.

The atmosphere at sea level exerts a pressure of 760 mm. Hg. It is composed of approximately 20 percent oxygen, 79 percent nitrogen, and less than 1 percent carbon dioxide.

According to Dalton's law, the pressure of a mixture of gases is equal to the sum of the pressures of the individual gases. Thus, the partial pressure of oxygen in the atmosphere is equal to $760 - 31.5$ mm. (pressure of water vapor at saturation and $30°$ C.) multiplied by 21 percent, or 153 mm. Hg. When several gases are in contact with a liquid, each is absorbed independently of the others and in relation to its pressure or tension.

The tension of the gases in arterial blood is dependent upon the partial pressures of the various gases in the alveolar air of the lungs. In man, the O_2 content of the alveolar air (expired air) is about 14 volumes percent and for CO_2 is 5.3 percent, about the same as in birds.

If the exchange of gases in the lungs is due to diffusion and is governed by physical laws, then it is to be expected that the tension of O_2 in venous blood coming to the lungs would be less than that of arterial blood and that the tension of CO_2 in venous blood would be higher than that in arterial blood. Determinations have shown such to be the case.

Since O_2 is consumed and CO_2 produced in the tissues, it is expected that O_2 tension in the tissues would be low and CO_2 tension high, and this has been demonstrated in mammals.

Oxygen and Carbon Dioxide Content of the Air in the Lungs and Air Sacs

The O_2 and CO_2 content of expired air and air in the air sacs are determined by absorption. An alkali is commonly used for absorption of CO_2, and alkalized pyrogallol for O_2. Air samples of inspired air in the air sacs are obtained by inserting a small cannula into the air sacs and withdrawing air at the end of inspiration. The O_2 and CO_2 content of expired air and air in the air sacs of the pigeon, duck, and chicken are shown in Table 20.

These figures show that the air in the abdominal sacs at the end of inspiration contain more oxygen than the other sacs and indicate (as discussed previously) that on inspiration almost pure air goes to the abdominal sacs. The oxygen content of the air in these sacs, 18 to 19 percent, is only slightly lower than that of atmospheric air.

Table 20. Oxygen and CO_2 (in percent) of the air in the sacs
at end of inspiration

Air sacs	Pigeon*		Duck†		Chicken‡	
	O_2	CO_2	O_2	CO_2	O_2	CO_2
Interclavicular	15.5	4.5	14.2	5.6	14.6	5.0
	12.8§	6.4§	13.1*	6.0*		
Anterior thoracic	15.0	4.8	14.9	5.1	16.3	3.2
Posterior thoracic	15.8	4.6	17.7	2.7	17.4	3.4
Abdominal	—	3.3	18.1	2.5	19.0	2.0
			17.2§	2.7§		
Cervical	—	—	—	—	—	—
Expired air	14.5§	3.9§	14.3	5.1	13.5	6.5
			15.8§	3.0§		

* Scharnke (1938).   § Wishart (see Graham, 1939).
† Vos (1934).   ‡ Soum (1896).

The O_2 content is lowest in the air of the interclavicular sac and is only slightly lower than that in expired air.

No appreciable exchange of gases occurs within the blood vessels of the air sacs, since these vessels are sparse and small.

Blood Gases of the Bird

Details as to the general methods of determining the content, capacity, tension, and saturation of the gases in the blood may be obtained from textbooks on physiology, and for details on avian blood, consult the references cited at the end of this chapter. Pertinent data on the blood gases of birds are shown in Table 21. Further details are shown in the O_2 dissociation curves of Figure 28.

Utilization of oxygen is determined by the percent difference in the saturation of arterial and venous blood with oxygen, or the difference in O_2 content of arterial and venous blood. It is observed from

Table 21. Data on blood gases for adult birds

	Species*	Arterial blood	Venous blood
O₂ content	Duck	16.32	6.55
Volumes percent	Pigeon	19.20	7.66
	Goose	—	—
	Chicken	12.10	5.50
CO₂ content	Duck	46.00	53.55
Volumes percent	Pigeon	34.00	40.70
	Goose	44–46	48–51
	Chicken	40.50	46.50
O₂ capacity	Duck	16.90	—
Volumes percent	Pigeon	20.00	—
	Goose	19.80	—
	Chicken	13.50	12.00
O₂ saturation	Duck	97.70	38.70
Percent	Pigeon	96.50	38.60
	Goose	96–97	69–73
	Chicken	88.00	40.00
O₂ tension	Duck	96–112	35–40
mm. Hg	Pigeon	98–114	35–40
	Goose	91–95	55–57
	Chicken	90.00	50.00
CO₂ tension	Duck	53–55	60–70
mm. Hg	Pigeon	53–55	60–70
	Goose	42–44	53–55
	Chicken	34.00	45.00

Utilization of O₂—duck, 60 percent; pigeon, 60 percent; goose, 26 percent; chicken, 54.6 percent. Obtained by the percent difference of arterial and venous blood.

* Figures on duck, pigeon, and goose taken directly or calculated from the data of Wastl and Leiner (1931a and 1931b). Data on chicken from Morgan and Chichester (1935).

the table and also is indicated in the dissociation curves that utilization of O_2 in the bird is high, ranging from 54 percent for the chicken to 60 percent for the duck and pigeon. This is much higher than the average figures for most mammals (20 to 30 percent). The efficiency for goose blood is about 26 percent. Thus, the degree of saturation of chicken arterial blood at a given O_2 tension or pressure and temperature (88 percent) is lower than for mammals (about 95 percent). The O_2 saturation of chicken venous blood (40 percent) is also lower than that for mammals.

Oxygen Dissociation Curves

These curves have been established for the duck, goose, and pigeon (Wastl and Leiner, 1931a and 1931b) and for the pheasant and chicken (Christensen and Dill, 1935; Morgan and Chichester, 1935). Figure 28 gives the curve for the chicken, as compared to that of the dog and of man (Morgan and Chichester). It is observed that the curve for the chicken is displaced to the right. The chicken blood was equilibrated at 40° C. (near the normal body temperature), and the dog blood at 37.5° C. (near the dog body temperature). Wastl and Leiner showed similar curves for the duck, goose, and pigeon, except that the curve for the goose showed only slight displacement to the right.

Christensen and Dill (1935) derived O_2 dissociation curves for the goose, duck, pheasant, and chicken. Their results on the duck and pigeon differ somewhat from those of Wastl and Leiner in that they found little difference between these species, and they state that the results of Wastl and Leiner are complicated by the fact that there was no control of the alkaline reserve in the different specimens and therefore no assurance of constant pH. The curve for chicken blood presented by Christensen and Dill appears to agree fairly closely with that of Morgan and Chichester. The differences observed were probably due to the fact that Christensen and Dill equilibrated the blood at 37° C. instead of 40° C. It is known that at a given pH and O_2 tension the degree of saturation with O_2 varies inversely with the temperature. This has been demonstrated by Wastl and Leiner and others. However, at the same temperature, pH, and O_2 and CO_2 tensions, the curve for chicken blood is displaced to the right of curves for mammalian blood. This means that avian blood has less affinity for oxygen than mammalian blood and releases its O_2 to the tissues more readily than the latter. The higher body temperature of the bird also facilitates this unloading.

Morgan and Chichester and also Wastl and Leiner have determined the effect of pH upon the affinity of chicken blood for oxygen.

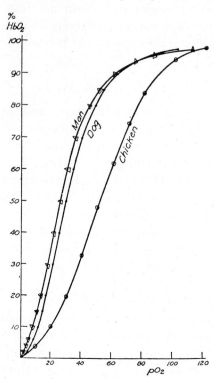

Here, as with mammalian blood, the affinity decreases with increase in acidity or with decrease in pH. It has been demonstrated in mammalian and avian blood that CO_2 tension affects the affinity of blood for O_2. Wastl and Leiner (1931b) have shown that in goose blood with a given pH, temperature, and O_2 tension the percent saturation with O_2 varies inversely with the CO_2 tension. For example, the percentage saturations of oxygen at an O_2 tension of 50 mm. Hg and at CO_2 tensions of 50 and 80 mm. Hg are 77 and 60 respectively.

Effects of age on oxygen dissociation curves. Rostorfer and Rigdon (1946) found a difference in O_2 dissociation curves of young and mature ducks. The O_2 capacities were 16.1 and 13.9 volumes percent respectively for mature and young ducks. The affinity of blood of

Figure 28. Oxygen dissociation curves of man, dog, and chicken.

O_2 saturation is in percent (ordinates), and O_2 tension (pO_2) in mm. Hg (abscissae). (From Morgan and Chichester, *J. Biol. Chem.*, 1935.)

young ducks for O_2 is therefore less than that of mature ducks.

It is known that hemoglobin in birds increases with age up to sexual maturity, but the authors demonstrated that this does not account for all of the increased O_2 combining ability of adult duck blood. Thus, there is also an increase with age in the efficiency of duck hemoglobin as an oxygen carrier. This, however, is not true for chicken blood. Hall (1934) has shown that O_2 dissociation curves for young and mature chickens are also different and that the affinity of hemoglobin of young chicks for oxygen is greater than that of adult birds.

Carbon Dioxide Dissociation Curves

Carbon dioxide dissociation curves for duck and goose blood have been determined by Wastl and Leiner (1931a and 1931b). At a given CO_2 tension, the curves for the goose and duck are very similar to those for man and some other mammals. At the same CO_2 tension, goose blood contains 5 to 10 volumes percent more CO_2 than duck blood. The difference in CO_2 tension of arterial and venous blood of birds (10 to 11 mm. Hg in chickens) is greater than that of mammals, and this facilitates the removal of CO_2.

REFERENCES

Christensen, E., and D. B. Dill 1935 Oxygen dissociation curves of bird blood. J. Biol. Chem. 109:443.

Graham, J. D. 1939 The air stream in the lungs of the fowl. J. Physiol. 97:133.

Hall, F. G. 1934 Hemoglobin function in the developing chick. J. Physiol. 83:222.

Morgan, V. E., and D. F. Chichester 1935 Properties of blood of the domestic fowl. J. Biol. Chem. 110:285.

Rostorfer, H. A., and R. H. Rigdon 1946 A study of oxygen transport in the blood of young and adult domestic ducks. Am. J. Physiol. 146: 222.

Scharnke, H. 1938 Experimentelle Beiträge zur Kenntnis der Vogelatmung. Z. vergl. Physiol. 25:548.

Soum, M. 1896 Recherches physiologiques sur l'appareil respiratoire des oiseaux. Ann. Univ. Lyon 28:1.

Vos, H. F. 1934 Über den Weg der Atemluft in der Entenlunge. Z. vergl. Physiol. 21:552.

Wastl, H., and G. Leiner 1931a Beobachtungen über die Blutgase bei Vögeln. I. Arch. ges. Physiol. (Pflügers) 227:368 (duck and pigeon).

Wastl, H., and G. Leiner 1931b Beobachtungen über die Blutgase bei Vögeln. II. Arch. ges. Physiol. (Pflügers) 227:421 (goose).

CHAPTER 8

Regulation of Body Temperature

WHEN food is oxidized in the body, heat is produced (Chapter 9). The production, loss, and conservation of this heat are concerned in the maintenance of body temperature. The body temperature of cold-blooded animals (poikilotherms) varies with environmental temperature, but that of warm-blooded mammals and birds (homeotherms) is largely independent of environmental temperature. The activity of the poikilothermal animal is influenced greatly by environmental temperature—in cold weather such animals become inactive and hibernate. Homeothermal animals and birds have well-developed temperature regulating mechanisms which enable them to maintain constant body temperature and to function under varying environmental temperatures.

Heat is lost from the body by radiation, conduction, and convection and by vaporization through the lungs and through the skin of those animals which have sweat glands. The bird has no sweat glands, and heat loss by vaporization is effected through the lungs by increased respiration and panting. Heat loss is also regulated by the pilomotor and vasomotor nervous mechanisms. Erection of hairs or feathers (pilomotor system) tends to conserve heat; in the non-erected state, heat loss is facilitated. When the air temperature is high, the blood vessels in the skin dilate, thus increasing heat loss, and when the temperature is low, the vessels constrict, which tends to conserve heat.

BODY TEMPERATURE OF BIRDS

The average body temperature of birds is higher than that of mammals, ranging from approximately 105° F. to 111° F., depend-

Table 22. Average body temperature (rectal) of adult birds

Species	Sex	Body temperature		Author
		°F	°C	
Eastern bobwhite	Male	111.2	44.0	Baldwin & Kendeigh (1932)
Eastern mourning dove	—	108.8	42.7	"
Hummingbird	Female	108.0	42.2	"
Crested flycatcher	Female	111.4	44.1	"
Eastern crow	Male	106.0	41.1	"
Eastern robin	Male	109.6	43.1	"
Eastern house wren	Male	108.6	42.6	"
Chicken (White Leghorn)	Female	106.6	41.47	Heywang (1938)
Chicken (Rhode Island Red)	Female	106.5	41.40	"
Chicken (White Leghorn)	Female	106.2	41.46	Robinson & Lee (1946)
Chicken (Australorp)	Female	106.2	41.46	"
Turkey	Female	105.4	40.97	"
Duck	—	106.0	41.10	"
Pigeon	—	105.08– 108.4	40.6– 41.9	Groebbels (1932)
Goose	—	105.08	40.6	"

ing on the species (Table 22). For a review of body temperatures in wild birds, see Baldwin and Kendeigh (1932). The average rectal temperature of the chicken is approximately 106° F. and is about the same as, or slightly higher than, the temperatures for the turkey, goose, duck, and pigeon.

The body temperature of the day-old chick is about 3° F. below that of the adult, but by 10 days of age, it is the same as that of the adult. This is illustrated by the data of Lamoreux and Hutt (1939), as follows:

Age of chicks in days
(Rhode Island Reds)   1   2   4   5   10
Mean body temperature
(rectal) in °F.   103.4 104.2 105.8 106.0 106.0

White Leghorn chicks have a significantly higher body temperature during the first week of life than Rhode Island Reds, according to these authors and to Scholes and Hutt (1942), and the higher temperature is associated with the chick's greater resistance to pullorum disease.

Diurnal Variation in Body Temperature

Chickens, like mammals, exhibit diurnal variation in body temperature (Simpson, 1911; Fronda, 1921). In the adult chicken the body temperature is lowest at 12 midnight (104.5° F.) and highest at 5 P.M. (106.9), according to Kaupp (1922; see also Fronda). The variation appears to be less, however, when the air temperature is

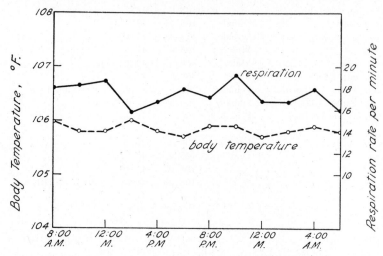

Figure 29. Diurnal variation in body temperature of chicken at 70° F. ambient temperature. (From Wilson, *Poultry Sci.*, 1948.)

constant (Wilson, 1948). When the ambient temperature is held constant at 70° F., the greatest variation observed is 0.3° F. (Figure 29).

Critical Temperature of the Hen

An environmental temperature above or below certain points raises the heat production of the body. There is a range of environmental temperature between these extremes that has little or no effect upon heat production. This is known as the range of thermal neutrality. It has a low point and a high point. When the environmental temperature drops to a certain low point, heat production increases in order to keep body temperature from dropping. This is the *lower* critical temperature. If, however, air temperature continues to drop, the increased heat production cannot keep pace with the heat loss from the body and the animal develops hypothermia, or subnormal body temperature (see also Chapter 9).

When the environmental temperature reaches a certain high point, heat loss cannot keep pace with heat production, the body temperature increases, and the animal develops hyperthermia. The highest environmental temperature at which no rise in body temperature results is the *upper* critical temperature.

The lower critical temperature in the chicken (hen), according to Mitchell and Haines (1927) and Dukes (1947), is approximately 16.5° C. (61.7° F.). The upper critical temperature in the fowl, according to Dukes and also Wilson (1948), is at approximately 27.5° C. (81° F.). See also Barott and Pringle (Chapter 9) for further details.

Lethal Temperatures

Lethal temperature is the temperature of the body above or below normal at which death occurs. Lethal temperatures are determined by subjecting the animal to high or low environmental air temperatures or by submerging the animal in water of the desired temperature.

Lethal temperatures for the bird, as determined by either of the methods, are approximately the same. However, the time of survival varies with the methods used. Where the animal is submerged in water, the survival time is relatively short even though the temperature is not low. When a bird is submerged in water at 6° C. with an air temperature of 21° C., the survival time is approximately one hour. Hypothermia may be induced in chickens with water at a temperature as high as 37° C. Air temperatures must be well below or above the critical temperatures to cause changes in body temperature. This difference in response is due to the fact that in water heat loss is at a maximum, because body heat is conducted into the water, whereas in air the insulating effect of the feathers is still intact.

Lethal temperatures of chickens of different ages and by different investigators are shown in Table 23. During the first week of life of the chick, the lower lethal temperatures are lowest and then rise slightly, but after 10 days, the temperature changes only slightly from this age to maturity. The lethal temperature of the adult male

Table 23. Lethal temperatures of the fowl

LOWER LETHAL

Breed	Age and sex	Body temperature °C	°F	Investigator
	1 day	15.5	60	Moreng & Shaffner (1951)
	2 days	15.5–16.1	60–61	"
	4 "	16.1–16.6	61–62	"
	6 "	17.2–18.0	63–64.5	"
	7 "	15.0	59	Randall (1943a)
	8 "	17.2–18.8	63–66	Moreng & Shaffner
	10 "	18.3–20.5	65–69	"
	21 "	18.8–20.0	66–68	"
	16 weeks	19.4–20.5	67–69	"
White Leghorn	Adult, hen	23.4	74.1	Sturkie (1946)
White Leghorn	Adult, male	20.7	69.3	"

UPPER LETHAL

White Leghorn	Young	46–47.8	114.8–118	Randall & Hiestand (1939)
White Leghorn	Adult	47	116.6	"
	1 day	46.6	116	Moreng & Shaffner
	3 days to maturity	47.2	117	"

(20.7° C., or 69.3° F.) is lower than that of the female (23.4° C., or 74.1° F.; Table 23). The upper lethal temperature of day-old chicks is 116° F., and at 3 days of age, 117° F., and from this age to maturity there is no change.

EXPERIMENTAL HYPOTHERMIA

In Chicks

The body temperature of the day-old chick, which is below the adult body temperature, begins to rise at about 4 days of age and reaches its maximum at 7 to 10 days. When day-old chicks are exposed to an air temperature of 26° C., their body temperatures rapidly fall to 31° or 32° C. (Randall, 1943a). Upon exposure to a temperature of 10° C., practically no resistance is shown to chilling. Shivering is not pronounced and is often absent. The 7-day-old chick, however, responds to low temperature with vigorous shivering and is capable of maintaining a body temperature of 41° C.

when exposed to a room temperature of 26° C., but when exposed to an air temperature of 10° C., body temperature drops quickly. Within 2 minutes after exposure to this temperature, shivering is pronounced, and heart rate and respiratory rate increase. After 10 minutes' exposure, body temperature drops, heart and respiratory rates increase from 300 to 360 and from 50 to 80 per minute respectively, and shivering continues. Heart and respiratory rates then begin to drop, and after 110 minutes of exposure, they fall to 108 and 40 respectively. After 150 minutes of exposure, shivering ceases, and body temperature drops to 20° C., heart rate to 20 per minute, and respiration to 14 per minute. Thirty minutes later, respiration ceases, at a body temperature of 15° C. and a heart rate of 12 per minute.

The 7-day-old chick has developed some measure of temperature control, but the mechanism is not fully developed until the down feathers are replaced by the juvenile plumage at about 3 weeks of age. This was demonstrated by Moreng and Shaffner (1951). From 1 to 20 days of age the ability to withstand low temperatures increases (Figure 30).

In Adults

The adult fowl is able to withstand very low air temperatures before body temperature drops. At air temperatures as low as 0° C., the body temperature is normal if the birds are not restrained, but are allowed free movement in the pen (Simpson, 1911). The survival time of birds in extremely low air temperatures (−34° to −37° C.), as reported by Horvath, Folk, Craig, and Fleischmann (1948), is shown as follows:

	Canary	Pigeon (carrier)			Chicken (White Leghorn)	
Number	2	5	4	2	8	3
Survival time (hours)	0.6	22–24	24–48	48–78	3.3–16	16–29.5

The pigeon is very resistant to low temperatures; the chicken is less so, but more resistant than the mouse, rat, or rabbit. Streicher,

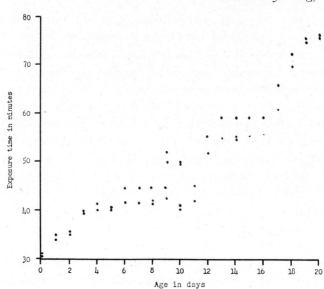

Figure 30. The response of chicks to an ambient temperature of −10° F.

Each dot, representing data collected on 24 chicks, shows the time of survival at this temperature. (From Moreng and Shaffner, *Poultry Sci.*, 1951.)

Hackel, and Fleischmann (1950) subjected fasted pigeons and ducks to ambient temperatures of −40° C. and found that most of the pigeons (19 out of 25) survived this treatment for 72 hours and that 4 birds were alive even after 144 hours. The pigeons, when plucked of feathers, survived only 20 to 30 minutes at this temperature.

Tolerance of Birds to Water Hypothermia

The bird's best protective measure against low air temperatures is its covering of feathers. Hypothermia can be induced more rapidly by placing the birds in cold water, because the feathers no longer offer protection, and the heat loss from the body is almost complete.

Sturkie (1946a) subjected adult hens and cocks to various degrees of hypothermia by submering the birds up to the neck in water at 6 to 11° C. The lethal body temperatures of 3 hens suspended in water at 6° C. were 23.3, 23.3, and 23.9° C., and their survival times were 50, 50, and 65 minutes respectively. The lethal temperatures of 5 hens exposed to water-bath temperatures of 9 to 11.7° C. were 22.8, 23.3, 23.6, 22.8, and 23.6° C., and their survival periods were 83, 65, 90, 90, and 79 minutes respectively. Thus, there was little difference in the lethal temperatures, but the periods of survival were in most hens directly proportional to the temperature of the water. The lethal temperatures of 4 males studied were slightly lower (19.4, 22.2, 21.1, and 20.0° C.), and their survival periods were 65, 75, 77, and 90 minutes respectively.

Within 10 to 15 minutes after the birds are placed in the water baths, they shiver violently. By the time that body temperature drops to approximately 26° C., the intensity of shivering decreases and continues to decrease, but does not cease until death. As degree of shivering diminishes, respiration decreases and becomes arrhythmic, and as the respiratory mechanism begins to fail, cyanosis of the head and comb develops. Heart rate continues to decline, and when respiration ceases, the rates range from 78 to 90 per minute. Many of the hypothermic birds can be resuscitated immediately after respiration ceases, by wetting their heads in warm water. Keeping the neck and head warm while the remainder of the body is submerged in water increases survival time; this demonstrates, as shown by Randall (1943a and 1943b), that the temperature of the blood flowing to the central nervous system is an important factor in the control of respiration.

Moderate Water Hypothermia

Moderate hypothermia can be induced in hens by placing them in water at temperatures ranging from 20 to 27.8° C., mainly the latter (Sturkie, 1946a). The lethal body temperatures for 5 hens thus treated were 27.8, 29.4, 27.8, 28.9, and 28.9° C., and their survival periods were 44, 42, 40.21, 36.5, and 35 hours respectively. The lethal temperatures for these birds were higher than for those placed in colder water. Obviously the body temperature can drop no lower than that of the water, and the lethal temperatures are the same as, or slightly higher than, the water temperature.

The results of these and other experiments indicate that the critical body temperature of cocks and hens is about 25 to 27° C. When body temperature reaches this level, the birds exhibit signs of respiratory failure, and body temperature continues to drop to the lethal level, unless the body is warmed.

Effects of Hypothermia on Specific Gravity of Blood

There is a significant increase in specific gravity of blood of hypothermic chickens, shown as follows (Sturkie, 1947):

No. of birds	Before hypothermia	After hypothermia	Body temperature
19	1.01904	1.02032	36.1°–26.7° C.

The degree of increase is independent of the degree and duration of hypothermia. Warming the birds from 1 to 7 hours after chilling decreases specific gravity, with values approaching normal, but none were significantly below normal. These results are contrary to those of Barbour, McKay, and Griffith (1943) for rats and monkeys, in which cases the increase reached a maximum at certain degrees of hypothermia, but then decreased and approached normal levels when body temperature was further depressed. They explained these changes as follows:

Exposure to cold with retention of protective reflexes leads to a gain in intracellular water throughout the body. When, however, the central nervous system becomes so chilled as to cause general neuro-muscular depression, the effect on the hypothalamus is to abolish the reflex responses to cold, which process includes a reversal of water shift with increased extra cellular fluid.

Since hemoconcentration accompanies hypothermia, it is presumed that blood volume may have been decreased. Rodbard, Saiki, and Malin (1950), in a preliminary report, studied the effects of hypothermia and hyperthermia upon the distribution of body fluid in chickens. They found that hypothermia increased the specific gravity of the blood slightly, but that plasma volume was decreased 30 percent below normal levels, and this was true also for thiocyanate space. Hyperthermia decreased hematocrit, specific gravity, and plasma volume slightly, but thiocyanate space was increased 30 percent.

These data suggest that hypothermia results in a marked shift of fluid from the plasma and interstitial spaces to the intracellular phase, state the authors. The fact that hematocrit and specific gravity do not rise commensurate with the decreased volumes suggests that blood cells and plasma proteins are removed from the circulating plasma and stored, according to the authors. The reverse processes are brought about by rewarming to normal temperature levels. Induction of hyperthermia causes water to leave the tissue cells and commensurate quantities of plasma protein and blood cells to be released to the circulating blood stream. Further studies on this subject should be conducted.

Other Effects of Hypothermia

Hypothermia (body temperature, 90 to 102° F.) causes contraction of the uterus of hens and premature laying of the egg (soft-shelled) when an egg is present in the organ, but has no effect upon ovulation or rate of passage of the egg from the ovary to the uterus (Sturkie, 1946b). When the egg is forcibly held in the uterus the normal length of time by stitching the cloaca, calcium deposition is inhibited, and the inhibitory effect lasts for several hours after resumption of normal body temperature (bird warmed). (See also Chapter 15.)

Various types of twins and duplicate embryos can be produced by inducing hypothermia in the hen before the egg reaches the uterus or during the early cleavage stages of the blastoderm (Sturkie, 1946c).

EFFECTS OF HIGH ENVIRONMENTAL TEMPERATURE ON THE FOWL

Changes in Air Temperature and Relative Humidity

Air temperatures up to 85° F. are without any constant effect on body temperature. At an air temperature of 90° F. there is a rise of 0.5 to 1.5° F. in rectal temperature (Heywang, 1938; Lee, Robinson, Yeates, and Scott, 1945; Wilson, 1948). As the air temperature rises, the effect upon rectal temperature becomes more pronounced (Figure 31). Most hens are able to withstand a 7-hour exposure at 105° F., but none are able to withstand 110° F. for this time.

The results of Yeates, Lee, and Hines (1941) show that at air temperatures of 85° F. or below relative humidity has little effect upon rectal temperatures. At 90° F., the average rectal temperature is appreciably raised only when the relative humidity is above 55 percent. At higher air temperatures, the degree of humidity has a greater effect upon elevation of body temperature. At a temperature of 105° F., for example, with a relative humidity of 75 percent, the body temperature is 118° F., as against 109° F. at 55 percent

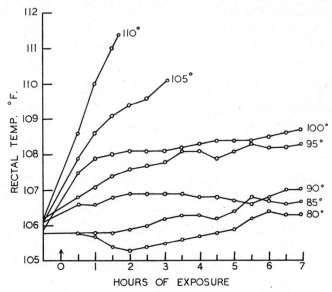

Figure 31. The effects of high ambient temperatures on body temperature of the fowl.

Air temperature is shown within the graph. (From Lee *et al.*, *Poultry Sci.*, 1945.)

humidity. No doubt this difference is due to the decreased evaporation at higher humidities.

Effect of High Temperature on Respiratory and Heart Rates

At 95° F. there is a definite increase in the respiratory rate, and when the air temperature is raised to 110° F., the respiratory rate reaches a maximum of 155 per minute (see Figure 32). The intake of water does not affect respiratory rate (Lee *et al.*, 1945; Wilson, 1948).

Hyperthermia, induced by high air temperatures, does not affect heart rate appreciably, according to Yeates *et al.* (1941) and Wilson (1948), except that with extremely high temperatures heart rate may be depressed slightly (Wilson). Rodbard and Tolpin, however, claim that heart rate increases directly with body temperature (see Chapter 4). At body temperatures of 41° and 45° C., the heart rates were 390 and 550 respectively. They produced hyperthermia by applying contact heat (heating pads) to the birds, and the conse-

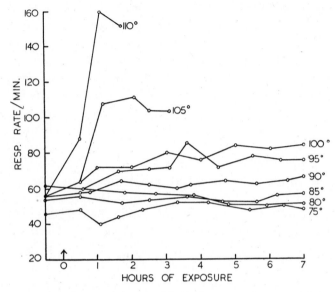

Figure 32. The effects of high ambient temperatures on respiratory rate of the fowl.

Air temperature is shown within the graph. (From Lee *et al.*, *Poultry Sci.*, 1945.)

quent handling of the birds and lower air temperature may have been influencing factors in their experiments.

Hyperthermia and Evaporation of Water

Water is lost from the body of birds by vaporization through the lungs (respiratory water), in the feces and urine, and through the skin. Total water loss from the body may be determined by recording changes in weight of the bird (Yeates, Lee, and Hines, 1941). Respiratory water may be determined indirectly by subtracting from the total weight loss the loss due to water in the feces, which must be determined or estimated (Barott and Pringle, 1946), or it may be determined directly by collecting expired air in a bag or container and measuring the amount of water in it.

The rate of water loss from the body of the chicken is fairly constant at temperatures from 40 to 85° F. (Lee, Robinson, Yeates, and Scott, 1945; Barott and Pringle, 1946). Above 90° F., total water loss is high, averaging approximately 18 grams per hour for a four-pound hen at 100° F., as contrasted with 5 grams or less at 80° F.

Relative humidity plays an important role in the evaporative loss. For example, at an air temperature of 85° F. and a relative humidity of 25 percent, the total water loss is appreciable and ranges from 11 to 17 grams per hour; but at the same temperature and a humidity of 51 percent, the water loss is negligible (0 to 3 grams per hour). At a temperature of 105° F., however, the water loss is greater at a relative humidity of 75 percent than at 25 percent (Lee et al., 1945).

The proportion of the total water loss, vaporized through the lungs at different temperatures, was determined indirectly by Barott and Pringle (1946). They found that respiratory water is higher per unit of body weight for immature chickens than mature ones, except at a temperature of 95° F. or above. The respiratory water for the adult chicken (weighing four pounds) averages 4.5 grams at 95° F. and 1.4 grams at 85° F. Thus, the respiratory water loss at 95° F. constitutes about half the total water loss, based on the figures of Lee et al. (1945) for total loss.

Fowls allowed free access to drinking water show a greater evaporative loss and more resistance to heat than do birds with restricted water supply. Hens supplied drinking water and exposed to high temperatures survive three times as long as those without drinking water (Fox, 1951). Water consumption at 95° to 100° F. is double that consumed at 70° F. (Figure 33).

Lee et al. (1945) suggested that the amount of water in the body and tissues is not the main factor governing the increased resistance to heat, because if water is added to the body orally in amounts sufficient to balance evaporative loss, this has no effect. It may be, as Fox suggested, that fowls supplied drinking water ad libitum wet their feathers and in this way cool themselves more by evaporative loss. Wetting the bird without increased water consumption appears not to have been tried. Evaporative loss is not changed in plucked birds exposed to high temperatures, according to Lee et al., but Benedict, Landauer, and Fox (1932) reported that it is less than normal in the Frizzle fowl, which is partially naked.

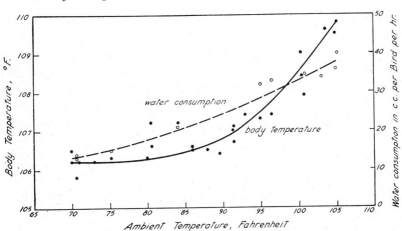

Figure 33. Body temperature and water consumption of the chicken at different ambient temperatures. (From Wilson, *Poultry Sci.*, 1948.)

Effects of Air Movement on Response of Birds to Heat

The effects of air movement on the response to heat are slight. The rise of rectal temperature is somewhat reduced by increased air movement (up to 300 feet per minute) in hot humid atmospheres, but not in dry atmospheres. The rise of respiratory rate is somewhat reduced in hot humid atmospheres (Lee *et al.*, 1945).

Effects of Caloric Intake on Response to Heat

Robinson and Lee (1947) have shown that caloric intake of chickens (White Leghorns and Australorps) has an important effect upon their response to heat. Hens exposed to air temperatures of 105° F. and allowed a high caloric intake exhibited an increase in rectal temperature (1 to 1.5° F.), pulse rate, and respiratory rate. Hens fed a diet with lower caloric intake reacted less to the same high temperature. The proportion of protein (5 to 28.5 percent) in the ration did not influence the response of the birds to heat.

Effects of Plumage, Combs, and Wattles upon Reaction to Heat

When the feathers are plucked from chickens which are exposed to heat, the birds show somewhat less rapid and extensive rises of temperature and respiratory rates than nonplucked fowls, but the heart rate of the plucked birds at a given air temperature is higher than in normal birds, according to Lee *et al.* (1945). They give no reason for this.

They revealed that there is some tendency for hens whose wattles have been removed to show increased reaction to hot air temperatures; however, this tendency is of no importance. Varnishing the combs and wattles of hens makes no difference in the hen's response to heat. These organs apparently are not important in cooling the body by evaporation or conduction.

Breed Variation in Response to Heat

Lee *et al.* (1945) studied the response of six different breeds of chickens to hot air temperatures. These breeds were White Leghorn, Brown Leghorn, Minorca, White Wyandotte, Australorp, and Rhode Island Red. At intermediate temperatures (85° F.), the reactions of all breeds are about the same, but at 105° F. and 25 percent relative humidity, the White Leghorn shows the least rise of body temperature and the Brown Leghorn the greatest, while the Australorp and Rhode Island Red are intermediate in response. If the humidity is raised to 75 percent, the order is completely changed. The Brown Leghorn is the least reactive and the Australorp and Rhode Island Red most reactive, with the White Leghorn and Minorca intermediate. In general, the Australorp and Rhode Island Red withstand heat the least. Hutt (1938) has also shown that White Leghorns are more resistant to heat than heavy breeds.

Fox (1951) also demonstrated a breed difference in response to high temperature. White Plymouth Rocks and Rhode Island Reds survived longer at a high temperature (108° F., relative humidity 30 percent) and without drinking water than did White Leghorns, but when water was available, the White Leghorns survived longer. His results (showing survival time in minutes) follow:

	Without drinking water	*With drinking water*
White Leghorn	89.7	281
White Plymouth Rock	104.5	—
Rhode Island Red	101.2	150

The White Plymouth Rock male is more resistant to high temperatures than the female according to Fox.

As to what determines the relative abilities of the different breeds to withstand high temperatures, there is little evidence. It is not likely that color of plumage plays a role, since under the conditions of the experiments of Lee *et al.* (1945) radiation was at a minimum. It is difficult to explain the different responses in terms of body size or conformation, particularly since the White and Brown Leghorns are of the same size. It is probable, as Hutt (1938) has suggested, that these differences in response to heat are genetic, but this does not explain the mechanism by which the differences are effected.

TEMPERATURE CONTROL MECHANISM

Control of Panting

Reflex panting of mammals has been demonstrated. Randall and Hiestand (1939) and Randall (1943b) devised experiments to determine how panting and shivering are controlled in birds (see also Chapter 6). They found that as body temperature rises, panting ensues, but the increased respiratory rate always lags behind the rise in temperature. They concluded that panting is not controlled reflexly in birds (chickens). They further showed (1939) that central nervous depressants (nembutal) have a depressing effect on respiration. They found, in anesthetized birds, that the onset of panting is delayed, the panting temperature threshold is raised, and the panting rate does not increase in proportion to body temperature as rapidly as in birds not anesthetized. Light narcosis raises the panting threshold, whereas deep anesthesia abolishes panting entirely. When central nervous stimulants, such as lobeline, are injected, a prompt increase in respiratory rate occurs, which, however, does not last long.

Randall (1943b) demonstrated that results obtained by chilling and then warming the birds are different from those obtained by warming and then chilling. When the birds are chilled (body temperature from 42.1 to 39.1° C.) and then warmed up again to 42.1° C., the birds began panting at a lower temperature than normally, that is, the "panting thermostat" was set at a lower level. When the birds are first warmed to 43.0° C. and then chilled to 39.0° C., shivering is initiated at a lower body temperature than normal. Thus, heat acts as a depressant of the shivering mechanism, and cold acts as a stimulant to the panting mechanism.

Randall (1943b) devised further experiments to determine the mechanism by which panting is controlled. He raised the skin temperature of chickens by placing them in a heating pad, and at the same time the temperature of the blood flowing through the carotid artery was lowered by placing a cold collar around the neck of the bird. Deep body temperature was not changed. With this treatment, respiratory rate did not change, indicating that cool blood flowing to the brain was sufficient to offset the heating effect of the skin. When the cold collar was removed, respiratory rate increased from 34 to 150. He concluded that this indicates a discrete central control of panting in the chicken. That inhibition of panting is mediated reflexly has been demonstrated by Randall and others. Blowing cool air on the head will slow respiratory rate.

Control of Shivering

According to Randall (1943a), shivering in birds appears to consist of two definite and distinct physiological components. The first is reflex shivering initiated by impulses arising in skin receptors. Reflexly increased breathing rate is associated with increased muscular contraction designed to increase metabolic production of heat. Since shivering may be produced by decreasing deep body temperature but at the same time holding skin temperature constant, centrally initiated shivering is indicated. In order to investigate the effect of reflexly induced and centrally induced shivering, a temperator tube was placed in the cloaca and body temperature was lowered without lowering skin temperature. Shivering first appeared only after a fall of 1.2° C. cloacal temperature, whereas if the skin temperature was lowered, shivering was initiated in the chick within two minutes, or before body temperature dropped. Sturkie (unpublished) has observed the same.

It is known that in mammals the level of blood sugar figures prominently in shivering. When blood sugar is lowered by the injection of insulin, shivering ceases. Cassidy, Dworkin, and Finney (1926) have shown the same to be true in the fowl. When the blood sugar fell to 40 mg. percent following insulin injection, the bird did not shiver when placed in water at 20° C. That hypothermia depresses and hyperthermia elevates blood sugar in the fowl has been demonstrated (see Chapter 12).

Center of Temperature Control

These and other experiments indicate that the control of body temperature is mediated through the central nervous system. Location of the panting center in the interbrain was discussed in Chapter 6. Further evidence that the temperature control center is located in the thalamus or hypothalamus of birds, as it is in mammals, is based upon the results of Rogers (1928), who stimulated directly with various stimuli the thalamus of the decerebrate pigeon. Applications of cold air and cold water or electrical stimulation usually caused shivering and an increase in body temperature and in some cases mild panting.

REFERENCES

Baldwin, S. P., and S. C. Kendeigh 1932 Physiology of the Temperature of Birds. Scientific Publications of the Cleveland Museum of Natural History, Cleveland, Ohio, Vol. III.

Barbour, H. G., E. A. McKay, and W. P. Griffith 1943 Water shifts in deep hypothermia. Am. J. Physiol. 140:9.

Barott, H. G., and E. M. Pringle 1946 Energy and gaseous metabolism of the chicken from hatch to maturity as affected by temperature. J. Nutrition 31:35.

Benedict, F. G., W. Landauer, and E. L. Fox 1932 The physiology of normal and Frizzle fowl with special reference to basal metabolism. Storrs Agr. Exp. Sta. Bull. 177.

Cassidy, G. F., J. Dworkin, and W. H. Finney 1926 The action of insulin on the domestic fowl. Am. J. Physiol. 75:609.

Dukes, H. H. 1947 The Physiology of Domestic Animals. 6th ed. Comstock Publishing Co., Inc., Ithaca, N.Y.

Fox, T. W. 1951 Studies on heat tolerance in the domestic fowl. Poultry Sci. 30:477.

Fronda, F. M. 1921 A comparative study of the body temperature of the different species and some representative breeds of poultry. Poultry Sci. 1:16.

Groebbels, F. 1932 Der Vogel. Erster Band: Atmungswelt und Nahrungswelt. Verlag von Gebrüder Borntraeger, Berlin.

Heywang, B. W. 1938 Effect of some factors on body temperature of hens. Poultry Sci. 17:320.

Horvath, S. M., G. E. Folk, F. N. Craig, and W. Fleischmann 1948 Survival time of various warm-blooded animals in extreme cold. Science 107:171.

Hutt, F. B.   1938   Genetics of the fowl. VII: Breed differences in suscep-
    tibility to extreme heat. Poultry Sci. 17:454.
Kaupp, B. F.   1922   Normal temperature of the adult domestic fowl.
    J. Am. Vet. Med. Assoc. 61:520.
Lamoreux, W. F., and F. B. Hutt   1939   Variability of body temperature
    in the normal chick. Poultry Sci. 18:70.
Lee, D. H. K., K. W. Robinson, N. T. M. Yeates, and M. I. R. Scott
    1945   Poultry husbandry in hot climates: Experimental inquiries.
    Poultry Sci. 24:195.
Mitchell, H. H., and W. T. Haines   1927   The critical temperature of
    the chicken. J. Agric. Res. 34:549.
Moreng, R. E., and C. S. Shaffner   1951   Lethal internal temperatures
    for the chicken from fertile egg to mature bird. Poultry Sci. 30:255.
Randall, W. C.   1943a   Factors influencing the temperature regulation
    of birds. Am. J. Physiol. 139:56.
Randall, W. C.   1943b   Hypothermia in chickens. Proc. Soc. Exp. Biol.
    & Med. 52:240.
Randall, W. C., and W. A. Hiestand   1939   Panting and temperature
    regulation in the chicken. Am. J. Physiol. 127:761.
Robinson, K. W., and D. H. K. Lee   1946   Animal behaviour and heat
    regulation in hot atmospheres. Univ. Queensland Papers 1:1.
Robinson, K. W., and D. H. K. Lee   1947   The effect of the nutritional
    plane upon the reactions of animals to heat. J. Animal Sci. 6:182.
Rodbard, R., H. Saiki, and A. Malin   1950   Body fluid redistribution in
    induced hypothermia and hyperthermia. Fed. Proc. 9:107.
Rogers, F. T.   1928   Studies of the brain stem. XI: The effects of artifi-
    cial stimulation and of traumatism of the avian thalamus. Am. J.
    Physiol. 86:639.
Romanoff, A. L.   1941   Development of homeothermy in birds.   Science
    94:218.
Scholes, J. C., and F. B. Hutt   1942   Cornell University Memoir 244.
Simpson, S.   1911   XI: An investigation into the effects of seasonal
    changes in body temperature. Proc. Roy. Soc. Edinburgh 32:110.
Streicher, E., D. B. Hackel, and W. Fleischmann   1950   Effects of ex-
    treme cold on the fasting pigeon with a note on the survival of fasting
    ducks at −40° C. Am. J. Physiol. 161:300.
Sturkie, P. D.   1946a   Tolerance of adult chickens to hypothermia. Am.
    J. Physiol. 147:531.
Sturkie, P. D.   1946b   The effects of hypothermia upon the reproductive
    tract of the hen. Poultry Sci. 25:369.

Sturkie, P. D. 1946c The production of twins in Gallus domesticus. J. Exp. Zool. 101:51.

Sturkie, P. D. 1947 Effects of hypothermia upon the specific gravity and proteins of the blood of chickens. Am. J. Physiol. 148:610.

Wilson, W. O. 1948 Some effects of increasing environmental temperatures on pullets. Poultry Sci. 27:813.

Yeates, N. T. M., D. H. K. Lee, and H. J. G. Hines 1941 Reactions of domestic fowls to hot atmospheres. Proc. Roy. Soc. Queensland 53: 105.

CHAPTER 9

Energy Metabolism

Production of Energy by the Body

ALL of the energy for the animal body is derived from the oxidation of organic foodstuffs—carbohydrates, proteins, and fats. Water, minerals, and vitamins, although essential, do not supply energy directly. When carbohydrates, fats, or proteins are oxidized or burned outside of the body, in a bomb calorimeter, they yield heat energy or calories, and this is usually expressed by the kilocalory (Cal.), which is equal to 1000 calories. The number of Calories produced by the oxidation of one gram of pure carbohydrate is 4.1 (average value of different types of carbohydrates), and for one gram of fat, 9.3; this is true also when oxidized in the body because the end products are CO_2 and H_2O. One gram of protein oxidized inside the body yields approximately 4.1 Calories, but about 25 percent more than this when oxidized outside the body. Thus, protein is not completely oxidized in the body, and protein nitrogen in the form of urea, and mainly of uric acid in the case of birds, is excreted in the urine. This energy is therefore lost to the animal. Other sources of losses are combustible materials in the feces and the increased heat production which occurs with eating (referred to as the calorigenic effect or the specific dynamic action of the food). This extra heat represents wasted energy except in cold weather when it is utilized in keeping the body warm. It may amount to 20 to 30 percent of the gross energy of the food for the animal on full feed. The figures for birds range from 20 to 30 percent (Groebbels, 1932). The specific dynamic action of protein is considerably higher than for carbohydrates or fats.

The total or gross energy of a food is the amount of heat energy (Calories) produced upon complete combustion of it. The amount of energy utilized by the animal, apart from the calorigenic heat, represents the net energy of food. By determining the amount of heat energy eliminated by the body, that is, the outgoing energy, and knowing the net income of energy, it is possible to determine the gain or loss of energy by the body.

CALORIMETRY

Outgoing energy can be determined directly by placing the animal in a closed chamber and measuring heat production by the change in temperature of a given volume of water surrounding the chamber. This is known as direct calorimetry. Energy produced may also be determined indirectly. See Brody's book (1945) for a review and discussion on calorimetry and energy metabolism.

Indirect calorimetry is based on the fact that normally the consumption of oxygen and the production of carbon dioxide are closely correlated with heat production. In the oxidation of pure carbohydrates, the volume of CO_2 produced is equal to the amount of O_2 consumed. This is illustrated as follows (Brody):

$$C_6H_{12}O_6 + 6\ O_2 = 6\ CO_2 + 6\ H_2O + 678\ Cal.$$

180	134.4	134.4
grams	liters	liters

Thus, in the oxidation of 1 mole of $C_6H_{12}O_6$ weighing 180 grams, 6 moles of O_2 are consumed and 6 moles of CO_2 are produced. Since 1 mole of a gas at standard conditions has a volume of 22.4 liters, then there are 134.4 liters of O_2 consumed and of CO_2 produced, as shown in the foregoing equation.

The Calories produced per 1 gram of glucose are 3.75, and the use of 1 liter of oxygen in oxidizing glucose represents 5.047 Calories. The caloric value of carbohydrates varies, depending on the type, but the figure 4.1 Calories is considered an average one for several types.

Heat production, or metabolism, can be determined by measuring the consumption of oxygen and the production of carbon dioxide in liters and if the animal is metabolizing carbohydrates, in which case the respiratory quotient (R.Q.) is 1, multiplying this value by 5.047.

For each liter of oxygen consumed in the oxidation of mixed fats, and with an R.Q. of 0.71, 4.69 Calories are generated, and for each liter of carbon dioxide produced, 6.6 Calories. The quantities of carbon dioxide produced and oxygen consumed depend upon the R.Q. Tables have been prepared showing the different values and R.Q.'s. Some of these values are shown as follows:

			R.Q.'s				
0.07	0.71	0.75	0.80	0.85	0.90	0.95	1.00

Calories per liter of

O_2	4.68	4.69	4.73	4.80	4.86	4.92	4.98	5.04
CO_2	6.69	6.60	6.32	6.00	5.72	5.47	5.25	5.04

The respiratory quotient, or R.Q., is the ratio of the volume of CO_2 produced to the volume of O_2 consumed: $R.Q. = \dfrac{CO_2}{O_2}$.

Thus, the R.Q. for pure carbohydrates is 1.00 and for fats it is less, because some of the O_2 is used in the oxidation of hydrogen as well as carbon. This is illustrated in the following equation:

$$C_{57}H_{104}O_6 \text{ (triolein)} + 80\ O_2 = 57\ CO_2 + 52\ H_2O$$

$$R.Q. = \frac{57}{80} = 0.71$$

The average R.Q. for mixed fats is 0.71.

The respiratory quotient for mixed proteins is approximately 0.80 for mammals and 0.705 for birds. In calculating the R.Q. of birds, the computations are based upon the heat of combustion of, and the amount of, uric acid in the urine (instead of urea, as in mammals), since uric acid is the end product of protein metabolism in birds (Barott, Fritz, Pringle, and Titus, 1938; Deighton and Hutchinson, 1940; Barott and Pringle, 1946).

Indirect Methods of Calorimetry

Metabolism may be determined by measuring the consumption of O_2 or the production of CO_2. The gases may be measured gravimetrically or volumetrically. The apparatus may be of the open-circuit or the closed-circuit types. Haldane's modification of the Pettenkofer open-circuit type is a gravimetric method. Atmospheric air is freed of water vapor and CO_2 by pumping it through bottles containing H_2SO_4 and soda lime, and then it is forced into the sealed animal chamber. Carbon dioxide and water vapor produced by the animal pass through the outgoing chain; the water vapor is absorbed by H_2SO_4 and CO_2 by soda lime. The carbon dioxide produced is determined directly by the change in weights of the soda lime and acid bottles of the outgoing chain. Oxygen consumed is determined indirectly by the gain in weight of the bottles containing water and CO_2, minus the loss in weight of the animal and chamber. After determining the R.Q., the caloric equivalent of the O_2 and CO_2 may be found in appropriate tables.

Heat production can be estimated from CO_2 production alone, if the R.Q. is assumed. If the animal has been fasted sufficiently, then no serious error is involved in assuming an R.Q. of 0.71.

There are several closed-circuit types of metabolism apparatus. One type commonly used clinically and on farm animals involves the use of a mask, into which the subject breathes, and a spirometer to measure the amount of O_2 consumed. Metered oxygen is introduced into the spirometer and is inhaled by the subject. Carbon dioxide and water are removed by appropriate absorbers. Thus, the amount of oxygen is determined directly and the circuit is closed to atmospheric air.

BASAL METABOLISM

Basal metabolism is the resting energy metabolism of an animal in the postabsorptive state and in a thermoneutral environment, uncomplicated by the heat increment of feeding (Brody, 1945). Thus, to determine basal metabolism, the animal must first be fasted. In the basal state the animal is metabolizing mainly fats.

Metabolic rate may be related to surface area or body weight. In general, heat production increases with surface area, but there are many variations and deviations. Brody sees no sound reason for relating it to surface area, as there is no method sufficiently accurate for determining surface area. He suggests that metabolism be referred to body weight raised to the 0.734 power. His equation is $y = 70.5x^{0.734}$, in which y represents Calories of heat produced and x the body weight in kilograms. The average numerical value of the ratio $\dfrac{\text{Cal./24 hours}}{\text{kg.}^{0.73}}$ equals 70.5, and this means that the average basal metabolism is 70.5 Calories per 24 hours per kg.$^{0.73}$. Thus, according to this equation, an increase of 1 percent in body weight is associated with an increase of 0.73 percent in metabolic rate.

Actual determinations on a large number of mature animals of different species shows a close relation between heat production and body weight to the 0.734 power. The value of the power for mature Rhode Island Red chickens is 0.73 (Brody).

FACTORS AFFECTING METABOLISM IN BIRDS

The fasting, basal metabolic rate for a number of avian and mammalian species is shown in Table 24. In general, the metabolic rate per unit of body weight is inversely proportional to total body weight. The principal factors affecting metabolic rate in birds, as in mammals, are food, work or exercise, age, environmental temperature, and disease.

Table 24. Basal metabolism of animals and birds, from data arranged and compiled by Brody (1945, p. 390) from work of his own, from Benedict (1938), and from others

Species	Body weight kg.	Basal heat production in 24 hours		
		Per kg. body wt.	Calories sq.m. mostly per $10W^{0.66}$	Per kg. weight$^{0.73}$
Man	65	25	917	78
Horse	703	17	1504	99
Cow	500	12	1094	66
Dog	14	35	745	71
Mouse	0.021	171	526	60
Fowl, hen	2.1	55	701	67
Fowl, cock	2.8	52	730	68
Goose	5.0	54	930	84
Duck	0.9	90	—	—
Pigeon	0.278	102	667	72
Dove	0.150	115	609	69
Canary	0.016	301	762	99
Sparrow	0.0225	231	652	83

Food

Because of the calorigenic action of food, the animal must be fasted if basal metabolic rate is determined. The required length of the fast and its effect upon the R.Q. of the chicken (Dukes, 1937) and the pigeon (Benedict and Riddle, 1929) are shown as follows:

Chicken		Pigeon	
Hours of fast	R.Q.	Hours of fast	R.Q.
1–5	0.96	0–2	0.81–1.01
22–29	0.74	4–6	0.83–1.03
48–53	0.70	8–10	0.72–0.82
88–101	0.71	16–18	0.73–0.78
		26–28	0.71–0.72

Thus, the fasting R.Q. is attained in the chicken in 48 hours or less and in the pigeon 28 hours after fasting. The fasting R.Q. of chickens of all ages is approximately the same (0.717), according to Barott and Pringle (1946). Chickens fed high energy diets (high caloric intake) have higher basal metabolic rates than chickens fed a standard, lower-energy ration, according to Mellen, Hill, and Dukes (1952).

Age and Growth

The metabolism of chickens of various ages has been determined by a number of investigators (see references). Most of these are agreed that basal metabolism is highest during the first 4 to 5 weeks of life and decreases with age up to one year of age (Figure 34). The higher metabolic rate during early life corresponds roughly with the higher growth rate observed during the same period (Mitchell, Card, and Haines, 1927; Kibler and Brody, 1944; Barott and Pringle, 1946; and others).

Effects of Environmental Temperature

The effects of environmental temperatures, ranging from 10° to 100° F., upon basal metabolic rate of the chicken were determined by Barott and Pringle (1946). See Figure 34. The birds were usually fasted for 12 hours before determinations were made. Relative humidities from 50 to 60 percent were maintained at all temperatures.

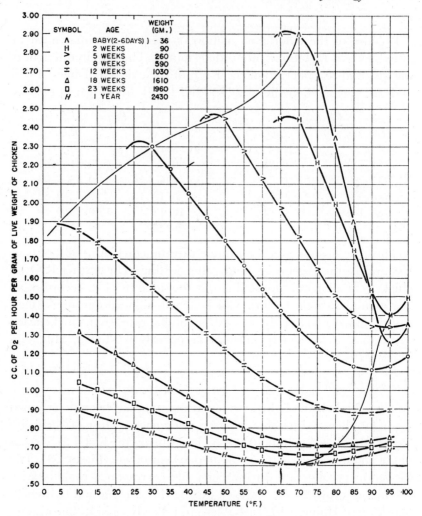

SYMBOL	AGE	WEIGHT (GM.)
∧	BABY(2-6DAYS))	36
H	2 WEEKS	90
>	5 WEEKS	260
o	8 WEEKS	590
�	12 WEEKS	1030
Δ	18 WEEKS	1610
□	23 WEEKS	1960
H	I YEAR	2430

Figure 34. Oxygen consumption of chickens at various temperatures. Rhode Island Red females, fasted for 12 hours. (From Barott and Pringle, *J. Nutrition* 1946.)

Oxygen consumption was determined during a 2-hour period. Chicks up to 2 weeks of age did not survive temperatures below 70° F. for as long as 24 hours. The upper temperature limits for survival for 24 hours was about 90° F. for most adult birds and 103° F. for baby chicks.

It is observed from Figure 34 that, for any given age of chicken, O_2 consumption decreases as environmental temperature increases up to the upper lethal range, and then it increases slightly. The drop in O_2 consumption for birds above 12 weeks of age is fairly steady and regular at environmental temperatures from 10° F. up to about 70° F.; there it tends to level off and remain relatively unchanged until a temperature of 80° to 85° F. is reached, at which point O_2 consumption begins to rise.

Oxygen consumption drops steadily for chickens 8 weeks old at temperatures from 30° F. to about 80° F. and reaches its low at 90° F., after which it rises again. For 5-week-old chicks about the same situation prevails, except the low point in O_2 consumption is at 90°. At 2 to 6 days and at 2 weeks of age, the low point is at 95° F.

Oxygen consumption at a constant environmental temperature is inversely proportional to age of the bird. The drop in O_2 consumption with increasing temperature is greater for younger birds. This is further evidence that the temperature-regulating mechanism in younger chicks is not fully developed. The range of thermal neutrality is narrower in younger chicks than in older ones. This range for chicks up to 2 weeks of age is about 1° to 2°, because metabolism begins to rise at temperatures above or below the critical temperature (95° F.).

The range of thermal neutrality then increases up to 18 weeks of age; thereafter it changes little with age. The range extends from about 65° to 80° or 85° F. for birds 18 weeks of age or over. The range of thermal neutrality for featherless chickens is shifted upward, because heat loss is greater, but the metabolic rate within this range for the bird without feathers is no greater than for normal birds (Benedict, Landauer, and Fox, 1932).

Individual Variation and Effects of Activity

Winchester (1940a) studied the individual variation in metabolism of four birds at frequent intervals for a one-month period. Heat production was determined when the bird was active, relatively inactive, and in the act of laying. He found that heat production and heart rate are closely related. The day-to-day variations in heat production and heart rate in some cases were considerable. The act of laying an egg, however, does not affect metabolism or heart rate appreciably, according to Winchester.

The effect of different types of activity on the metabolic rate of hens was studied by Deighton and Hutchinson (1940), who reported as follows. (1) Metabolism in the standing position is 40 to 50 percent higher than in the sitting position. (2) Stretching of the neck in any direction, so that feathers are separated, increases metabolism as much as 20 percent. (3) Crowing produces a momentary increase in metabolism. (4) In rising to the standing position, metabolism may go up 200 percent, but this increase is momentary. (5) When the bird goes to sleep with head under wing, metabolism drops about 12 percent and remains at this level. These changes do not affect average metabolism, particularly if the determinations are made over a period of one-half hour or longer and on a fairly large number of birds.

Basal metabolism is higher in the morning than in the afternoon or evening (Deighton and Hutchinson, 1940; Barott and Pringle, 1946).

Seasonal Metabolic Rhythms and Egg Production

Winchester (1940b) made a detailed one-year study of the metabolism of birds at different rates of laying. He found that heat production increases steadily beginning in October and reaches its peak in February. Usually, egg production also increases during this period, but the peak of egg production is in April, when metabolism is dropping. Heat production usually reaches its low point in July and August and in general appears to be inversely related to environmental temperature; however, there are exceptions. In one flock, heat production remained low during the cold months of December and January. Egg production declined after April, but environmental temperature remained relatively low during May and June. Winchester (1940b) concluded that the seasonal rhythm of heat production is not simply an effect of changes in environmental temperature, but that the level of metabolism is influenced by the rate of egg production and other energy exchanges in the body. However, he did not show how rate of production, apart from that associated with season, affects metabolism. Dukes (1937) reported that metabolic rate of high laying hens is slightly greater than in poor laying hens.

Molting and Its Effect on Metabolism

Perek and Sulman (1945) measured basal metabolism of hens during the summer, fall, and winter. They found that metabolic rate is highest during the period of molting. Their data, showing the average O_2 consumption (in cc. per kilogram of body weight per hour), follow:

No. of hens	Summer laying	Autumn molting	Winter laying
8	460	666	448

The birds, before and after molting (summer and winter layers), ranged from 50 to 80 percent in egg production, and the metabolic rate of these did not differ. It is apparent from their data that metabolic rate increases about 50 percent during molting, but some of the increase may be due to greater heat loss resulting from the loss of feathers. It is known that molting can be induced by feeding large doses of thyroid-active substances, particularly at or near the time when birds molt. The relationship of molting to thyroid activity is discussed in Chapter 19.

Effects of Altered Thyroid Activity

Metabolic rate is influenced greatly by the activity of the thyroid gland. Overactivity of the gland (hyperthyroidism) elevates and underactivity (hypothyroidism) depresses metabolic rate. Removal of the thyroid depresses metabolism in pigeons (Marvin and Smith, 1943), geese (Lee and Lee, 1937), and chickens (Winchester, 1939). The heat production of thyroidectomized chickens averages 2.81 Calories per kg.$^{0.73}$ compared to 3.27 for the normal bird. The drop in heat production of the thyroidectomized goose ranges from 15 to 33 percent, depending upon the temperature. At temperatures of 21° to 24° C., the heat production of normal geese ranges from 58 to 70 Calories per kilogram of body weight for 24 hours.

Mild hyperthyroidism and hypothyroidism, induced by administration of small amounts of iodinated casein and thiouracil respectively, increase and decrease metabolic rate respectively without affecting laying rate or fertility appreciably (McCartney and Shaffner, 1950). See Figure 35. The metabolic response to graded doses of iodinated casein (5, 10, and 15 grams per 100 pounds of feed) is proportional to dosage above the 5 gram level. Increasing the

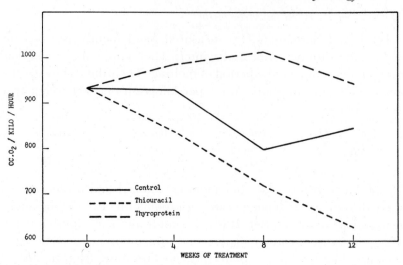

Figure 35. Effects of thyroprotein (0.022 percent in feed) and thiouracil (0.1 percent in feed) upon basal metabolism of laying chickens. (From McCartney and Shaffner, *Poultry Sci.*, 1950.)

caloric value of the diet also increases the metabolic response to iodinated casein (Singh and Shaffner, 1950).

Effects of Disease on Metabolism

Diseases affecting the function of the thyroid gland may increase or decrease metabolic rate. Disorders which increase (fever) or decrease body temperature produce changes in metabolic rate. Very few studies have been conducted upon the metabolism of diseased birds. Olson and Dukes (see Dukes, 1947) reported that transmissible lymphomatosis in chickens causes a slight increase in basal metabolism and that two cases of lymphocytoma were associated with a marked increase in basal heat production.

REFERENCES

Barott, H. G., J. C. Fritz, E. M. Pringle, and H. W. Titus 1938 Heat production and gaseous metabolism of young male chickens. J. Nutrition 15:145.

Barott, H. G., and E. M. Pringle 1946 Energy and gaseous metabolism of the chicken from hatch to maturity as affected by temperature. J. nutrition 31:35.

Benedict, F. G.   1938   A study in comparative basal metabolism. Carnegie Institution of Washington, Publication 503.

Benedict, F. G., W. Landauer, and E. L. Fox   1932   The physiology of normal and Frizzle fowl with special reference to basal metabolism. Storrs Agr. Exp. Sta. Bull. 177.

Benedict, F. G., and O. Riddle   1929   The measurement of the basal heat production of pigeons. I: Physiological technique. J. Nutrition 1:497.

Brody, S.   1945   Bioenergetics and Growth. Reinhold Publishing Co., New York.

Deighton, T., and J. C. D. Hutchinson   1940   Studies on metabolism of fowls. II: The effect of activity on metabolism. J. Agric. Sci. 30:141.

Dukes, H. H.   1937   Studies on the energy metabolism of the hen. J. Nutrition 14:341.

Dukes, H. H.   1947   The Physiology of Domestic Animals. 6th ed. Comstock Publishing Co., Ithaca, N.Y.

Groebbels, F.   1932   Der Vogel. Erster Band: Atmungswelt und Nahrungswelt. Verlag von Gebrüder Borntraeger, Berlin.

Kendeigh, S. C.   1944   Effect of air temperature on the rate of energy metabolism in the English sparrow. J. Exp. Zool. 96:1.

Kibler, H. H., and S. Brody   1944   Metabolic changes in growing chickens. J. Nutrition 28:27.

Kleiber, M., and J. E. Dougherty   1934   The influence of environmental temperature on the utilization of food energy in baby chicks. J. Gen. Physiol. 17:701.

Lee, M., and R. C. Lee   1937   Effect of thyroidectomy and thyroid feeding in geese on the basal metabolism at different temperatures. Endocrinol. 21:790.

McCartney, M. G., and C. S. Shaffner   1950   The influence of altered metabolism upon fertility and hatchability in the female. Poultry Sci. 29:67.

Marvin, H. N., and G. C. Smith   1943   Technique for thyroidectomy in the pigeon and early effect of thyroid removal on heat production. Endocrinol. 32:87.

Mellen, W. J., F. W. Hill, and H. H. Dukes   1952   Effect of dietary energy level on the basal metabolism of growing chickens. Poultry Sci. 31:927 (Abs.).

Mitchell, H. H., L. E. Card, and W. T. Haines   1927   The effect of age, sex, and castration on the basal heat production of chickens. J. Agric. Res. 34:945.

Mitchell, H. H., and W. T. Haines   1927   The basal metabolism of mature chickens and the net-energy value of corn. J. Agric. Res. 34: 927.

Perek, M., and F. Sulman 1945 The basal metabolic rate in molting and laying hens. Endocrinol. 36:240.

Singh, H., and C. S. Shaffner 1950 Effect of thyroprotein and caloric level of diet on metabolic rate of chickens. Poultry Sci. 29:575.

Winchester, C. F. 1939 Influence of thyroid on egg production. Endocrinol. 14:697.

Winchester, C. F. 1940a Lability of metabolic processes in laying hens. Poultry Sci. 19:233.

Winchester, C. F. 1940b Seasonal metabolic rhythms in the domestic fowl. Poultry Sci. 19:239.

Winchester, C. F., and M. Kleiber 1938 The effect of environmental temperature on mortality, rate of growth, and utilization of food energy in White Leghorn chicks. J. Agric. Res. 57:529.

CHAPTER 10

Alimentary Canal: Anatomy, Prehension, Deglutition, Passage of Ingesta, Motility

ANATOMY OF THE ALIMENTARY CANAL

THE organs of the digestive tract of the bird include the beak, mouth, tongue (but no teeth), pharynx, esophagus, crop, proventriculus, gizzard, intestines, ceca, rectum, and cloaca (see Figure 36). The length of various parts of the tract is shown in Table 25.

Mouth and pharynx. There is no sharp line of demarcation between the mouth and pharynx, and there is no soft palate in most birds.

Table 25. Length of the digestive tract of chickens
(five birds: Calhoun, 1933)

	Age	
	20 days	1.5 year
Entire digestive tract	85 cm.	210 cm.
Angle of beak to crop	7.5 "	20 "
Angle of beak to proventriculus	11.5 "	35 "
Duodenum (complete loop)	12 "	20 "
Ileum and jejunum	49 "	120 "
Cecum	5 "	17.5 "
Rectum and cloaca	4 "	11.25 "

The hard palate is pierced by a median slit which communicates with the nasal cavities. The cavity of the mouth is lined with stratified squamous epithelium. Branched tubular salivary glands are present (Calhoun, 1933; Halnan, 1949).

Esophagus and crop. The esophagus of the mature fowl is 6 to 8 inches long and is lined with stratified squamous epithelium. Mucous glands are present.

The crop has essentially the same structure as the esophagus, though mucous glands are absent in the crop except at the juncture of the esophagus (Calhoun). The crops of certain grain-eating birds, such as the chicken, duck, and pigeon, are well developed, but in some other species they may be rudimentary, and in some insect-eating birds, absent (Browne, 1922).

Proventriculus and gizzard. The proventriculus, or glandular stomach, is lined with columnar epithelium, formed into simple tubular glands. The underlying mucous layer contains well-developed glands, which communicate with the lumen of the proventriculus by a duct. The outer muscular coats are similar to those of the esophagus. The gastric glands of birds contain only one type of cell, which produces both acid and pepsinogen granules, unlike the gastric glands of mammals, in which different cell types produce the two secretions (Bowie, 1936).

The gizzard, or ventriculus, of the fowl is lined by keratinized, columnar epithelium. Tubular glands which empty on the surface are arranged in groups in the tunica propria. A muscularis mucosae is absent, but a submucosa is present. A very prominent striated muscular layer surrounds the organ and is composed of a thick layer of parallel fibers which extend from one aponeurosis to another. Surrounding the outer muscular layers ia a thin layer of connective tissue, containing blood vessels and nerves (Calhoun, 1933). The gizzard is large and well developed in grain-eating birds, but in carnivorous birds, it is small and poorly developed and may be regarded as a simple expansion of the proventriculus (Browne, 1922).

Small intestine. The small intestine consists of the duodenum (loop) and a jejunum and ileum, according to the terminology of some authors, but beyond the duodenum there are no delimited areas in

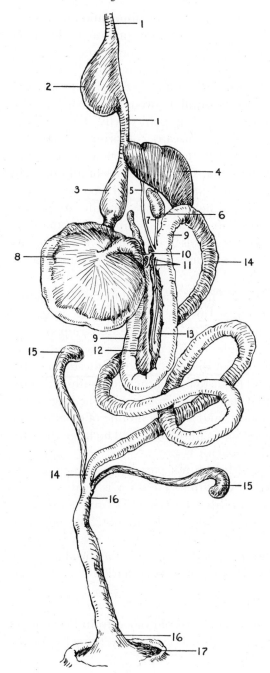

Figure 36. Digestive tract of the chicken.

1 and 2, esophagus and crop; 3, proventriculus; 4, liver; 5, hepatic duct; 6, gall badder; 7, cystic duct or duct from gall bladder; 8, gizzard; 9, duodenum; 10, pancreatic ducts from dorsal lobe; 11, pancreatic ducts from ventral lobe; 12, dorsal lobe of pancreas; 13, ventral lobe of pancreas; 14, upper and lower segments of small intestine; 15, ceca; 16, large intestine or rectum; 17, cloaca.

the small intestine. Some authors refer to the upper and lower ileum as corresponding to the jejunum and ileum in mammals. The remnant of the attachment of the yolk stalk may be found about midway of the small intestine. In relation to body length, the intestines of birds are shorter than those of mammals (Browne, 1922). The histology of the small intestine is similar throughout. It is lined by simple columnar epithelum with many goblet cells. The layers or coats from the epithelial surface outward comprise a muscularis mucosae and a thin submucosa, both containing few blood vessels and nerves, and an outer muscular layer, made up of an inner circular and an outer longitudinal layer, rich in blood vessels and nerves. Projections from the epithelial surface, or villi, are present in all of the small intestine, but are most prominent in the duodenum. Simple tubular mucous glands (Leiberkühn) and crypts are present in the mucosa, but there are no Brunner's glands, as in mammals (Calhoun, 1933).

Ceca, large intestine, and cloaca. The ceca are situated at the juncture of the small and large intestines. In some species they are large and prominent (about 6 inches long in the chicken) and are paired; in other species they may be single, rudimentary, or absent (Browne, 1922). Guarding the entrance of the ceca into the intestine are the muscular ileocecal valves. The histology of the ceca is similar to the rest of the tract, except that the villi are not as tall. The large intestine in birds is relatively short, and there is no line of demarcation between the rectum and colon, as in mammals. The large intestine or rectum empties into the cloaca.

The liver and pancreas, although not part of the alimentary canal, are organs concerned in digestion. The liver is relatively large and bilobed. Some species of birds (chicken, duck, and goose) have gall bladders, and others, such as the pigeon, do not. The gall bladder is located on the dorsal surface of the liver and gives rise to the bile ducts, which open into the duodenum, near the distal loop (see Figure 36). The pancreas is discussed in Chapter 20.

Circulation in the Digestive Tract

The esophagus and crop receive arterial blood from branches of the external carotid arteries and are drained by branches of the jugular veins. The celiac artery and its branches supply the liver, proventriculus, gizzard, pancreas, duodenum, and small intestine. The caudal mesenteric artery supplies the cloaca and rectum. Blood is drained from the stomach, gizzard, and intestines by the gastro-duodenal, cranial, and caudal mesenteric veins. These veins empty into the portal vein, which carries the blood to the liver (Bradley and Grahame, 1950).

The nerves of the alimentary canal are discussed under motility of the tract.

PREHENSION AND DEGLUTITION

The bird picks up feed with the beak, and the food is mixed with saliva in the mouth and swallowed. The act of swallowing (deglutition) differs in certain species. The food mass (bolus) or water is forced downward in the goose, chicken, and duck by gravity and the negative pressure produced in the esophagus as the bird raises its head and extends the neck. These birds do not possess a soft palate, which in certain mammals and birds (the pigeon) aids in forcing the bolus downward (Cannon and Moser, 1898; Halnan, 1949). The pigeon, like the horse, can drink with its head down.

PASSAGE OF INGESTA THROUGH THE TRACT

The time required for feed to pass through the alimentary canal can be studied in several ways. (1) Birds may be killed at different intervals to observe the location of feed in the tract. (2) The food may be stained with certain dyes so that it may be identified in the feces. (3) Certain types of feed, such as oats, may be recognized in the feces without marking (Browne, 1922). (4) The passage of the food may also be observed with X-rays, or (5) the food may be collected by placing cannulas in the different portions of the tract, a method employed by a number of German workers (see Groebbels, 1932, for a review).

Passage of food down the alimentary canal of birds has been studied by a number of workers with considerable variation in the results (for review, see Keith, Card, and Mitchell, 1927; Groebbels, 1932; Heuser, 1945). Some of these results, based on the chicken, are shown as follows:

Type of feed	Amount of feed in crop	Time required for feed to disappear from crop		Author
	Grams	Hours	Amount	
Wheat, oats, or corn	5	1½–2	all	Ihnen (1928)
"	30	7–9½	"	"
"	60	10–18	"	"
Oats	full crop	18–20	"	Browne (1922)
Corn	30	12	"	Schwarz & Teller (1924)
"	35–65	70	"	Hubeck (1930)
Wheat	"	102	"	"
Barley	"	119	"	"
Grain	40–60	4	20–30%	Heuser (1945)
"	"	24	90%	"

The data of Ihnen show that the amount of feed consumed influences greatly its passage from the crop. This has also been reported by Steinmetzer (1924) and Henry, MacDonald, and Magee (1933). Halnan (1949) showed that when the crop of the chicken is full, the lower half of the contents passes to the gizzard much faster than the upper half.

The rate of passage of ingesta is also influenced by the consistency, hardness, and water content of the feed. Dry oats remain in the crop longer than corn or wheat and longer than boiled oats, according to Heuser (1945). He revealed, also, that wet mash passes faster from the crop than an equal quantity of dry mash. Whether or not dry oats are whole, ground, or crushed does not materially affect their sojourn in the crop according to Henry *et al.* (1933). Soft potatoes leave the crop more rapidly than grain, but chopped meat remains longer in the crop of the goose than grain (Groebbels, 1932).

Most of the studies reported above were based upon the disappearance of feed from the crop. A better idea of the speed of passage of ingesta in the tract may be gained by the use of X-rays and by the first appearance, after feeding, of the feed in the feces.

Henry *et al.* (1933), who fed 2 ounces of oats mixed with barium sulfate to hens, reported the complete disappearance of feed from the tract (based on X-ray shadows) within 16 to 25 hours. Most investigators who have used markers have shown that some of the feed first ingested appears in the feces within $2\frac{1}{2}$ to 12 hours, depending on the type and amount fed and physiological state of the bird. Kaupp and Ivey (1923), who fed corn meal and wheat middlings mixed with various dyes, reported the appearance of the dye in the feces within approximately 4 hours for growing and laying chickens, 8 hours for nonlaying hens, and approximately 12 hours for broody hens.

The results obtained with the use of dyes are subject to error, according to Browne (1922). He showed that soluble dyes tend to pass through the tract faster than hard particles, particularly when large amounts are ingested. If the food to be tested is impregnated with an insoluble dye, this objection is overcome. Such a substance is chromic oxide. Preliminary experiments indicate that it can be detected in the feces within $2\frac{1}{2}$ hours after feeding.

MOTILITY OF THE TRACT

Crop Motility

The crop undergoes contractions which vary considerably in rhythm and amplitude. The irregularity of movements is influenced by the nervous state of the animal, hunger, and other factors. Extreme excitement, fear, or struggling may inhibit or retard crop contractions in the chicken and pigeon (Rogers, 1915; Henry, MacDonald, and Magee, 1933). In order to study crop movements supposedly not influenced by nervous impulses reaching the central nervous system, the cerebral hemispheres have been removed (decerebration) from pigeons and chickens (Rogers, 1915 and 1916; Paterson, 1927; Ashcraft, 1930). Rogers and also Ashcraft concluded that hunger produces restlessness and irregular crop activity in normal and decerebrate pigeons and chickens, but fear has no effect upon crop activity of the decerebrate pigeon (Rogers). Paterson (1927), however, reported that crop motility in hungry decerebrate pigeons is fairly regular.

Peristaltic contraction begins in the esophagus and spreads down the crop to the gizzard (Halnan, 1949). This usually occurs in groups of varying number and speed, depending upon state of hunger, amount of food in the crop, and other factors. The waves usually appear in groups of 2 to 15, at intervals of 1 to 40 minutes, according to Ashcraft (1930), and at intervals of 1 per minute, according to Groebbels (1932). The speed of contraction is greater when the crop is empty, as illustrated in the chicken as follows (from data of Lieberbarb; see Groebbels, 1932):

Hours of starvation	$1\frac{1}{2}$	6	10	27
No. of contractions per hour	13	36	55	75
Duration of contractions in seconds	42	45	30	26

When the gizzard and crop are full, crop contractions may cease (Halnan) or, in the pigeon, may be absent for 30 to 40 minutes (Rogers, 1916; Paterson, 1927).

Within 1 to 2 hours after feeding the pigeon, peristaltic waves appear in groups of 3 to 4, and at intervals of 15 to 20 minutes. After 5 to 12 hours, they appear in groups of 6 to 20 and at intervals of 10 to 30 minutes. In the hungry bird with an empty crop, the contractions occur in groups of 8 to 16 and at intervals of 10 to 60 minutes.

The pressure in the crop of the hen ranges from 7 to 18 cm. of water (Groebbels).

Nervous control. The motility of the esophagus and crop is under nervous control. These organs receive parasympathetic excitatory fibers from the vagus, according to Ihnen (1928), and also both excitatory and inhibitory fibers from the sympathetic system, according to Nolf (see Babkin, 1950). Stimulation of the peripheral end of the left vagus causes contraction in the left side of the crop (cephalic and dorsal region), and stimulation of the right vagus causes contraction of the right side (Ihnen).

Transection of the right vagus alone has little effect upon crop motility, but ligation of the left vagus inhibits motility and particularly the ability of the crop to empty itself (Mangold, 1929). According to Ihnen, the left vagus nerve controls the peristaltic movements of the esophagus, because after ligation of this nerve, these movements are abolished. The parasympathomimetic drugs, acetylcholine and pilocarpine, produce strong contraction in the crop (see Groebbels, 1932).

Motility of Proventriculus

Apparently few observations have been made on the motility of the glandular stomach. Ashcraft (1930) stated that the wave of contraction in the proventriculus of the chicken is fairly regular and rhythmical and of high amplitude. Rate of contraction is approximately 1 per minute in the hungry chicken. Amplitude and frequency of contractions are greater in the male, and this is due to the hormone, androgen, according to Ikegami (1938). He castrated male chickens and reported a decrease in frequency and amplitude of contraction, which could be restored to normal after injections of androgen.

Motility of Gizzard

The gizzard exhibits regular and rhythmic contractions. Motility has been studied by observing the organ in the opened bird, by fluoroscopic examination, and by placing balloons, attached to a suitable manometer and recording device, in the gizzard (for details, see Mangold, 1929; Ashcraft, 1930; Groebbels, 1932; Henry, MacDonald, and Magee, 1933). The type of wave produced varies some with the location of the balloon in the gizzard.

The contractions or grinding sounds of the gizzard in the bird can be heard with a stethoscope, particularly when coarse or hard food and grit are present (Groebbels, 1932). The movements appear to be rotary in nature, judging from the circumferential arrangement of fibrous food in the gizzard (Browne, 1922).

The frequency of contractions appears to vary little in the hen and ranges from 2 to 3 per minute, according to most investigators (Ashcraft, Mangold, Henry *et al.*, and others). To what extent state of hunger influences frequency is not clear. Henry *et al.* (1933) and also Mangold (1929) reported a slightly higher frequency in fed birds as compared with those starved, but Rossi's results (see Groebbels, 1932) showed the opposite effect. Gizzard contractions in hens starved for 1 to 2 days ranged from 2.5 to 3 per minute, and in those fed, 1.5 to 2 per minute.

The duration of contractions ranges, in most cases, from 20 to 30 seconds and is influenced by hunger and also by the type of feed ingested (Mangold, 1929). Starvation of birds previously fed wheat increases the amplitude and duration of individual contractions from 15 to 25 seconds to 30 to 50 seconds. Ingestion of hard or fibrous food shortens contraction time. For example, when wheat and barley are fed, the durations range from 15 to 22 seconds, and after the feeding of potatoes and cornmeal, from 22 to 30 seconds.

The amplitude of gizzard movements is greater when grit is present (Groebbels). Apparently grit remains in the gizzard for a considerable time and is not ordinarily passed out with the feed, particularly when small amounts are present. Browne (1922) fed, to a bird that had been denied access to grit, four small pebbles, and three of these were found in the gizzard three weeks later. Groebbels (1932), with the duodenal cannula, reported that very little grit was collected in the cannula, yet the gizzard of the domestic goose may contain as much as 30 grams, and the duck, 10 grams.

The pressure exerted by the gizzard has been measured by Mangold and co-workers, Kato, and others (see Mangold, 1929) in a number of birds, as follows (in mm. Hg):

Buzzard	8–26	Duck	180
Hen	100–150	Goose	265–280

The pressure is much lower in carnivores, such as the buzzard, in which the gizzard is poorly developed. Feeding of hard fibrous feeds, for example barley, produces higher gizzard pressure than the feeding of wheat. The amplitude of contractions is greater in males than in females.

Nerves. The gizzard receives extrinsic fibers from the vagus and the sympathetic system. Nolf and also Doyon (see Groebbels, 1932) reported the presence of excitatory and inhibitory fibers in the vagus. Nolf also reported these types of fibers in the sympathetic nerves to the gizzard, but Doyon reported only inhibitory fibers. Ligation of the vagus causes slowing of the gizzard movements, which, however, soon return to normal (Mangold, Nolf, and others). Cutting both nerves produces permanent slowing in the movements of the organ.

The gizzard is capable of automatic movements, which are governed by its intrinsic nerve supply. When the gizzard is deprived of its extrinsic nerve supply, by ligation of such nerves or by removal of the organ from the body, it continues to undergo movements (see Babkin, 1950, and Groebbels, 1932).

The excitatory and inhibitory effects of parasympathomimetic and sympathomimetic drugs on the gizzard have been reported (Henry *et al.*, 1933). Pilocarpine increases the rate of contraction, and adrenaline, as well as atropine, decreases it.

Motility of Intestines

The intestines of birds undergo peristaltic movements characteristic of the intestines of mammals (Mangold, 1929; Groebbels, 1932). This has been demonstrated also in *in vitro* studies, in which the intestine was placed in oxygenated Ringer's solution at 40 to 43° C. (Sugano; see Mangold).

The peristaltic wave proceeds aborally. Nolf (see Groebbels), who stimulated the cephalic end of an intestinal preparation in Ringer's solution, reported the spread of the wave aborally. Stimulation of the caudal end, however, produced contraction only a short distance orally. In the opened bird, with a balloon in the intestine, the wave is always aboral, according to Groebbels.

Since regurgitated material from the duodenum has been reported in the gizzard, proventriculus, and even the crop, this suggests reverse peristalsis at certain times.

Motility of Ceca

According to Browne (1922), the ceca undergo peristalsis, and the wave passes from the intestinal junction to the blind end of the organ. He believed that the ceca are filled in this manner. Other workers have suggested that they are filled by antiperistaltic movements of the intestines or by pressure in the latter. In order for the ceca to fill and empty, the valves guarding their entrance into the intestines must open and close, but the physiology of these in the filling and emptying of the structures is not understood.

The contents of the ceca are homogeneous and pultaceous in consistency and are usually chocolate-colored. Cecal contents or droppings can be readily distinguished from rectal feces. Such knowledge has been used in determining when the bodies are evacuated. The ratio of cecal to rectal evacuations for the hen ranges from 1 to 7.3, following the feeding of barley, to 1 to 11.5 after the ingestion of corn (Röseler, 1929).

The mechanism for the evacuation of the ceca is unknown. It is believed by some (see Mangold, 1929) that as the ceca are filled the pressure builds up to a point such that the iliocecal valves are opened or that the pressure in the cecal walls mechanically stimulates and causes contraction of the organs.

It is presumed that the ceca, like the rest of the digestive tract, receive sympathetic and parasympathetic fibers, which are concerned in their motility. It is known that the automatic movements of the organs *in vitro* are inhibited by epinephrine and stimulated by acetylcholine. In fact, the chicken cecum is a very sensitive indicator of epinephrine and related substances and is used for assaying the potency of such substances in the blood and other solutions.

REFERENCES

Ashcraft, D. W. 1930 Correlative activities of the alimentary canal of fowl. Am. J. Physiol. 93:105.

Babkin, B. P. 1950 Secretory Mechanism of the Digestive Glands. 2d ed. Paul B. Hoeber, Inc., New York.

Bowie, D. J. 1936 A method of staining the pepsinogen granules in gastric glands. Anat. Rec. 64:357.

Bradley, O. C., and T. Grahame 1950 The Structure of the Fowl. 3d ed. J. P. Lippincott Co., Philadelphia.

Browne, T. G. 1922 Some observations on the digestive system of the fowl. J. Comp. Path. & Thera. 35:12.

Calhoun, M. L. 1933 The microscopic anatomy of the digestive tract of Gallus domesticus. Iowa State College J. Sci. 7:261.

Cannon, W. B., and A. Moser 1898 The movements of the food in the esophagus. Am. J. Physiol. 1:435.

Groebbels, F. 1932 Der Vogel. Erster Band: Atmungswelt und Nahrungswelt. Verlag von Gebrüder Borntraeger, Berlin.

Halnan, E. T. 1949 The architecture of the avian gut and tolerance of crude fiber. Brit. J. Nutrition 3:245.

Henry, K. M., A. J. MacDonald, and H. E. Magee 1933 Observations on the functions of the alimentary canal in fowls. J. Exp. Biol. 10:153.

Heuser, G. F. 1945 The rate of passage of feed from the crop of the hen. Poultry Sci. 24:20.

Hubeck, R. 1930 Wiss. Arch. Landwirtschaft 2:626. Cited by Groebbels, 1932.

Ihnen, K. 1928 Beiträge zur Physiologie des Kropfes bei Huhn und Taube. I: Bewegung und Innervation des Kropfes. Arch. ges. Physiol. (Pflügers) 218:767.

Ikegami, Y. 1938 The function of the testes and the stomach movement. Jap. J. Gastroenterol. 10:103 (Biol. Abs. 14547, 1940).

Kaupp, B. F., and J. E. Ivey 1923 Time required for food to pass through the intestinal tract of fowls. J. Agric. Res. 23:721.

Keith, M. H., L. E. Card, and H. H. Mitchell 1927 The rate of passage of food through the digestive tract of the hen. J. Agric. Res. 24:759.

Mangold, E. 1929 Handbuch der Ernährung und des Stoffwechsels der Landswirtschaftlichen Nutztiere. Zweiter Band. Verlag von Julius Spring, Berlin.

Paterson, T. L. 1927 Crop movements in the pigeon. J. Lab. & Clin. Med. 12:1003.

Rogers, F. T. 1915 The hunger mechanism in birds (prelim. report). Proc. Soc. Exp. Biol. & Med. 13:119.

Rogers, F. T. 1916 Contribution to the physiology of the stomach: The hunger mechanism of the pigeon and its relation to the central nervous system. Am. J. Physiol. 41:555.

Röseler, M. 1929 Die Bedeutung der Blinddärme des Haushuhnes für die Resorption der Nahrung und Verdauung der Rohfaser. Z. Tierzücht und Züchtungsbiol. 13:281.

Schwarz, C., and H. Teller 1924 Beiträge zur Physiologie der Verdauung. VIII: Mitteilung über die Kropfverdauung des Haushuhnes. Fermentforschung 7:269.

Steinmetzer, K. 1924 Die zeitlichen Verhaeltnisse beim Durchwandern von Futter durch den Magendarmkanal des Huhnes. Arch. ges. Physiol. (Pflügers) 206:500.

CHAPTER 11

Alimentary Canal: Digestion, Absorption, Secretion of Gastric Juice, pH

RELATIVELY little is known about digestion in birds, and practically no work has been conducted upon it in recent years. (For reviews, see Mangold, 1929 and 1934; Groebbels, 1932; Dukes, 1947; Halnan, 1949.) Digestion involves all of the physical and chemical changes which ingested food must undergo before it can be absorbed in the intestines. These processes include swallowing, maceration, and grinding of food in the gizzard; the action of digestive enzymes from the saliva, stomach, intestines, and pancreas, bile from the liver, and hydrochloric acid from the stomach; and the action of bacteria.

Ingested carbohydrates must be converted into the simple sugars, the monosaccharides, before they are absorbed. Some of the enzymes which are concerned in the breakdown of the complex carbohydrates are ptyalin and amylopsin (amylases), lactase, maltase, and invertase.

The fats must be hydrolyzed into fatty acids and glycerol before absorption in the small intestine. This is accomplished by the action of bile, which emulsifies the fats, and the fat-splitting enzyme, lipase.

Ingested proteins are hydrolyzed into amino acids, in which form they are absorbed in the intestines. In this process, the primary protein derivatives, which are insoluble, are broken down into the secondary proteins, mainly proteoses, peptones, and peptides. Though these are soluble, they normally are not absorbed; instead they are converted finally into amino acids. The enzymes concerned in the cleavage of proteins in the bird are pepsin from the stomach and trypsin and possibly erepsin from the pancreatic and intestinal juices respectively.

In the digestion of fats, carbohydrates, and proteins, a number of intermediary products are formed. For details, consult chapter 12 and textbooks on biochemistry and nutrition.

The principal enzymes present in the digestive tract of the chicken and their effects are shown in Table 26. Further details concerning these are discussed in following sections.

DIGESTION IN MOUTH, ESOPHAGUS, AND CROP

The amylase, ptyalin, is present in saliva and scrapings from the mouth and esophagus of the fowl (Shaw, 1913; Leasure and Link, 1940), and although the concentration is not as high as in the saliva of humans (Leasure and Link), there is enough present to hydrolyze starch into sugar within one hour (Shaw). However, Jung and Pierre (1933), who fed chickens carbohydrates, found little or no conversion of starch into sugar in the crop and concluded that saliva plays a very minor role in enzymatic digestion.

The presence of enzymes in the crop and their role in digestion have been a subject of controversy. A number of workers have reported the presence of proteolytic and amylolytic enzymes in the crop or its contents, whereas others have not (see Groebbels, 1932). Klug (1891) and Shaw (1913) found no enzymes present in extracts of crop tissue or crop mucosa, but Plimmer and Rosedale (1922) did find proteolytic and carbohydrate-splitting enzymes (amylase and lactase) in crop tissue; Hamilton and Mitchell (1924) also found lactase in crop tissue. The presence of such enzymes in crop tissue, however, does not mean that they play a significant role in digestion, nor does their presence in the contents of the crop prove that they are normally produced there. In fact, diastase found in the crop is usually from an exogenous source, the feed itself. Since regurgitation of contents from the proventriculus, gizzard, and duodenum, including bile, into the crop has been demonstrated (Klug, 1891, and others), it is likely that most of the enzymes found in the crop come from the duodenum and pro-

Table 26. Enzymes of the digestive tract of the chicken

Organ and secretion	Enzyme	Substance acted upon	Intermediate or end product
Saliva	Amylase (ptyalin)	Starch	Maltose
Crop and contents	Lactase	Lactose	Glucose and galactose
Proventriculus (gastric juice)	Pepsin	Protein	Proteoses and peptones
Gizzard and extracts	Pepsin (from proventriculus)		
Pure intestinal juice or tissue	Amylase* Invertase* Trypsin*	Proteoses, peptones, and peptides	Amino acids
	Amylase	—	—
	Invertase	Sucrose	Simple sugars
Pancreas or pancreatic juice	Trypsin	—	—
	Erepsin*	Intermediate N products	Amino acids
	Lipase	Fat	Fatty acids and glycerol
	Amylase	—	—
Bile	Amylase	—	—

* See text.

ventriculus. Thus, the crop appears to play a minor role in enzymatic digestion and also absorption. Introduction of botulinus toxin into the crop, where the crop was separated from the proventriculus by a ligature, had no ill effect upon the bird, indicating that the toxin was not absorbed (Leasure and Foltz, 1940).

DIGESTION IN THE PROVENTRICULUS

The proteolytic enzyme, pepsin, is preformed in the cells of the proventriculus as pepsinogen, and its presence has been reported by many workers (Groebbels, 1932). In the mammal, pepsinogen granules are secreted by the chief cells and hydrochloric acid by the parietal cells of the gastric glands, but in birds both are secreted by the chief cells. The bird has no cells comparable to parietal cells of mammals. Bowie (1936) and others, using a method specific for pepsinogen granules, found them in all cells of the body of the gastric glands. Before feeding, the pepsinogen granules are abundant, but shortly after feeding, they virtually disappear, indicating that they are concerned in digestion (see Groebbels, 1932).

Shaw (1913) and Plimmer and Rosedale (1922) found only pepsin in the tissues of the proventriculus, and this appears to be the only enzyme formed by it. Although it is believed that peptic digestion begins in the proventriculus, the pH of the organ (3 to 4.5) is higher than the optimum pH (about 1 to 2) for peptic digestion. This and the short time that the food spends here suggests that peptic digestion in the proventriculus is not extensive.

DIGESTION IN THE GIZZARD

Pepsin is always present in the contents of the gizzard, and the pH of the latter is 2 to 3.5. This pH is more nearly optimum for peptic digestion than other parts of the tract, and might suggest that most of peptic digestion occurs in the gizzard. Removal of the gizzard, whose chief function is grinding food, however, has little effect upon digestion if the food is soft (Fritz, Burrows, and Titus, 1936). This suggests that peptic digestion may take place in the intestine, where the pH is much higher (6 to 7), or that most of the protein digestion is accomplished by other enzymes (trypsin or erepsin) which are more active at this pH than pepsin. The optimum activity of these enzymes in the mammal, however, is at pH 7.5 to 8.5

The pepsin in the gizzard comes from the stomach, but one investigator (Paira-Mall, according to Mangold, 1929) claims to have extracted minute amounts from the epithelial lining of the gizzard. Carbohydrate-splitting enzymes have also been reported in the gizzard contents. Bernardi and Schwarz (1932) extracted invertase from the epithelium of the gland. Groebbels (1932) reportedly demonstrated the digestion of carbohydrates in the gizzard, but Mangold (1929 and 1934) believes that the gizzard's role in carbohydrate digestion is of no importance.

Grit and digestion. Grit is essential for optimum digestion because it increases the motility and grinding action of the gizzard and the digestibility of coarse feed (Fritz, 1937). With grit, the digestibility of whole grains and seeds may be increased about 10 percent, and all-mash by about 3 percent (Titus, 1949). Grit is not indispensable, because chicks can be raised to maturity (8 months of age) without it, and growth and egg production are not affected (Bethke and Kennard, 1926; Buckner, Martin, and Peter, 1926).

Gizzard Erosion

Lesions of the epithelial lining of the gizzard (gizzard erosion), comparable to peptic ulcers in mammals, have been reported in chickens under a variety of conditions. Some workers believe that there is one anti-gizzard-erosion factor or nutrient, while others think that a number of factors may be concerned in the prevention of the lesions. Evidence from Almquist and Mecchi (1941), Manwaring (1942), and others suggests that cholic acid and oxycholic acid (constituents of bile) are the principal factors, since the lesions occurring normally or produced by cinchophen can be prevented, improved, or cured by these bile acids. However, a number of feedstuffs, such as alfalfa meal, oats, wheat by-products, milk, and pork liver and kidney, will reduce the incidence and severity of gizzard erosion (Titus, 1949) and suggests that several factors may be involved.

Chickens afflicted with gizzard erosion secrete hyperacid gastric juice (Cheney, 1938). The hyperacidity appears not to be the cause of the lesions, but develops as a result of them.

DIGESTION IN THE INTESTINES

Enzymes in the Small Intestine and Pancreas

Extracts of ground whole intestine of chickens contain protease, amylase, and invertase (Plimmer and Rosedale, 1922), but not lactase (Plimmer and Rosedale, 1922; Hamilton and Mitchell, 1924).

Pancreatic juice and bile are emptied into the distal end of the loop of the duodenum. Pure pancreatic juice is obtained by cannulating the pancreatic ducts. Langendorff (1879), who obtained pancreatic juice from the pigeon in this manner, found it to be slightly alkaline, and it contained proteolytic enzymes and amylase and lipase. He further demonstrated that pancreatic juice is essential for life, because when the pancreatic ducts were ligated, the bird, deprived of pancreatic enzymes, died within 6 to 12 days.

The presence of amylase in the pancreatic tissues of birds was demonstrated as early as 1846 by Bonchardat and Sondras and by Claude Bernard in 1856 (see Groebbels, 1932, and also Mangold, 1929). Later work by Shaw (1913) and Plimmer and Rosedale (1922) also shows that the pancreas of the adult chicken contains proteolytic, amylolytic, and lipolytic enzymes, but that in the very young chick, before 7 days of age, all enzymes are not present.

The proteolytic enzymes present in intestinal tissue exhibit maximum activity in an acid and only slight activity in an alkaline medium, suggesting that the enzyme in greatest concentration is pepsin or is pepsinlike in activity.

The enzymes contained in pure intestinal juice apparently have not been determined, but mixed intestinal juice contains pancreatic juice (which contributes proteases acting principally in an alkaline medium) and presumably trypsin or trypsin and erepsin. The isolation and identification of these in the bird intestinal tract have not been made. From the meager data available, it appears that digestion by pepsin, trypsin, and possibly erepsin takes place in the bird intestine, but which of these enzymes play the dominant role is unknown. The hydrogen ion concentration of the intestine (see later section) is slightly acid (pH about 6), and at this pH, digestion by pepsin or trypsin probably would not be appreciable, if the pH requirement for activity of these is similar to that in the mammal. The higher body temperature of the bird, however, could increase the activity even though pH is not optimum.

Secretin

One of the factors influencing the secretion of pancreatic juice in mammals is secretin, a hormone which is formed in the walls of the intestine. This hormone, which has been crystallized, causes when injected a copious secretion of pancreatic juice. Its distribution in the intestine varies. It is present in the duodenum in all species of mammals, and in some is found in other parts of the intestine also. In the chicken and pigeon it has been isolated from the walls of the duodenum and other segments of the small intestine, but not in the large intestine, rectum, cloaca, eosphagus, or crop (Koschtojanz, Mirjeeff, Korkjieff, and Otschakowskaja, 1933).

Bile

The pH of avian bile is acid (consult Table 28), unlike that of mammals, which is usually alkaline. Otherwise, the composition of avian bile is similar to that of mammals, according to Mangold (1929). Amylase is found in chicken bile, and its activity in bile from the gall bladder is greater than in bile from the liver. It is present in all chickens above eight weeks of age, but is absent in some at four weeks (Farner, 1943c). Little is known about the function of bile in birds, but presumably it aids in the absorption of fats by its emulsifying action and activating effects on pancreatic lipase and in the digestion of carbohydrates by virtue of the amylase present.

DIGESTION IN THE CECA

This subject has been reviewed by Mangold (1929 and 1934), Groebbels (1932), and Halnan (1949). For many years it was thought that little or no crude fiber was digested by birds. Although it is now recognized that birds can digest appreciable quantities of crude fiber of certain types, they digest considerably less than mammals. Cellulose, lignin, and pentosans from corn fodder are almost completely indigestible, but lignin and pentosans from grains are digestible to the extent of 10 to 40 percent (Tscherniak, 1936).

The coefficients (percents) of digestibility of crude fiber for poultry are variable even within the same species and with different varieties of the same grains (Mangold, 1934). The coefficients for crude fiber digestion for different grains, as reported for the hen by a number of workers, are shown as follows. Most of these figures are taken from Groebbels (1932).

> Corn, 0.12 to 28.2, 17.2, 19.2, up to 43.5
> Wheat, 0.0 to 3.5, 5.1, 4.6 to 5.7, 9.8, 0.0 to 16.9, 17.7, 29.8
> Barley, 0.0 to 0.24, 0.0 to 13.3, 8.9 to 13.4
> Oats, 0.0 to 6.6, 9.25
> Cellulose, 0.0

Mangold believed that much of the variation in digestibility is due to the varietal differences in the chemical and structural makeup of the cell membranes of the feedstuffs.

The site of digestion of most of the crude fiber is the ceca (Mangold, 1934). Radeff (1928) and Henning (1929) determined the coefficients of digestibility of corn crude fiber before and after surgical removal of the ceca of hens. The coefficients for corn before cecectomy were 17.1 (Radeff, 1928) and 19.7 (Henning, 1929), and 0.0 after the operation. The figures for oats and wheat with ceca intact were 9.25 and 5.7, and after the operation, 1.31 and 1.4, respectively. The digestibility of crude fiber in the pigeon, a species with rudimentary ceca, is less efficient than in the chicken (Radeff, 1928; Mangold and Hock, 1938). The ceca are not essential structures, however, as they can be removed without ill effect on the bird (Dukes, 1947).

Synthesis of Vitamins by the Ceca

Digestion of crude fiber is facilitated by enzymes in the cecal juice (Maumus and Launoy, 1901) and by the presence of bacteria.

The cecal contents contain considerably higher concentrations of the B-vitamins than other parts of the digestive tract (Couch *et al.*, 1950; Sunde *et al.*, 1950), suggesting that these vitamins may be synthesized in the ceca and that the required level of these in the feed might be less for birds with ceca. Removal of the ceca, however, did not increase the required vitamin level in the feed or affect the concentration of these vitamins in the feces. This indicates that B-vitamins are not synthesized in the ceca. In fact, the requirement for biotin is slightly less after cecectomy than before, suggesting that some of the biotin present in the ceca is normally used by bacteria (Sunde *et al.*).

Absorption of Water in the Ceca and Rectum

Evidence that the ceca absorb some water is based upon the findings of Röseler (1929), who demonstrated that the amount of water in cecal contents is lower than that of feces and rectal contents. He further revealed that after cecectomy the water content of the feces is higher than in unoperated birds.

DIGESTIBILITY OF FEEDSTUFFS

In order to determine the digestibility coefficient of each nutrient in the feed, it is necessary to determine the composition of the feed and, after feeding, to collect the feces, not mixed with urine, and determine quantities of the nutrients present or undigested. Separation of the feces and urine in birds presents difficulties because both are voided together in the cloaca. Therefore, to determine the digestibility of the feed, the feces must be separated from the urine; this involves surgery, or the preparation of an artificial anus, or the exteriorizing of the ureters (see Chapter 13). If feces and urine are collected together, a correction for the amount of nitrogen contained in the urine must be made. The results thus obtained compare favorably with determinations made on uncontaminated feces.

The coefficients of digestibility of some common feeds for the chicken follow (Titus, 1949):

Feed	Organic matter	Crude protein	Crude fiber	Nitrogen-free extract	Fat	Total digestible nutrients
Barley	76	74	9	82	69	67
Corn, whole	87	76	12	90	86	80
Oats	65	73	13	72	82	61
Wheat	84	79	9	88	50	73
Wheat bran	45	61	8	46	58	41

Except for crude fiber, the coefficients of digestibility of these feeds for chickens compare favorably with those for mammals.

GASTRIC JUICE

Collection of Gastric Juice

Gastric juice of the fed bird may contain feed and also contents from the gizzard and duodenum as a result of regurgitation. Minute amounts of pure gastric juice may be obtained by starving the bird, because normally little is secreted under such conditions unless some other stimulus is employed. Even under these conditions, the juice, while free from food, may contain intestinal juice; this can be overcome by cannulating the proventriculus or the gizzard. In order to study the stimulating effects of food ingestion upon rate of secretion and the composition of pure gastric juice, one of two methods may be used: (1) preparation of a fistula or opening in the esophagus, so that when food is ingested it does not pass to the stomach, but instead drops out of the opening (sham feeding); (2) preparation of a pouch in the stomach which opens to the outside through the body wall (Pavlov or Heidenhain pouch). Food entering the main stomach, but not the pouch, stimulates both parts, and pure juice is collected from the pouch. Apparently no studies employing the stomach pouch in the secretion of gastric juice in birds have been made, but the esophageal fistula has been used.

Most of the studies on the gastric juice of birds are based upon samples collected by cannulation of the proventriculus (Friedman, 1939) of starved birds (relatively pure juice), or by aspiration of stomach contents through catheters inserted through the mouth and crop of the starved bird (Cheney, 1938), or by insertion of needles into the gizzard of the fed bird (Collip, 1922; Farner, 1943a).

Composition of Gastric Juice

Gastric juice of the bird contains a large proportion of water and smaller amounts of hydrochloric acid, pepsin, mucin, and certain salts. (See Table 27.) The composition varies according to rate of secretion as well as other factors.

The pH of mixed gastric juice collected by aspiration from the gizzard of the live bird averages 2.05 (Farner, 1943c). The pH of the tissues or of the contents of the proventriculus of dead birds is considerably higher (see Tables 28 and 29). The total acidity and free HCl in the gastric juice of fed chickens average 59.2 and 25.0 milliequivalents (m.eq.) per liter respectively (Farner, 1943c), and for chickens starved for 12 to 24 hours, the range is from 40 to 75 for total acidity and 30 to 55 m.eq. for free HCl (Cheney, 1938). In the starved pigeon, total acidity ranges from 60 to 148, and free HCl from 60 to 148 m.eq. (Friedman, 1939).

The pH of stomach contents is ordinarily not influenced appreciably by a normal feeding regime. When excessive amounts of basic salts, such as $CaCO_3$ or bone meal, are fed, the hydrogen ion concentration decreases (Mussehl, Blish, and Ackerson, 1933; Heller and Penquite, 1936; Farner, 1943b). Farner reported that diets high in protein or milk products increase the pH of mixed gastric juice. Among the different feeds and combinations fed, the highest

Table 27. Gastric secretion of birds under different conditions

Species	No. of birds	Treatment	Rate of secretion* cc.	Acidity in m.eq. per liter		Pepsin activity Mett units	Author
				Free	Total		
Pigeon	13	Normal, starved 24 hours	*per hour* 0.2–4.2	40–136	60–148	0–36	Friedman
"	1	Histamine	1.3	70–160	120–195	0	"
"	1	Pilocarpine	*per 15 min.* 0.9	—	—	16	"
"	1	Acetylcholine	0.9	Not given, but high		64	"
"	1	Acetylcholine & histamine	1.6	—	150	52	"
Chicken	—	Normal, starved 24 hours	—	—	—	700–1,000	"
"		Normal, starved 12–24 hours	*per hour* 7.0	30–55	40–75	—	Cheney
"	22	Normal, fed	—	25	59.2	—	Farner
"	—	Histamine, starved	—	80–150	120–180	125	Friedman
"	—	"	15.0	110	125–160	—	Cheney

* The data of Friedman (1934) and of Cheney (1938) are based on starved birds, in which the rate of secretion is low and highly variable (see text). Cheney's figures on secretion are based upon contents withdrawn from the stomach (mixed juice) with catheter and are only rough estimates of amount secreted.

and lowest pH's recorded in the gastric juice were 3.02 and 2.01 respectively.

The pepsin content of avian gastric juice has received little study. According to Friedman (1939) the concentration of pepsin in relatively pure gastric juice of starved pigeons ranges from 0 to 38 Mett units, and the chicken from 700 to 1000 Mett units. Thus, the pepsin concentration of the pigeon stomach is much lower than that of the chicken stomach and is much lower than that in certain mammals, particularly the dog. This is true also for the goose stomach, in which the pepsin concentration is about one-tenth that in the dog (Karpov, 1919). The Mett unit refers to the ability of the pepsin to digest egg albumin when both are placed in small glass tubes.

Factors Affecting Secretion of Gastric Juice

Braitmaier, according to Friedman (1939), reported that the secretion of gastric juice in the chicken is regular and continuous; however, the experiments of Friedman and of Cheney (1938) show that it is not continuous, but intermittent. This was demonstrated in starved chickens and pigeons before and after injection of certain drugs. In the studies of Friedman (1939) and Cheney (1938), food was withheld for 12 to 24 hours, and the tract was presumably free from food. This is particularly true of the stomach, where food remains for a very short time. Starvation decreases or inhibits flow of gastric juice in the pigeon (Friedman), chicken (Collip, 1922), and duck (Keeton, Koch, and Luckhardt, 1920). Friedman showed that in 87 per cent of the pigeons starved for at least 24 hours, gastric secretion was practically inhibited. At autopsy, starved birds had no feed in the gizzard or proventriculus. In the remaining starved pigeons, some juice was collected, but the rate of secretion and amount collected varied considerably, ranging from 0.2 to 4.2 cc. per hour (see Table 27). Cheney (1938), who withheld feed 12 to 24 hours from chickens, reported, in a few individuals, a volume of about 7 cc. per hour, but the figure is only a rough approximation.

The stimulating effects of food ingestion on rate of gastric secretion was studied by Collip (1922) on the chicken and Karpov (1919) on the goose, who employed the esophageal fistula. Sham feeding, where food does not reach the stomach, stimulates the proventriculus and increases the rate of gastric secretion. This is known as the cephalic phase of stimulation; the sensations of eating evoke the discharge of impulses from the gastric secretory center in the brain, probably by way of nerve fibers in the vagi to the gastric glands.

The stimulating effect of food as it enters the stomach (gastric phase of stimulation) on gastric secretion in birds apparently has not been determined.

Effects of drugs. Histamine, injected into the pigeon, chicken, or duck, increases the rate of gastric secretion within 7 to 15 minutes Keeton, Koch, and Luckhardt, 1920; Cheney, 1938; Friedman, 1939). It increases the acidity of the secretion and diminishes the pepsin concentration considerably (Table 27). Continued injections of histamine decrease the volume of flow and increase the pepsin concentration of the secretion (Friedman). The volume dropped from about 1.3 cc. to 0.2 cc. per hour after histamine, and the pepsin increased from a low of 10 to 130 Mett units. There was also a slight increase in acidity. These changes are due to dehydration and a loss in blood volume. When saline or glucose solutions are injected, the birds respond as before to histamine, with an increased rate of flow.

Administration of ethyl alcohol to the pigeon increases the volume of secretion after a latent period of 35 minutes and otherwise has an effect similar to histamine, except that the effect is usually not as pronounced (Friedman).

Pilocarpine (0.5 mg./kg.) produces a secretion of moderate volume and peptic activity in the pigeon (Friedman, 1939). Acetylcholine (0.1 mg./kg.) induces the secretion of only small amounts of gastric juice in the pigeon, which is very rich in pepsin and mucin and high in acidity, according to Friedman, but his data on volume are inconclusive, and he shows none on acidity. When pilocarpine or acetylcholine is injected one to two hours after the histamine, the volume of secretion increases and there is a decrease in pepsin content, but apparently no change takes place in acidity of the secretion. Pilocarpine is not as effective as acetylcholine in increasing pepsin content.

According to Friedman, adrenaline alone (1 cc. of 1/10,000) has no effect on gastric secretion in the pigeon, but when injected after the bird has received histamine, there is a diminution in rate of secretion, but no marked effect on the concentration of pepsin (no data given).

In mammals, histamine stimulates the parietal cells of the gastric glands to produce acid, and parasympathomimetic drugs stimulate the production of pepsin from the chief cells. The effects of these agents in birds are the same except that one type of cell produces both products. The volume and rate of gastric secretion is influenced by the volume of fluid in the blood and tissues.

Nervous Control of Gastric Secretion

The results obtained with acetylcholine and pilocarpine (parasympathomimetic agents) suggest that the secretion of pepsin and possibly acid (although data on the latter are inconclusive) are controlled by parasympathetic nerves. The negative results obtained with adrenaline suggest that sympathetic nerves are not concerned in gastric secretion.

It is known that the proventriculus is innervated by both sympathetic and parasympathetic fibers, but apparently no studies have been made on the effects of stimulation of these nerves on gastric secretion.

HYDROGEN ION CONCENTRATION OF THE DIGESTIVE TRACT

The hydrogen ion concentration, or pH, of the different regions of the digestive tract is dependent mainly upon the amount of HCl secreted in the proventriculus and the action of bile and pancreatic juice, which in the mammal tend to neutralize the acid in the tract. The pH of the alimentary canal of birds, and particularly that of the chicken, has been determined by a number of workers. The results of some of these are presented in Tables 28 and 29. For a review of the earlier work, see Farner (1942). Most of the determinations have been made on the contents of different parts of the tracts of dead birds not previously starved. When food is in the tract, the secretion of gastric and intestinal juices is at a maximum. Steinmetzer (1924) believed that if the crop and gizzard were empty, then the secretion of gastric juice would be low in relation to the

Table 28. The pH of the contents of the digestive tract of different species of dead adult birds (Farner, 1942). All birds had food in the digestive tract

Species	Crop	Proven-triculus	Gizzard	Duodenum	Jejunum	Ileum	Rectum or colon	Ceca	Bile
Chicken	4.51	4.40	2.60	5.76–6.01	5.78–5.90	6.27–6.42	6.26	5.71	5.88
Pigeon	4.28	4.80	2.00	5.23–5.39	5.32–5.89	5.59	5.43	—	—
Pheasant	5.78	4.74	2.06	5.62–6.01	6.18–6.81	6.77	6.61	5.39	6.18
Duck	4.92	3.41	2.33	6.01–6.19	6.11–6.69	6.87	6.73	5.88	6.14
Turkey	6.07	4.72	2.19	5.82–6.52	6.71–6.95	6.85	6.46	5.86	6.01

amount of intestinal juice formed, and this would tend to make the lower tract more alkaline. However, if the upper tract is empty, then the lower tract would, except for a short time, be empty or contain little food, and the secretion of intestinal juice might also be low. The pH under these conditions has not been determined. Some of the investigators used pH meters (quinhydrone electrode), and others used a colorimetric method to determine pH. Farner (1942) believed that some of the variation in the reported results is due to difference in methods employed. Inspection of data in the tables reveals that the variation in results among investigators using one method is as great as for those employing a different method.

According to Farner (1942; see Table 28), all parts of the alimentary canal of chickens, pigeons, ducks, turkeys, and pheasants are acid, with the lowest pH recorded in the gizzard (2.0 to 2.6) and the highest in the lower half of the small intestine (5.59 to 6.87). The pH of the chicken gizzard is significantly higher than that of the other species, and the pH of the pigeon duodenum is lower than that of the other species. The upper portions of the small intestine of the pigeon and chicken are more acid than in the other species. In the ileum, or lower part of the small intestine, the pH increases in the following order: pigeon, chicken, pheasant, turkey, and duck. There are no significant differences in the pH of the bile, ceca, or large intestines of these species (Farner).

Farner's results for the chicken are compared with those of five other investigators in Table 29. The reports of Mussehl, Blish, and Ackerson (1933) and of Buckner, Insko, and Henry (1944) agree with Farner that all parts of the digestive tract are acid, and all investigators show that the duodenum and upper tract are acid except Olson and Mann (1935), whose average figure for the duodenum approaches neutrality (pH 7.04). The figures of Olson and Mann for all parts of the intestinal tract are higher (pH above 7) than all others shown in the table. Whether or not the determinations were made on the contents of the organs concerned or on scrapings from the mucosa of the organs does not affect the results, according to Buckner, Insko, and Henry (1944).

Thus, the digestive tract of birds, according to most authors, is acid. All reports show that the bile of birds is acid (pH 5.0 to 6.8), unlike that of mammals, which is alkaline (pH about 7.5 to 8.5).

Table 29. The pH of the digestive tract of adult chickens of both sexes, from different authors. All determinations were made on the contents of the organs of dead birds, and all birds had food in the digestive tract.

	Farner (1944)	Olson and Mann (1935)			Heller and Penquite (1936)	Mayhew* (1935)	Mussehl et al. (1933)	Buckner et al.* (1944)	
		Low	Mean	High				Contents	Mucosa
Mouth									6.7
Crop	4.51	4.00	5.37	6.37	4.44	4.7–5.4	—	4.6	4.5
Proventriculus	4.40†	3.07	4.69†	6.09	3.61	4.5–5.1	4.8	4.4	4.4
Gizzard	2.60	3.05	4.06	5.02	2.99	—	2.9	3.3	3.0
Duodenum	5.76–6.01	5.64	6.31	7.10	5.94	5.9–6.2	6.1	6.3	6.3
Jejunum or upper ileum	5.78–5.90	6.12	7.04	8.01	5.94	5.8–6.9	6.2	—	—
Ileum or lower half	6.27–6.42	6.93	7.59	8.42	7.21	6.1–7.3	6.9	—	—
Large intestine or rectum	6.26	6.29	7.38	8.18	6.92	—	6.6	6.4	6.4
Ceca	5.71	5.90	7.12	8.20	6.98	6.6–7.4	6.3	5.5	5.6
Bile	5.88				6.49	5.0–6.8	—	6.1	—
Pancreas (tissue)								6.6	—

* The pH was determined colorimetrically; all others by quinhydrone electrode.
† Samples taken by scraping of mucosa.

This difference may account, in part, for the higher pH in the intestinal tract of mammals as compared to birds.

Age appears to have little effect on pH in birds above 13 to 17 weeks of age. In younger birds, 10 to 11 weeks of age, the pH of the lower intestinal tract is higher according to Mayhew (1935), but his data on this point are inconclusive. According to Vonk, Brink, and Postma (1946), the pH of the gizzard of young chickens (23 days of age) is lower (pH 2.7) than in adults (3.06).

Buckner *et al.* (1944) found no difference in the pH of the digestive tract of male and female chickens one and two years of age. Moreover, the pH was not influenced by molting or state of reproduction.

The effect of different feeding regimes on pH of the digestive tract has been studied by a number of researchers (Beach, 1925; Ashcraft, 1933; Mussehl *et al.*, 1935; Heller and Penquite, 1936; Farner, 1943b; and others). The effects of pH of the gizzard have been discussed previously, and the effects on the remainder of the tract are similar. The ingestion of very large quantities of basic salts tends to lower the acidity of all parts of the tract. Diets high in milk products tend to increase the pH of certain parts of the tract (Ashcraft, Farner), and diets high in protein increase the pH of gastric juice, according to Farner, but decrease it, according to Vonk, Brink, and Postma (1946). The fiber of the diet in amounts ranging from 13.6 to 14.9 percent has no effect upon pH of the tract (Heller and Penquite).

REFERENCES

Almquist, H. J., and E. Mecchi 1941 Influence of bile acids, vitamin K, and cinchophen on erosions of the chick gizzard lining. Proc. Soc. Exp. Biol. & Med. 46:168.

Ashcraft, D. W. 1933 Effect of milk products on pH of intestinal contents of domestic fowl. Poultry Sci. 12:292.

Beach, J. R. 1925 The effect of feeding various milk products on the hydrogen ion concentration of the contents of the ceca of chickens. Hilgardia (Calif. Sta.) 1:145.

Bernardi, A., and M. A. Schwarz 1932 Über das Verkommen einer Invertase im Kaumagen der Hühner. Biochem. Ztschr. 256:406.

Bethke, R. M., and D. C. Kennard 1926 Does the growing chick require grit? Poultry Sci. 5:285.

Bowie, D. J. 1936 A method of staining the pepsinogen granules in gastric glands. Anat. Rec. 64:357.

Buckner, G. D., W. M. Insko, and A. H. Henry 1944 Does breed, age, sex, or laying condition affect the pH of the digestive tract system of chickens? Poultry Sci. 33:457.

Buckner, G. D., J. H. Martin, and A. M. Peter 1926 Concerning the growth of chickens raised without grit. Poultry Sci. 5:203.

Cheney, G. 1938 Gastric acidity in chicks with experimental gastric ulcers. Am. J. Digest. Dis. 5:104.

Collip, J. B. 1922 The activation of the glandular stomach of the fowl. Am. J. Physiol. 59:435.

Couch, J. R., H. L. German, D. R. Knight, P. S. Parks, and P. B. Pearson 1950 Importance of the cecum in intestinal synthesis in the mature domestic fowl. Poultry Sci. 29:52.

Dukes, H. H. 1947 The Physiology of Domestic Animals. 6th ed. Comstock Publishing Co., Inc., Ithaca, N. Y.

Farner, D. S. 1942 The hydrogen ion concentration in avian digestive tracts. Poultry Sci. 21:445.

Farner, D. S. 1943a Gastric hydrogen ion concentration and acidity in the domestic fowl. Poultry Sci. 22:79.

Farner, D. S. 1943b The effect of certain dietary factors on gastric hydrogen ion concentration and acidity in the domestic fowl. Poultry Sci. 22:295.

Farner, D. S. 1943c Biliary amylase in the domestic fowl. Biol. Bull. 84:240.

Friedman, M. H. F. 1939 Gastric secretion in birds. J. Cell. & Comp. Physiol. 13:219.

Fritz, J. C. 1937 The effect of feeding grit on digestibility in the domestic fowl. Poultry Sci. 16:75.

Fritz, J. C., W. H. Burrows, and H. W. Titus 1936 Comparison of digestibility in gizzardectomized and normal fowls. Poultry Sci. 15:239.

Groebbels, F. 1932 Der Vogel. Erster Band: Atmungswelt und Nahrungswelt. Verlag von Gebrüder Borntraeger, Berlin.

Halnan, E. T. 1949 The architecture of the avian gut and tolerance of crude fiber. Brit. J. Nutrition 3:245.

Hamilton, T. S., and H. H. Mitchell 1924 The occurrence of lactase in the alimentary tract of the chicken. J. Agric. Res. 27:605.

Heller, V. G., and R. Penquite 1936 Effect of minerals and fiber on avian intestinal pH. Poultry Sci. 15:397.

Henning, H. J. 1929 Landw. Versuchs stat. 108:253. Cited by Groebbels, 1932.

Jung, L., and M. Pierre 1933 Sur le rôle de la salive chez les oiseaux granivores. Comp. Rend. Soc. Biol. 113:115.

Karpov, L. V. 1919 Russ. Physiol. J. 2:185 (abstracted in Physiol. Abs. 5:469, 1920).

Keeton, R. W., F. C. Koch, and A. B. Luckhardt 1920 Gastrin studies. III: The response of the stomach mucosa of various animals to gastrin bodies. Am. J. Physiol. 51:454.

Klug, F. 1891 Beiträge zur Kenntnis der Verdauung der Vögel. Ztbl. Physiol. 5:131.

Koschtojanz, I. I., M. Mirjeeff, P. Korjuieff, and S. Otschakowskaja 1933 Zur Frage der Spezifität des Sekretins: Vergleichendephysiologische Untersuchung. Z. vergl. Physiol. 18:112.

Langendorff, O. 1879 Versuche über die Pankreasverdauung der Vögel. Arch. f. Anat. u. Physiol. 18:1.

Leasure, E. E., and V. D. Foltz 1940 Experiments on absorption in the crop of the chicken. J. Am. Vet. Med. Assoc. 96:236.

Leasure, E. E., and R. P. Link 1940 Studies on the saliva of the hen. Poultry Sci. 19:131.

Mangold, E. 1929 Die Verdauung des Geflügels im Handbuch der Ernährung und des Stoffwechsels der lanswirtschaftlichen Nutztiere. Zweiter Band. Verlag von Julius Springer, Berlin.

Mangold, E. 1934 The digestion and utilization of crude fiber. Nutrition Abs. and Rev. 3:647.

Mangold, E., and A. Hock 1938 Die Verdaulichkeit der Futtermittel bei der Taube. Arch. f. Geflügelkunde 12:334.

Manwaring, W. H. 1942 Bile deficiency and gizzard erosion. Calif. and West. Med. 56:61 (abstracted in Biol. Abs. 16531, 1942).

Maumus, J., and L. Launoy 1901 La digestion caecale chez les oiseaux. Bull. Mus. d'Hist. Mat., Paris 7:361.

Mayhew, R. L. 1935 The hydrogen ion concentration of the digestive tract of the fowl. J. Am. Vet. Med. Assoc. 86:148.

Mussehl, F. E., M. J. Blish, and C. W. Ackerson 1933 Effect of dietary and environmental factors on the pH of the intestinal tract. Poultry Sci. 12:120.

Olson, C., and F. C. Mann 1935 The physiology of the cecum of the domestic fowl. J. Am. Vet. Med. Assoc. 87:151.

Plimmer, R. H. A., and J. L. Rosedale 1922 Distribution of enzymes in the alimentary canal of the chicken. Biochem. J. 16:23.

Radeff, T.   1928   Die Verdaulichkeit der Rohfaser und die Funktion der Blinddärme beim Haushuhn. Arch. f. Geflügelkunde 2:312.

Röseler, M.   1929   Die Bedeutung der Blinddärme des Haushuhnes für die Resorption der Nahrung und Verdauung der Rohfaser. Z. f. Tierzücht und Züchtungbiol. 13:281.

Shaw, T. P.   1913   Digestion in the chick. Am. J. Physiol. 31:439.

Steinmetzer, K.   1924   Die zeitlichen Verhaeltnisse beim Durchwandern von Futter durch den Magendarmkanal des Huhnes. Arch. ges. Physiol. (Pflügers) 206:500.

Sunde, M. L., W. W. Cravens, C. A. Elvehjem, and J. H. Halpin   1950   The effect of diet and cecectomy on the intestinal synthesis of biotin in mature fowl. Poultry Sci. 29:10.

Titus, H. W.   1949   The Scientific Feeding of Chickens. 2d ed. Interstate Press, Danville, Ill.

Tscherniak, A.   1936   Über die Verdauung der Zellwandbestandteile des Futters (Lignin, Pentosone, Cellulose, und Rohfaser) durch das Haushuhn. Biedermans Ztbl. B. Tierernahrung 8:408 (abstracted in Nutrition Abs. and Rev. 6:1127, 1937).

Vonk, H. J., G. Brink, and N. Postma   1946   Digestion in the stomach of birds. I: The acidity in the stomach of young chickens. Proc. K. Nederland Akad. Wetenschap. Amsterdam 49:972 (abstracted in Biol. Abs. 20863, 1949).

CHAPTER 12

Carbohydrate Metabolism

CHEMICAL MECHANISMS INVOLVED

STARCH and common sugars are hydrolyzed in the alimentary canal to the monosaccharides glucose, fructose, and galactose, which are absorbed into the portal blood and transported to the liver, where they are converted into glycogen. Glycogen is a colloidal polysaccharide, whitish in color and soluble in water, which upon hydrolysis produces glucose.

Glucose and glycogen may also be formed in the liver from amino acids and from lactic and pyruvic acid, which are products of muscle metabolism. Certain fatty acids, such as propionic, and others containing an odd number of carbon atoms, and glycerol can also be converted into glucose and glycogen by the liver.

The conversion of glucose into glycogen (glycogenesis)' takes place in liver, muscle, and tissues, whereas the conversion of glycogen to glucose (glycogenolysis) is limited essentially to the liver. The conversion of nonglucose substances into glucose (gluconeogenesis) takes place principally in the liver and to a very limited extent in the kidney.

When blood glucose is plentiful, it is converted and stored in the liver as glycogen, and when the supply is diminished or depleted, as in starvation, the liver converts glycogen into glucose in an attempt to maintain a normal blood sugar level. The rate of storage and release of glucose by the liver is influenced by the amount of glucose absorbed and by starvation, certain hormones, and other factors, which will be discussed later.

The principal carbohydrate in the blood is glucose, and in muscle and tissues, glycogen. Blood glucose, carried to the muscles, is converted to glycogen, which, in turn, is broken down to pyruvic and lactic acids (glycolysis); the pyruvic acid is finally oxidized to CO_2 and water, and muscle energy is released.

The process of conversion of glucose to glycogen and the breakdown of glycogen in the liver and in muscles involve a series of chemical reactions called phosphorolysis, in which phosphate is essential. Some of these reactions are shown in the abridged diagram which follows:

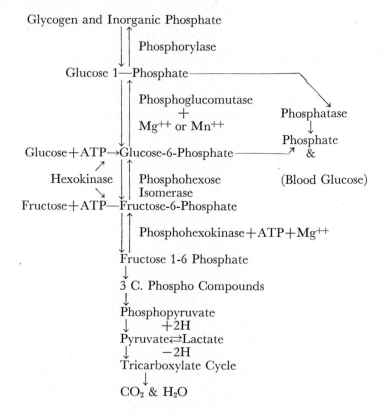

It is observed from the diagram that the glucose-glycogen reaction in the liver is a reversible one.

Muscle and tissue glycogen, other than that in the liver, cannot revert directly to glucose, apparently because of the absence of the necessary phosphatase enzyme (West and Todd, 1951). Fructose-6-phosphate (see diagram) is further phosphorylated by ATP to fructose 1-6 phosphate. By a series of reactions, the latter is finally degraded to pyruvic acid, which is then oxidized to CO_2 and H_2O by reactions of the tricarboxylic acid cycle.

BLOOD SUGAR

Normal Values

As early as 1901, Saito and Katsuyama presented evidence that the blood sugar of birds is in the form of D-glucose, as it is in mammals. In Chapter 2, normal blood glucose values for the chicken are presented. The values exhibit considerable variation, ranging from 161 to 280 mg. percent with most of the values between 180 and 200. The values for the turkey range from 175 to 210 (Dukes, 1947), and for the female pigeon from approximately 190 to 255, depending on the stage of the reproductive cycle (Riddle, 1937). Scott and Honeywell (1921) reported average values of 185 mg. percent for 11 adult nonfasted pigeons.

Weintraud (1894) reported that the blood sugar of normal fasted ducks averaged 160 mg. percent, with a range of 117 to 198. The very meager data of Mirsky, Nelson, Grayman, and Korenberg (1941) reveal a blood sugar level of approximately 115 mg. percent. Mirsky (1945) reported an average value of 114 mg. percent for 8 ducks. The limited data of Nelson, Elgart, and Mirsky (1942) indicate a level of about 150 mg. percent for the depancreatized duck, which they state is no higher than the level of the normal duck. The blood sugar of the ducks of Kausch (see Scott and Honeywell) averaged 140 mg. percent.

Blood sugar of the carnivorous horned owl ranges from 200 to 350 mg. percent according to Nelson *et al.* (1942), but according to Scott, Harris, and Chen (1945), it averages 194 mg percent in this species. The latter workers reported for the barn owl (not fasted) average blood sugar values of 130 mg. percent (4 birds). The blood sugar level in birds is therefore about double that in man and certain other mammals.

For reviews on carbohydrate regulation in birds see Riddle (1937) and Golden and Long (1942a).

Role of Liver in Control of Blood Sugar Level

The liver provides glucose from two sources: (1) breakdown of glycogen to glucose (glycogenolysis) and (2) gluconeogenesis from proteins, glycerol and certain fatty acids, lactic acid, and other substances. Gluconeogenesis is the more important function, because the amount of glycogen present in the liver is not sufficient to play a major role in maintaining blood sugar.

During fasting or starvation, stored liver glycogen derived from carbohydrate sources is soon depleted, and then the liver's main source of glycogen is from tissue proteins and other noncarbohydrates. The rate of formation of glucose from protein can be estimated by determining the amount of urinary nitrogen excreted, which is increased in such cases.

Removal of the liver (hepatectomy) in mammals causes a drastic fall in blood sugar, and death occurs within a short time unless glucose is administered. Continued administration of glucose, however, will not prevent ultimate death because of other effects resulting from the operation. Ablation of the liver in ducks also causes a significant drop in blood sugar (Kausch, 1897; Mirsky *et al.*, 1941). The hepatectomized birds of Kausch developed glycosuria, and most of them died within 15 hours after the operation. (See also Minkowski, 1893.)

Fasting Blood Sugar Level

According to the limited data of Honeywell (1921) on the pigeon and Nelson *et al.* (1942) on the horned owl, fasting does not affect blood sugar level appreciably in these species. This has not been confirmed in the duck and chicken. There is usually a significant drop in blood sugar of the chicken after 14 to 24 hours of fasting (Burrows, Fritz, and Titus, 1935; Golden and Long, 1942a). See Table 30. There is also a pronounced drop in liver glycogen, but there appears to be no appreciable change in muscle glycogen, although the data on the latter are limited.

Some of the earlier investigators reported a marked rise in the blood sugar of fasting chickens on the fourth day after withdrawal of feed. Burrows, Fritz, and Titus, who studied the effects of fasting for 7 to 10 days on the blood sugar of intact and gizzardectomized chickens, found no indication of the fourth-day rise. This was true also of the same birds fed coarsely ground corn. They showed that the blood sugar level dropped about 10 percent after 15 hours of fasting (Table 30) and changed only slightly from then on, even

Table 30. Carbohydrate levels of fed and fasted chicks
(weighing 250 to 400 grams) and adult males

Number	Hours fasted	Blood glucose mg. percent	Liver glycogen mg. percent	Muscle glycogen mg. percent	Author
			Chicks		
68	0	188±1.49	2,550±19	—	*
30	0	191±3.40	2,784±343	1,093±34	†
388	14	152±0.56	153±17.7	—	*
14	24	148±1.96	260±22.1	—	*
27	24	182±3.9 (12)	364±36	773±20	†
12	48	153±3.9 (7)	326±33.5	—	*
15	48	—	498±50	889±26	†
10	72	169±3.0	248±34.7	—	*
			Adult Males		
5	0	200.5	—	—	‡
5	15–18	178.0	—	—	‡

The figures for liver and muscle glycogen are based on a smaller number of birds than for blood glucose.

  * Opdyke (1942).
  † Golden and Long (1942a).
  ‡ Burrows, Fritz, and Titus (1935).

after 7 days of fasting. The normal nonfasting levels ranged from 180 to 230 mg. percent. Gizzardectomy had no effect on the blood glucose levels.

Thus, the ability to maintain a normal blood sugar level after fasting varies among the species of birds as it does among mammals. The blood sugar level of the dog, cat, and pig and of man is little affected by fasting, but this is not true for the cow (Dukes, 1947). The maintenance of normal blood sugar levels after fasting appears to be due to a well-developed gluconeogenic mechanism in these species.

Starvation diabetes in carnivores may represent the decreased capacity of the pancreas to secrete insulin and also decreased efficiency of some or all of the enzyme systems concerned with carbohydrate metabolism (West and Todd, 1951). In the graniverous birds, the latter factor is probably more important.

Glucose Tolerance

Hyperglycemia is produced in birds and mammals when excessive amounts of glucose are ingested or injected, because the liver and tissues cannot store the sugar as glycogen as readily as it is absorbed. When the blood glucose reaches such a high level that the kidney tubules can no longer reabsorb it, glucose appears in the urine (alimentary glycosuria). The blood sugar level at which glycosuria occurs is known as the renal threshold for glucose. Since the normal blood sugar of birds is higher than mammals, the threshold is higher. In the normal chicken, it ranges from 275 to 300 mg. percent (Batt, 1940), and in man it is about 160 mg. percent.

One means of determining the capacity of an animal to metabolize and utilize carbohydrates is the glucose tolerance test, which measures the response of the animal (its blood sugar) to the administration of a definite amount of glucose. A large amount of glucose (usually 50 to 100 grams for humans) is administered orally, and blood sugar determinations are usually made at 30-minute intervals up to two hours or more after administration. In a normal subject, the blood sugar level usually reaches a peak in 30 minutes, then decreases steadily and returns to normal within approximately two hours.

The glucose may also be administered intravenously, but in smaller amounts. Since absorption is no longer a factor, sugar determinations are made sooner after administration, usually within the first 5 to 10 minutes, and at 15 to 20 minute intervals for the first hour after injection and at 30-minute intervals thereafter (Wiggers, 1949).

The level that the blood sugar reaches and the time required for it to return to normal are influenced by (1) the amount of glucose ingested or injected, (2) the rate of absorption, (3) the rate of glycogenesis in the liver, (4) gluconeogenesis, and (5) the rate of utilization of carbohydrates by the tissue. A decreased tolerance is indicated by a more marked hyperglycemia and by a slower rate of fall of blood sugar and return to normal, after a given period of time. Glucose tolerance is decreased in diabetes, starvation, fasting, or any condition in which liver glycogen drops to a low level. It is increased by insulin and hypopituitarism (Dukes, 1947).

Few glucose tolerance tests have been made on birds. When the nonfasted duck was injected with 1.75 grams of glucose per kilogram of body weight, the level of blood sugar was elevated, after 30 minutes, 50 mg. percent above the preinjection level. One hour after the injection, blood sugar was only slightly above the normal level (Mirsky *et al.*, 1941). Fasting, however, decreased the tolerance of the duck to glucose, as it does in mammals, but pancreatectomy had no effect on the tolerance curve. When the normal duck was fasted for 10 to 20 days and given glucose intravenously, its blood sugar increased to 325 mg. percent within 30 minutes.

When 1.75 grams of glucose per kilogram were injected intravenously in the horned owl, the blood sugar rose, after 30 minutes, from a normal level of 250 to approximately 550 mg. percent, according to Nelson *et al.* (1942). These data are based on a few observations, and the authors admitted that the quantity administered may have been too high.

The determinations for the tolerance curves presented by Mirsky *et al.* were made at 30-minute intervals. Determinations made at shorter intervals on the fowl reveal a different picture. Booker (unpublished) determined blood glucose on nonfasting cocks injected intravenously with 1.75 grams of glucose per kilogram at intervals of 5 and 10 minutes. Glucose rose from a preinjection normal of 200 mg. to 485 mg. percent within 5 minutes. The level had dropped only slightly after 10 minutes, but after 20 minutes it was 285 mg. percent. One hour after injection, the value was 250 mg. percent. When glucose is administered to the fowl via the gizzard, absorption is also rapid, and blood glucose usually reaches a peak within 15 to 30 minutes, depending upon the amount administered (Booker; also Blech, 1937).

Four hundred milligrams of glucose per 100 grams of body weight can be absorbed over a four-hour period by the chicken (Golden and Long, 1942b). Twelve percent of the absorbed glucose could be accounted for as liver glycogen, but not more than 8 percent was deposited in the muscles. The authors concluded that the bird metabolizes carbohydrates at a rapid rate or is able to convert considerable proportions of the absorbed glucose into fat. The ability to convert carbohydrates to fats is marked in birds, particularly so in the duck and goose.

Effects of Body Temperature on Blood Sugar

That hypothermia depresses blood sugar in the chicken was reported by Guttman (1938) and by Rodbard (1947). Rodbard lowered the body temperature of 10-week-old chicks to 35° C. and then raised it to 44° C. (above normal). Blood sugar dropped from 166 mg. percent at 41.5° C. (normal body temperature) to 133 at 35° C. When the birds were warmed to 44° C., blood sugar rose to 209. Streicher, Hackel, and Fleischman (1950), who exposed pigeons to an air temperature of −40° C. for 1 to 72 hours, found, contrary to results on the chicken, that blood sugar was not affected appreciably. There was, however, a significant decrease in liver glycogen of the fasted pigeon exposed to cold.

The thermoglycemic response in chickens is mediated via the vagi, according to Rodbard and Goldstein (1950), because they demonstrated that bilateral vagotomy at the level of the proventriculus modified the blood sugar response to changes in body temperature. Blood sugar after vagotomy did not fall with body temperature, but in some instances increased. When both vagi were sectioned in the normothermic bird, there was a transient increase in the blood sugar level, which, however, soon returned to normal. This indicates that other mechanisms for regulating blood sugar are more important. The authors postulate the release of a hypoglycemic factor from the abdominal organs as a result of vagal stimuli.

ENDOCRINE CONTROL OF CARBOHYDRATE METABOLISM

Pancreatectomy

The pancreas of birds and mammals produces the hormone, insulin, which in mammals plays an important role in carbohydrate regulation. This can best be demonstrated by removal of the pancreas (pancreatectomy). For details of the operation in birds, see Chapter 20.

Pancreatectomy in man and a number of mammalian species produces extreme hyperglycemia and diabetes. In all species of grain-eating birds depancreatized, a mild hyperglycemia results which usually disappears one week after the operation. The increase in blood sugar in these species immediately following the operation usually averages about 50 mg. percent, but in some individuals, it rises considerably higher. Although mild hyperglycemia is usually the rule, glycosuria is seldom observed and if observed is usually transient.

Pancreatectomy in the carnivorous horned owl, however, results in extreme hyperglycemia. The blood sugar may rise from a normal of 250 to 300 mg. percent to 750 mg. within 24 hours after the operation, and the birds develop diabetic symptoms and usually die within one week after the operation (Nelson, Elgart, and Mirsky, 1942).

That the type of diet influences the degree and severity of diabetic symptoms is well known. Carnivorous mammals or birds exhibit more extreme symptoms following pancreatectomy than do herbivorous or graniferous species. The depancreatized duck on a grain diet exhibits only mild and transient diabetes, but when it is fed meat, the hyperglycemia may reach extreme levels (Mirsky *et al.*, 1941). This is apparently due to the fact that liver gluconeogenesis is stimulated by ingested protein and by pancreatectomy, which increases glucose formation from tissue proteins. High carbohydrate diets tend to depress gluconeogenesis.

Not only is gluconeogenesis increased in the diabetic animal, but so is the rate of glycogenolysis, and the liver stores less carbohydrate as glycogen while the blood accumulates more glucose.

Liver and tissue glycogen. In the diabetic mammal, the capacity to store liver glycogen is impaired so that the level drops markedly. Pancreatectomy in those bird species not exhibiting diabetes does not impair liver-glycogen storage. This was reported in the chicken by Koppanyi, Ivy, Tatum, and Jung (1926) and in the duck by Sprague and Ivy (1936) and Minkowski (1893).

Apparently no studies have been made on muscle or liver glycogen of the diabetic horned owl or on muscle glycogen of other depancreatized birds. In the diabetic mammal, the muscle glycogen level is low, because the rate of glycogenesis is decreased. Similarly, the ability of the diabetic to oxidize glucose appears to be impaired.

Effects of Alloxan on Pancreas

Alloxan (mesoxalyl urea) when administered to certain mammals causes a selective necrosis of the beta cells of the pancreas, inhibits insulin secretion, and therefore produces diabetes, as does pancreatectomy. Since ablation of the pancreas does not produce diabetes in graniverous birds, it is not expected that alloxan would produce diabetes even if the beta cells were destroyed.

According to Scott, Harris, and Chen (1945), alloxan does not affect the beta cells of the duck, chicken, barn owl, or horned owl, nor does it produce diabetes. In some of the pigeons studied, there was occasional destruction of the beta cells, and a few birds developed transient diabetes, but most of them showed no symptoms even upon continued administration of alloxan. Mirsky (1945) reported that alloxan caused necrosis of the beta cells in the duck pancreas, but did not produce diabetes.

The effects of alloxan on different avian species (taken from the review of Lukens, 1948) are shown as follows:

Species	Lesions of islet cells	Hyper- glycemia	Alloxan dosage mg./kg.	Uratic deposits
Pigeon	+	+	75–200	+
Duck	+	0	50–750	0
	0	0	200–300	0
Chicken	0	0	75–400	+
Barn Owl	0	0	50–200	+
Horned Owl	0	0	100–250	0

The minimum lethal doses in milligrams per kilogram of body weight for the chicken and the pigeon were 199.8 and 111.8 respectively (Scott *et al.*).

Lukens stated that deposition of sodium urate on the serous surfaces in certain bird species is apparently a nondiabetic complication; this makes it possible that alloxan may be useful in the experimental study of gout. Blood uric acid reached extremely high levels 24 hours after injection of alloxan, and death occurred in 48 hours when the response was severe. In birds which survived the initial rise in blood uric acid, the normal level was restored in two or three days, and at autopsy little or no uratic deposition was found.

Lukens stated that alloxan may be neutralized in the blood by its conversion to alloxantin and dialuric acid by the thiol groups in plasma. It is possible that the bird is able to neutralize alloxan in this fashion more readily than mammals. Goldner and Gomori (1945) reported that dialuric acid was just as effective as alloxan in increasing blood uric acid in the pigeon, but it had no effect on the beta cells of the pancreas, as alloxan did in some cases.

Insulin in Bird Pancreas

Since pancreatectomy in most birds does not cause diabetes, it has been postulated that insulin is not necessary in the control of blood sugar or that the bird pancreas does not contain insulin or contains less insulin than the mammalian gland. However, the amount of insulin is as high in the chicken pancreas, per unit of tissue, as in the glands of calves (Redenbaugh, Ivy, and Koppanyi, 1926; Koppanyi *et al.*, 1926), but is lower than in some mammals (Haist, 1944). Extracts, which presumably contained insulin, from the pancreas, liver, and other tissues of ducks decreased blood sugar when injected into normal ducks, but such extracts from depancreatized ducks had no effect.

Ketosis

Diabetes in mammals is accompanied by abnormal fat metabolism and the accumulation of excessive amounts of ketones in the blood (ketonemia) and urine (ketonuria). The ketones, acetoacetic acid and beta hydroxybutyric acid, and acetone are produced in the liver and carried by the blood to the tissues, where they normally are oxidized to CO_2 and H_2O. When the rate of ketone formation in the liver exceeds the capacity of the tissues to oxidize the ketones, they accumulate in the blood and tissues. This occurs in starvation and on high fat diets, as well as in diabetes.

Fasted ducks, either normal or depancreatized, also exhibit a marked increase in ketones in the blood (Mirsky *et al.*, 1941). This is true as well for the fasted and depancreatized horned owl (Nelson *et al.*). When the ducks were fed, pancreatectomy had no effect on the ketones of the blood.

Effects of Insulin

Chen, Anderson, and Mage (1945) and others have shown that most birds, and particularly the chicken, are unusually resistant to insulin and that typical convulsions are not produced in the chicken, even with lethal doses. The lethal doses for some birds and mammals are shown in Table 31.

Golden and Long (1942a), however, reported a few cases of shock and death in the chicken with 200 units of insulin, but no convulsions. Opdyke (1942) produced convulsions in a few young fasted chicks with small doses, but not in the fed chick, where liver glycogen was not depleted.

On blood sugar and liver glycogen. Some workers have claimed that extremely large doses of insulin are required to depress blood sugar in the intact or depancreatized bird, but extensive work by Opdyke

Table 31. Lethal doses of insulin (Chen, Anderson, and Mage, 1945)

Species	Body weight kg.	Median lethal or convulsive dose (CD_{50}) Units insulin/kg. body wt.
Chicken (male)	3.0	5,000
Canary	0.016	2,396
Pigeon	0.2998	705
Duck	2.189	157
Dog	7.03	23.5
Rat	0.0905	20.7
Rabbit	1.89	5.1

and by Golden and Long (1942a) demonstrates that moderate to small doses of insulin depress blood glucose and glycogen in the liver, but not in the muscles of the chicken (Table 32). Small doses of insulin (0.5 to 2 units per kilogram) administered to 30-day-old chicks caused a progressive decrease in blood sugar within 1 to 1½ hours after injection, and the depression persisted for 3 hours after the injection. But within 5 hours the values returned to normal. With dosages from 0.5 to 1.5 units per kilogram, the percentage decrease in blood sugar exhibited a straight-line function of logarithm of dose. At 2 units, however, the increase was not proportional and suggests overcompensation. The higher dose probably resulted in adrenal stimulation with the release of adrenaline or cortical hormones which tend to increase blood sugar.

The values for liver and muscle glycogen are considerably higher than those reported by earlier workers. It is now known that tissue for glycogen analysis should be taken from the anesthetized but otherwise intact animal in order to prevent rapid glycogenolysis (Golden and Long).

The effects of small doses of insulin upon the depression of blood glucose and the glycogen stores are transient. With large doses of insulin (80 units per kilogram), Riddle and Opdyke (1942) reported elevated blood glucose and liver glycogen in the pigeon 24

Table 32. Effects of small doses of insulin and other hormones on blood glucose and liver and muscle glycogen of the fasted chick, weighing 200 to 400 grams (data from Golden and Long, 1942a)

No. of chicks	Insulin dosage Units/kg./day	No. of days	Hours fasted	Hours since last injection	Blood glucose mg. percent	Liver glycogen mg. percent	Muscle glycogen mg. percent
15	1	1	24	2	87±5.4	154± 32	763±24
21	2	1	24	2	66±4.6	132± 21	814±10
8	5	1	24	2	49±6.5	192± 23	844±41
27	0	—	24	—	182±3.9	364± 36	773±20
7	5+cortical extract*	1	24	2	88±7.5	426± 54	804±54
13	cortical extract alone	1	24	8–11	259±5.2	1,046±124	623±34

* 1 cc. per hour for 8 to 11 hours, then 5 units of insulin 2 hours before killing birds.

hours after the last injection, and similar results were reported by Honeywell and Riddle (1923) for the ringdove. Opdyke studied the long-term effects of moderately high doses of insulin on the blood sugar and liver glycogen of fasted and nonfasted chicks from 10 to 24 hours after administration (Table 33).

Large doses of insulin injected over a period of one to four days did not depress blood glucose or liver glycogen in the nonfasted chick when determinations were made 10 to 24 hours after the last injection. In fact, there was an increase in blood glucose and liver glycogen in those birds receiving the larger doses, suggesting again that insulin stimulated the release of adrenal hormones which are responsible for the rise. Six to ten hours after injections, the non-fasted chick began to eat, and it is possible that the high liver glycogen values are a result of ingested carbohydrate and may be

Table 33. Effects of large doses of insulin on blood glucose and liver glycogen of fasted and nonfasted chicks (from Opdyke, 1942)

No. of chicks	Dosage Units kg./day	Dosage No. of days	Hours fasted	Hours since last injection	Blood glucose mg. per- cent	Liver glycogen mg. percent	
7	60	$\frac{1}{2}$	0	10	189± 6.0	150±	26*
24	60	1	0	24	226±10.2	4,950±	202*
23	60	2	0	24	248±11.6	6,840±	659*
16	60	3	0	24	259± 3.2	3,990±1,133*	
5	60	4	0	13	274±24.1	4,960±	382
68	Control		0		188±14.9	2,550±	195†
12	120	1	24	24	182± 7.5	434±	119
12	120	2	48	24	201±10.4	494±	82
8	120	3	72	24	223±11.8	412±	64
14	Control		24		148± 1.9*	260±	22*
12	Control		48		153± 3.9*	326±	33.5
10	Control		72		169± 3.0	248±	34.7

* Mean of 7 determinations.
† Mean of 21 determinations.

of no endocrine significance except to show that the liver is capable of storing glycogen (Opdyke) or that the effects of the insulin are dissipated six to ten hours after injection. In the fasted chick receiving large doses of insulin, blood glucose and liver glycogen were much lower than in the fed, insulin-treated birds, but actually somewhat higher than for the fasted nontreated birds.

The depancreatized horned owl, which becomes diabetic, is very sensitive to insulin. One unit of insulin per kilogram of body weight produces hypoglycemia (Nelson *et al.*, 1942). Two to five units of insulin injected into five-day-old chick embryos produced marked hypoglycemia which persisted to the fourteenth day (Zwilling, 1948).

Pituitary Hormones

The anterior pituitary of mammals may affect carbohydrate metabolism directly by the action of certain hormones elaborated by it and indirectly through the action of trophic hormones which regulate the activity of other endocrine organs, such as the thyroids and adrenals.

Hypophysectomy in mammals decreases the rate of absorption of glucose by decreasing the activity of the thyroid. In the fasted animal, there is marked depletion of liver and muscle glycogen and hypoglycemia. The hypoglycemia can be prevented by feeding a diet rich in carbohydrate or protein or by administration of anterior pituitary extracts (Houssay *et al.*, 1951).

Severe diabetes can be prevented in depancreatized animals by ablation of the pituitary (Houssay preparation) and can be induced again by injecting anterior pituitary extracts. The anterior hypophysis apparently regulates carbohydrate metabolism by mobilizing body proteins and fats for liver gluconeogenesis.

The meager data concerning the effects of hypophysectomy in birds indicate that the operation also causes hypoglycemia. The results on the effects of pituitary hormones are inconclusive and conflicting. Riddle (1937) reported that the blood glucose levels of a few hypophysectomized pigeons were slightly subnormal. In three hypophysectomized chickens, blood glucose dropped from 200 mg. percent to as low as 119 mg. 48 hours after the operation, according to Hill, Corkill, and Parkes (1934). Most of their birds, however, died less than 48 hours after the operation, but death was not due to hypoglycemic shock. Among the five birds which survived the operation for 30 days or longer, the blood sugar ranged from 130 to 175 mg. percent. Injections of anterior pituitary extracts to four birds decreased or prevented the fall in blood sugar resulting from pituitary ablation. The hypophysectomized chicken withstands large doses of insulin as well as the intact bird, according to Hill *et al.*, but pituitary removal in the pigeon increases the sensitivity to insulin, as it does in the mammal (Riddle).

Golden and Long (1942a) injected anterior pituitary extracts of known diabetogenic activity in young chicks. There was no clearcut effect of the pituitary extracts on the blood sugar of the chick, nor on that of the duck (Mirsky *et al.*), but such extracts increased the pigeon's blood sugar (Riddle, 1937). Posterior lobe extracts containing the oxytocic and pressor factors had no effect on blood sugar in the chicken (Sprague and Ivy, 1936) or the pigeon (Funk, 1919).

Prolactin injected into pigeons induces a marked and prolonged hyperglycemia, and the maximum effect is obtained one to two days after the injection, according to Riddle (1937) and to Riddle and Dotti (1934). They concluded that prolactin is the essential diabetogenic principle of the anterior pituitary in birds.

Adrenal Cortical Hormones

Riddle and co-workers (see Riddle, 1937) reported that adrenal cortical extracts (ACE) injected into normal, hypophysectomized, thyroidectomized, or partially adrenalectomized doves and pigeons increase blood sugar by 15 percent seven hours after the injection. Likewise, in the normal fed or fasted chicken, ACE (8 to 11 cc. administered over an 8-hour period) increases significantly blood glucose and liver glycogen, but has no significant effect, in most cases, on muscle glycogen, according to Golden and Long (1942a). Their results follow:

Treatment	No. of chickens	Liver glycogen mg. percent	Muscle glycogen mg. percent	Blood glucose mg. percent
Fasted (control)	9	430	676	187
Fasted (ACE, 8–11 cc. over 8 hours)	13	1,046	634	259
Fed (controls)	6	1,520	957	193
" (ACE, as above)	6	1,970	891	255

The increased deposition of liver glycogen and hypoglycemia in the fasted, ACE-treated birds indicate increased gluconeogenesis from body protein. The increased liver glycogen in the fed chick receiving ACE is derived from ingested carbohydrates and from body protein. Adrenal cortical hormones also decrease the utilization of carbohydrates in the animal.

Not only does ACE produce hyperglycemia in normal or de-pancreatized chicks, but so does compound F, another adrenal steroid (Stamler and Pick, 1950; Stamler, 1952). Preliminary work by Stamler (1952) suggests that cortisone has no appreciable effect on blood sugar. Sames and Leathem (1952), however, reported that cortisone and several other adrenal steroids increase liver glycogen of chick embryos and ACE produces hyperglycemia (Zwilling, 1948).

Adrenalectomy, as expected, depresses blood sugar in the chicken and the normal level can be restored with cortical extracts (Parkins, 1931).

Epinephrine

Hyperglycemia is produced in ducks, geese, and chickens when epinephrine or adrenaline is injected (Paton, 1905; Fleming, 1919; Henry, Magee, and Reid, 1934; Sprague and Ivy, 1936; Golden and Long, 1942a). This occurs in normal fed, fasted, or depancreatized birds. An example of the effects of epinephrine on blood glucose and muscle glycogen of the fasted chick follows (Golden and Long, 1942a):

Treatment	Muscle glycogen mg. percent	Blood glucose mg. percent
Controls	910 ± 56	189 ± 14.6
Epinephrine, 0.5 mg./kg. (1 hour later)	687 ± 31	224 ± 5.8

Epinephrine, therefore, produces hyperglycemia and glycogenolysis in the chicken as it does in the mammal, and the chicken is apparently no more sensitive to the action of this hormone than the mammal, according to Golden and Long (1942a).

Emotional hyperglycemia can be induced in certain animals by fright and excitement, because epinephrine is released from the adrenals, but it cannot be produced in the duck (Koppanyi *et al.*, 1926; Sprague and Ivy, 1936).

Thyroxine and Parathormone

The thyroid hormone accelerates energy production in the body and carbohydrate metabolism. It also increases the rate of absorption of sugar from the intestines. Guttman (1938) reported that thyroidectomy in the fowl reduces blood sugar. Thyroxine produces hyperglycemia in pigeons and depletion of liver glycogen, according to Funk (1919).

Parathormone (hormone from the parathyroids) increases blood glucose and liver glycogen in intact pigeons (Funk) and also in those hypophysectomized (Riddle and Dotti, 1934; Riddle, 1937).

Gonadal Hormones

Results showing the effects of sex hormones on carbohydrate regulation in birds are limited, conflicting, and inconclusive. According to Rogemont (1930), the blood glucose in laying hens is 30 percent higher than in males, but the levels in sexually immature males and laying females are approximately the same. The glucose level decreases in the male at sexual maturity, suggesting the depressing effect of androgen. Castration resulted in an elevation of blood sugar to prepuberal levels. These results are at variance with those of Riddle (1937), in which he reported that the blood sugar level of the pigeon increased with the increase in production of estrogen coincident with ovulation. He reported that blood glucose increased from 190 mg. percent at the resting stage to 255 mg. preceding ovulation and 280 mg. at ovulation. According to Mirsky *et al.* (1941)- the administration of estrogen to ducks did not influence blood sugar level.

The work of Heller and Purcell (Chapter 1) showed no difference in blood glucose of mature and sexually immature female chickens under one year of age. Further studies on the effects of sex hormones on blood sugar are needed.

Summary

The hyperglycemia which results in mammals and in birds from the administration of thyroxine, adrenal cortical hormones, and pituitary hormones is due mainly to increased gluconeogenesis by the liver. Insulin, when administered in sufficient quantities, depresses blood sugar in birds and mammals; but in the amounts normally secreted by the pancreas of most birds, it has little effect upon glucose level in this species. Thus, in the bird, unlike mammals, hormones other than insulin, and probably adrenal cortical hormones, appear to play a more important role in the regulation of carbohydrate levels of the blood and tissues. The generally higher blood sugar levels of birds appears to be associated with their higher body temperature and higher metabolic rates.

REFERENCES

Batt, H. T. 1940 The pancreas of the fowl. Thesis. University of Toronto, Toronto.

Blech, K. 1937 Blutzuckerstudien am Huhn. Thesis. Fredrick-Wilhelm University, Berlin.

Burrows, W. H., J. C. Fritz, and H. W. Titus 1935 The blood sugar of the fasting, gizzardectomized fowl. J. Biol. Chem. 110:39.

Chen, K. K., R. C. Anderson, and N. Mage 1945 Susceptibility of birds to insulin as compared with mammals. J. Pharm. & Exp. Thera. 84:74.

Dukes, H. H. 1947 The Physiology of Domestic Animals. 6th ed. Comstock Publishing Co., Inc., Ithaca, N. Y.

Fleming, G. B. 1919 Carbohydrate metabolism in ducks. J. Physiol. 53:236.

Funk, C. 1919 Action of substances influencing the carbohydrate metabolism in experimental beriberi. J. Physiol. 53:245.

Golden, W. R. C., and C. N. H. Long 1942a The influence of certain hormones on the carbohydrate levels of the chick. Endocrinol. 30: 675.

Golden, W. R. C., and C. N. H. Long 1942b Absorption and deposition of glucose in the chick. Am. J. Physiol. 136:244.

Goldner, M. G., and G. Gomori 1945 Effect of alloxan on carbohydrate and uric acid metabolism of the pigeon. Proc. Soc. Exp. Biol. & Med. 58:31.

Guttmann, A. 1938 Über den Einfluss niedriger Aussentemperaturen auf den Blutzuckergehalt nach der Thyreodektomie bei Kaninchen und Hühnern. Weiner Tier Monat. 25:546.

Haist, R. E. 1944 Factors affecting the insulin content of the pancreas. Physiol. Rec. 24:409.

Henry, K. M., R. E. Magee, and I. Reid 1934 Some effects of fasting on the composition of the blood and respiration exchange in fowls. J. Exp. Biol. 11:58.

Hill, R. T., A. B. Corkill, and A. S. Parkes 1934 Hypophysectomy of birds. II: General effects of hypophysectomy of fowls. Proc. Roy. Soc. London 116:208.

Honeywell, H. E. 1921 Studies of the sugar in the blood of pigeons. Am. J. Physiol. 58:152.

Honeywell, H. E., and O. Riddle 1923 The action of iletin (insulin) on the blood sugar of pigeons. Proc. Soc. Exp. Biol. & Med. 20:248.

Houssay, B. A., J. T. Lewis, O. Orias, E. B. Menendez, E. Hug, V. G. Foglia, and L. F. Leloir 1951 Human Physiology. McGraw-Hill Book Co., Inc., New York.

Kausch, W. 1896 Über den Diabetes Mellitus der Vögel nach Pankreasexstirpation. Arch. f. Exp. Path. u. Pharm. 37:274.

Kausch, W. 1897 Der Zuckerverbrauch im Diabetes Mellitus des Vogels nach Pankreasexstirpation. Arch. f. Exp. Path. u. Pharm. 39: 219.

Koppanyi, T., A. C. Ivy, A. L. Tatum, and F. T. Jung 1926 Absence of permanent diabetes following pancreatectomy in the domestic fowl. Am. J. Physiol. 76:212.

Lukens, F. D. W. 1948 Alloxan diabetes. Physiol. Rev. 28:304.

Minkowski, O. 1893 Untersuchungen über den Diabetes Mellitus nach Exstirpation des Pankreas. Arch. f. Exp. Path. u. Pharm. 31:85.

Mirsky, A. 1945 Alloxan administration to the duck. Proc. Soc. Exp. Biol. & Med. 58:31.

Mirsky, A., N. Nelson, I. Grayman, and M. Korenberg 1941 Studies on normal and depancreatized domestic ducks. Am. J. Physiol. 135: 223.

Nelson, N., S. Elgart, and I. A. Mirsky 1942 Pancreatic diabetes in the owl. Endocrinol. 31:119.

Opdyke, D. F. 1942 Response of fasted and non-fasted chicks to insulin. Endocrinol. 31:363.

Parkins, W. M. 1931 An experimental study of bilateral adrenalectomy in the fowl. Anat. Rec. 51:39.

Paton, W. 1905 The effect of adrenaline on sugar and nitrogen excretion in urine of birds. J. Physiol. 32:59.

Redenbaugh, H. E., A. C. Ivy, and T. Koppanyi 1926 The presence of insulin in chicken tissues. Proc. Soc. Exp. Biol. & Med. 23:756.

Riddle, O. 1937 Carbohydrate metabolism in pigeons. Cold Spring Harbor Symposia on Quantitative Biol. 5:362.

Riddle, O., and L. B. Dotti 1934 Action of parathyroid hormone in normal and hypophysectomized pigeons. Proc. Soc. Exp. Biol. & Med. 32:507.

Riddle, O., and D. F. Opdyke 1942 Gross differences in response of the liver to first and later daily dosage with insulin and prolactin. Fed. Proc. 1:72.

Rodbard, S. 1947 Relationship between body temperature and blood sugar in the chicken. Am. J. Physiol. 150:67.

Rodbard, S., and M. S. Goldstein 1950 Neurogenic control of the blood sugar elicited by induced variations in the body temperature of the chick. Am. J. Physiol. 162:175.

Rogemont, L. 1930. Variations de la glycémie pendant la puberté du coq domestique. Comp. Rend. Soc. Biol. 104:154.

Sames, G. L., and J. H. Leathem 1952 Influence of adrenal steroids on chick embryo. Anat. Rec. 113:568 (Abs.).

Scott, C. C., P. N. Harris, and K. K. Chen 1945 Effects of alloxan in birds. Endocrinol. 37:201.

Scott, E. L., and H. E. Honeywell 1921 A study of sugar in blood of normal pigeons. Am. J. Physiol. 55:362.

Seitz, I. J., and A. C. Ivy 1929 The effects of pancreatectomy in ducks. Proc. Soc. Exp. Biol. & Med. 26:463.

Sprague, R., and A. C. Ivy 1936 Studies in avian carbohydrate metabolism. Am. J. Physiol. 115:389.

Stamler, J. 1952 Effects of adrenal steroid compound F in depancreatized cholesterol-fed cockerels. Fed. Proc. 11:153.

Stamler, J., and R. Pick 1950 Marked acute hyperglycemic response of depancreatized chicks to adrenal cortical extracts. Proc. Soc. Exp. Biol. & Med. 75:803.

Streicher, E., D. B. Hackel, and W. Fleischmann 1950 Effects of extreme cold on the fasting pigeon with a note on the survival of fasting ducks at −40° C. Am. J. Physiol. 161:300.

Weintraud, W. 1894 Ueber den Pancreas—Diabetes der Vögel. Arch. f. Exp. Path. u. Pharm. 34:303.

West, E. S., and W. R. Todd 1951 Textbook of Biochemistry. Macmillan Co., New York.

Wiggers, C. I. 1949 Physiology in Health and Disease. Lea and Febiger, Philadelphia.

Zwilling, E. 1948 Association of hypoglycemia with insulin micromelia in chick embyros. J. Exp. Zool. 109:197.

CHAPTER 13

Kidneys and Urine

STRUCTURE OF KIDNEY

THE urinary organs of birds consist of paired symmetrical kidneys and ureters. The ureters transport the urine to the cloaca, where it is voided with the feces. The folded, delimited area of the cloaca which receives the urine is termed the urodaeum. There is no urinary bladder birds.

The kidneys of birds are relatively larger than those of mammals, ranging from 1 to 2.6 percent of the body weight, depending on the species (Benoit, 1950). They comprise three lobes which are attached to the vertebral column and occupy the depression formed by the vertebrae and the ilia, caudal to the lungs (Bradley and Grahame, 1950). See Figure 58, Chapter 16.

The kidneys are usually brownish in color and friable in texture. There is no sharp line of demarcation between the cortex and the medulla of the organ in birds and reptiles, as there is in mammals. Each lobe is divided into lobules, which are bounded by interlobular veins (see Figure 37). Within each lobule are found the nephrons, the functional units of the kidney which are structurally similar to those of mammals. The nephron includes the glomerulus and the tubule. The part of the tubule extending from the glomerulus is thin and straight and is called the descending limb of Henle's loop (absent in some birds). The thicker ascending (distal) limb of the loop opens into the collecting tubules. These, in turn, empty into the ureter (Figures 37 and 38).

The dimensions of the nephron of the hen kidney, according to Groebbels (1932), are as follows (see also Marshall, 1934):

	Diameter in microns	Length in mm.
Glomerulus	86.00	—
Principal part of proximal tubule and descending limb	62.90	4.5–5.5
Thinner part (descending loop)	18.60	2.1
Thick part (ascending loop)	34.40	2.4
End part	29.00	2.7–3.0

The glomeruli of birds are considerably smaller and more numerous than those of mammals. The number of glomeruli of certain birds, according to Marshall (1934) and others, reviewed by him, are as follows (*shown at top of next page*):

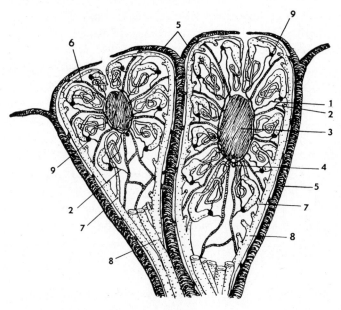

Figure 37. Diagram of the bird kidney showing the arrangement of the glomeruli and tubules in two lobules and blood vessels supplying them.

1, afferent artery of glomerulus; 2, efferent artery of glomerulus; 3, intralobular vein; 4, intralobular artery; 5, interlobular vein; 6, branch of interlobular vein which empties into intralobular vein; 7, end of tubules, emptying into excretory duct; 8, urinary collecting tubules leading to ureters which are not shown; 9, glomerulus. (Modified slightly from Spanner, *Morph. Jahrb.*, 1925.)

Species	Body weight Grams	No. of glomeruli in both kidneys Thousands	Author
Chicken	2,500	840	Marshall
Duck	3,670	1,989	Kunkel
Goose	5,400	1,659	"
Pigeon	232–420	274–353	"

The numbers of glomeruli range from 30,000 in small passerines to 200,000 for the chicken according to Benoit (1950). The glomerulus is formed by a network of capillary loops, surrounded by a capsule (Bowman's).

The structure of the renal corpuscles of birds is similar to that of mammals, except that they contain fewer capillary loops and the thin segment of Henle's loop is absent in some species of birds (Marshall, 1934).

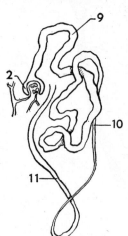

The bird kidney is supplied by sympathetic fibers, and the ureters receive parasympathetic fibers from the vagus, according to Portmann (1950); but Gibbs (1929c) reported that stimulation of the vagus had no effect on the ureters, nor did atropine, suggesting the absence of vagal fibers or parasympathetic control. He demonstrated that adrenaline caused contraction of the ureters and suggested that they are under sympathetic control.

Figure 38. Diagram of glomerulus and tubule of bird kidney.

2, glomerulus with blood vessels; 9, proximal convoluted tubule; 10, descending limb of Henle's loop; 11, ascending limb of Henle's loop.

Circulation in Kidney

The main blood vessels which supply and drain the kidney and the arrangement of these vessels within the lobules are shown in Figures 37 and 39. There are three main arteries branching from the aorta, each of which supplies a lobe of the kidneys (Spanner, 1925). These send branches into each of the lobules, forming the intralobular arteries, and these ramify to supply the glomeruli.

The afferent and efferent branches of the intralobular arteries carry blood to and away from the glomeruli, and these enter and leave by way of the same opening in the capsule. The efferent arterial

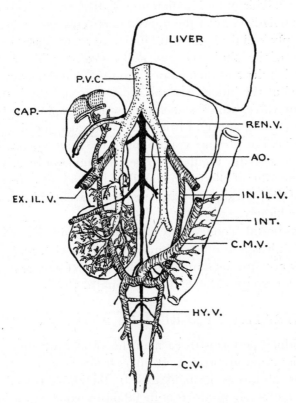

Figure 39. Diagram of circulation of bird kidney.

Black represents arteries; stippling, efferent veins; and crosshatching, afferent veins. P.V.C., posterior vena cava; EX.IL.V., external iliac vein; REN.V., renal vein; AO., aorta; IN.IL.V., interval iliac vein; INT., intestine; C.M.V., coccygeo-mesenteric vein; HY.V., hypogastric vein; C.V., coccygeal vein. (Modified slightly from Spanner, *Morph. Jahrb.*, 1925.)

blood empties into the branches of the interlobular veins (Figures 37 and 39), which in turn drain into the intralobular veins. The arterial blood supply of the bird kidney is sparse in relation to the venous supply (Spanner, 1925; Gordeuk and Grundy, 1950).

The kidney receives venous blood from the renal portal system, which includes blood from the coccygeo-mesenteric, caudal hypogastric, ischiatic, and iliac veins (Spanner; Gordeuk and Grundy, and others). This system is afferent and distributes blood to tubules of each lobule by way of the interlobular veins and their branches. These empty into the large intralobular veins, which course through the center of the lobule. The intralobular veins, which are efferent, drain the lobules and then empty into the main renal veins.

Located at the juncture of the renal vein and the iliac vein is a prominent valve, which somehow governs the flow of blood into the renal vein (Spanner). Little is known concerning the physiology of this valve, but pressure conditions in the renal portal vessels and renal veins probably regulate its opening and closure, as well as the relative amounts of afferent venous blood, which supplies the kidney by way of the interlobular veins, and of extrarenal blood, which bypasses the kidney.

A renal-portal blood supply does not exist in mammals, but is present in birds and other submammalian species, and this difference may account for some of the differences in renal function between these groups (Marshall, 1934; Smith, 1951).

FILTRATION, EXCRETION, AND ABSORPTION

The kidney performs three main functions: filtration, excretion or secretion, and absorption. It filters from the blood excess water and other substances normally used by the body, as well as foreign products and waste products of metabolism which are voided in the urine. It conserves needed body water, glucose, and other substances by reabsorption into the blood. By these processes the kidney becomes an important homeostatic mechanism, by which the internal environment is maintained at a fairly constant level. (For details concerning kidney physiology, see the book by Smith, 1951.)

Filtration takes place in the glomeruli, where crystalloids and substances with medium to small size molecules pass through the capillary walls of the glomeruli into the capsule. The plasma proteins, with large molecules, do not pass through the capillary walls and are not filterable. Some of the filterable substances of the blood include sodium, potassium, chlorides, inorganic phosphate, glucose, urea, creatinine, and uric acid. These substances have the same concentration in the capsular fluid as in the blood plasma, and this is evidence of filtration. The concentration of some of these in the urine may be higher or lower than that in the blood plasma. When the concentration is lower, this indicates that the substance is being reabsorbed by the kidney tubules. Glucose normally does not appear in the urine, but it is completely filterable, and therefore it must be reabsorbed. When the kidney tubule suffers impairment, such as follows administration of the glucoside, phlorizin, or when the blood sugar level is inordinately high, all of the glucose that is filtered is not reabsorbed and some appears in the urine. The kidney tubules also reabsorb water, which aids in maintaining normal blood volume.

The concentration of certain substances in the tubules and urine may be higher than that in the plasma or glomerular filtrate. When the increased concentration cannot be accounted for by filtration and reabsorption of water in the tubules (and this can be determined by comparing the clearance rate of the substance with that of inulin), this is evidence of tubular secretion. When the concentration of a substance in the tubules and urine is higher than that in the plasma or glomerular filtrate, this is evidence of tubular secretion.

In the aglomerular kidney of lower vertebrates, where there is no filtration, the kidney tubules secrete the urine. Tubules of the mesonephric kidney of chick embryos, cultured *in vitro*, containing dye (phenol red), are able to pick up the dye and transport it across the tubular cells without storage and discharge it into the tubular urine highly concentrated (Chambers and Kempton, 1933). Certain metabolites are excreted by the tubules, including uric acid in birds and some reptiles and creatinine in fishes, chick, man, and anthropoid apes (Smith). A number of foreign substances, such as phenol red, diodrast, and hippuran, when administered to animals and birds, have a higher renal clearance than inulin, or they are more concentrated in the urine, indicating tubular secretion.

Energy is expended by the tubular cells in secretion and reabsorption. Reabsorption occurs even when the substance reabsorbed may be many more times concentrated in urine than in the blood and could therefore not be accomplished by simple diffusion. Changes in arterial pressure do not appreciably affect secretion or reabsorption, but do affect rate of filtration.

Filtration and Renal Blood Flow in Birds

The pressure required to drive the fluid through the glomerular blood vessels must be sufficient to overcome the pressure exerted by the capsular membrane and the osmotic pressure of blood colloids. Thus, the effective filtration pressure (Pf) equals the pressure in the glomerular blood vessels (Pb) minus the capsular pressure (Pc) and the osmotic pressure of the blood colloids (Po). Thus: $Pb - (Po + Pc) = Pf$. (See Houssay *et al.*, 1951.)

Direct measurements of glomerular capillary pressure (Pb) have not been made on the intact avian or mammalian kidney. Pb and Pf can be estimated by determining the pressure required in the kidneys or ureters to stop urine flow. This can be done by cannulating the ureter or pelvis of the kidney and connecting the cannula to a vertical glass tube until its hydrostatic pressure equals the filtration pressure and urine flow ceases. Such determinations indicate that glomerular capillary pressure in the dog is approximately 60 percent of mean arterial pressure. If mean arterial pressure in the dog equals 150 mm. Hg, then capillary pressure equals 90 mm. Hg. If osmotic blood pressure equals 25 mm. Hg and capsular pressure 10 mm. Hg., effective filtration pressure is as follows:

$$Pf = Pb - (Po + Pc)$$
$$55 = 90 - (25 + 10)$$

The ureteral or intrapelvic pressure required to stop urine flow would be the capillary pressure minus the osmotic pressure, or $90 - 25 = 65$ mm. Hg.

The pressure required to stop urine flow in the chicken ureter varies considerably, but may range as high as 32 mm. Hg, according to Gibbs (1929a). However, part of this pressure is due to the milking action of the ureters, which, when in an active state, forces the urine along. Gibbs estimated that the highest pressure at which urine is formed, independent of the ureter action, ranges from 7.5 to 15 mm. Hg. Thus, the effective filtration pressure represented by the figure $15 - 10$ mm. Hg. or the figure $32 - 10$ mm. Hg is considerably lower than that for the dog and man.

It would appear that pressure in the glomerular capillaries of the bird should be as high as that in man and some mammals, since arterial blood pressure of birds, particularly that of the male, is higher than in man and some other mammals. If Gibbs's high figure of 22 mm. Hg is used as effective filtration pressure in birds, and 12 mm. Hg as the blood colloid osmotic pressure (lower in birds because total proteins are lower and the globulin content is higher in bird blood than albumin), then capillary pressure equals 34 mm. Hg. This figure appears low. Further studies are necessary.

Gibbs (1929a) and Marshall (1934) believed that filtration plays a less important role in kidney function of birds than mammals, because of the smaller number of capillary loops and poorer filtering areas in bird glomeruli. The rate of filtration in the bird kidney, as determined by inulin clearance, indicates that it is as high, per unit of body weight, as in man. (See later section.)

The amount of urine formed by filtration varies directly with blood pressure and blood flow. Constriction of the efferent glomerular arteries of mammals by the vasoconstrictor nerves (sympathetic) or by small doses of epinephrine causes an engorgement of the glomerulus with blood and an enlargement of the kidney. Accompanying these changes, there may be dilatation of the afferent arterioles, and thus a greater volume of blood with higher pressure is available to the glomerulus and a higher filtration pressure results (Smith). Constriction of the efferent arterioles, as occurs with large doses of epinephrine, decreases the blood flow and filtration pressure.

The renal blood flow in the chicken kidney is considerable, averaging according to Mayrs (1924) 150 cc. per kidney per hour, or 0.4 cc. per gram of kidney per minute. Gibbs (1928) reported a much higher rate, but showed that the rate was variable, ranging from 400 to 4,000 cc. per kidney per hour. One bird showed a rate of 10 cc. per gram of kidney per minute.

Adrenaline, which increases blood pressure, may cause an increase in urine flow in the chicken (Sharpe, 1912; Mayrs, 1924; Gibbs, 1928; Korr, 1939) and an increase in renal blood flow (Mayrs, 1924; Gibbs, 1928), but the effect is inconstant, according to Gibbs. There is a momentary decrease in renal blood flow followed by an increase, but no great change in urine flow. Korr showed, like Gibbs, that adrenaline increases filtration rate markedly (inulin clearance) and presumably renal blood flow, but increases urine flow only slightly. He believed that adrenaline caused a constriction of the efferent glomerular arterioles and dilatation of the afferent ones, as is believed to occur in mammals.

Ergotoxin, which produces hypertension, also decreases renal blood flow, and acetylcholine, which decreases blood pressure, increases renal blood flow (Gibbs, 1928). Changes in urine flow do not always parallel the changes in renal blood flow and pressure and led Gibbs to conclude that renal blood flow and pressure were not the most important factors controlling renal function in the bird, but that other factors, particularly O_2 tension, may be important.

Pitts (1938) and Shannon (1938a and 1938b) demonstrated that glomerular filtration in the chicken (inulin clearance) remains fairly constant over a wide range of changes in urine flow and concluded that urine flow is affected mainly by reabsorption and excretion in the tubules.

RENAL CLEARANCE

Renal clearance may be defined as the volume of blood which one minute's excretion of urine suffices to clear of a given substance (Moller, McIntosh, and Van Slyke, 1928) or as the minimum volume of blood required to furnish the quantity of substance excreted in the urine in one minute's time (Smith, 1951). It should be understood that the cleared volume of plasma represents the volume that, is virtually cleared, since it is not completely cleared of any substance by the kidney. The volume of blood which is cleared of a particular substance by the kidney in one minute may be expressed as follows:

Ux = concentration of x in each cc. of urine
V = rate of urine formation in cc. per minute
Px = concentration of x in each cc. of plasma
UxV = rate of excretion of x in mg. per minute

Then $\dfrac{UxV}{Px}$ = volume of plasma required to supply the quantity of x excreted in each minute's time. Thus UV/P equals the clearance of a given substance, x, in the plasma (Smith).

The substance to be tested is usually infused at a constant rate, and urine samples are collected at regular and frequent intervals (usually at 2 to 7-minute intervals in the chicken). Blood samples are as a rule taken near the middle of the collection periods. The plasma concentrations are plotted against time, and the exact values at the middle of each urine collection period are determined by interpolation.

Inulin Clearance

A substance suitable for measuring glomerular filtration must be completely filterable, physiologically inert, and must not be reabsorbed or excreted or synthesized by the kidney tubules (Smith). Such a substance is inulin, a starchlike polymer containing 32 hexose molecules with a molecular weight of 5200. Inulin is not reabsorbed or excreted by the kidney tubules in mammals, amphibia, or birds, and therefore its clearance is a measure of filtration (Smith).

The ratio of the inulin clearance to the simultaneous clearance of other substances, such as urea, uric acid, creatinine, and phenol red, indicates whether the substance in question is reabsorbed or secreted by the kidney tubules. Thus, a ratio of less than 1 indicates reabsorption, and a ratio greater than 1, excretion or secretion by the tubules.

Figures for inulin clearance in the chicken are shown as follows:

Mean inulin clearance per kg./min. In cc.	*Conditions*	*Mean urine flow per bird per minute In cc.*	*Author*
1.84	Hydration	0.89	Pitts (1938)
1.87	"	0.90	Shannon (1938a)
1.70	"	1.20	" (1938b)
2.15	"	1.13	Pitts & Korr (1938)
1.71	—	—	Lambert (1945)
1.37	No water given	0.33	Korr (1939)
0.60	Dehydrated 48–60 hours	0.16	"
2.45	Bird very hydrated	1.4	"

Korr's data indicate that rate of urine flow increases with inulin clearance and that both are influenced by degree of hydration of the body, but that hydration increases filtration rate more than it does urine flow. The data of Pitts (1938) and Shannon (1938a) based on birds hydrated to a lesser extent show, however, only a slight increase in inulin clearance with urine flows from 0.4 to 1.8 cc. per minute.

An inulin clearance of 1.8 cc. per kilogram of body weight per minute means that for a chicken weighing 2 kilograms the fluid filtered through the kidneys in 1 minute amounts to 3.6 cc., or 216 cc. in 1 hour, or 5.18 liters in 24 hours. On a body weight basis, this rate compares favorably with that in man. Since approximately 130 cc. of urine are voided by the chicken in 24 hours (Hester, Essex, and Mann, 1940), most of the water filtered through the kidney (nearly 98 percent) is reabsorbed in the tubules, and this figure is of the same order as that for man.

Inulin is completely filterable and is not reabsorbed or excreted by the tubules; therefore, the inulin clearance varies directly with the concentration of inulin in the plasma, and UV/P is constant and independent of plasma concentration.

An increase in renal blood flow, induced with epinephrine, increases filtration rate in the chicken (Pitts, 1938; Korr, 1939). Plasma hypertonicity, induced by injections of sodium chloride or sucrose, also increases filtration rate (Korr).

Phenol Red Clearance

The dye, phenol red, is filtered by the glomeruli and is also secreted or excreted by the tubules of man, dog, and chicken, as indicated by ratios of phenol red to inulin. Some of the dye is bound by the plasma proteins, and only the free dye is filterable. The amounts bound and free depend upon the concentration of the dye in the plasma. At very low concentrations in chicken plasma (1 mg. percent), only 15 to 20 percent of the dye is free or filterable, but at concentrations of 15 mg. percent, 60 percent is filterable, and at higher concentrations more is filterable because more is free (Pitts, 1938).

Unlike inulin, the ratio of free phenol red in the plasma to that in the urine is not constant, and this ratio decreases after the concentration in the plasma reaches a certain point. At low plasma levels of the dye (1 to 3 mg. percent), the ratio of the phenol red to inulin clearance ranges from a low of 10 to 1 to a high of 17 to 1 in the chicken (Pitts), as contrasted with ratios of 3.3 to 1 in man and 1.7 to 1 in the dog (Smith).

Thus, tubular excretion of the dye is much greater in the chicken than in the mammal, and this may be due to the fact that the tubules of birds receive an independent blood supply by way of the renal portal system. At high concentrations of the dye, the phenol red /inulin clearance ratio approaches 1 (Figure 40). This means that as the plasma concentration reaches a certain point less and less of

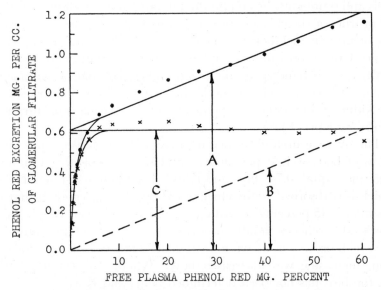

Figure 40. Excretion of phenol red by the chicken kidney in relation to concentration of free phenol red in plasma.

A, total excretion; B, that filtered; C, that excreted by tubules. The amount of phenol red filtered increases with plasma concentration, but this is not true for that excreted by tubules. (From Pitts, *J. Cell. & Comp. Physiol.*, 1938.)

the dye is handled or excreted by the tubules; in other words, the tubules have a limited capacity to excrete the dye. The absolute clearances of phenol red and inulin in the chicken at low plasma concentrations are 25 and 1.8 cc. per kilogram per minute, and at high concentrations (100 mg.) 2.59 and 2.57 respectively (Pitts). The differences in the excretion of phenol red in relation to that filtered by the bird and mammal have been calculated by Smith, who showed that the quantities of dye excreted by the tubules per cc. of dye filtered for the dog, man, and the chicken are 0.079, 0.21, and 0.62 mg., respectively. Phlorizin, which impairs or inhibits tubular function, depresses the excretion of phenol red in the chicken (Pitts).

Urea Clearance

Urea is the chief nitrogenous constituent of the urine of mammals and represents the end product of protein metabolism, but this is not true for the chicken, in which uric acid is the chief end product of protein metabolism and the principal constituent of avian urine. Urea represents the end product of purine metabolism in birds, yet it is handled by the avian kidney like that of mammals; that is, it is completely filterable, but it is partially reabsorbed by the kidney tubules and independently of the plasma concentration (Pitts and Korr, 1938).

The average urea clearance in the chicken is 1.50 cc. per kilogram of body weight per minute, and the ratio of urea to inulin clearance equals 0.74 (Pitts and Korr). The fraction of filtered urea which is reabsorbed in the chicken (25 percent) is less than that in mammals (45 percent) according to these authors, but whether the species difference is significant is not known, because in mammals urea reabsorption is known to be influenced by rate of urine formation (increasing with decreased flow). Whether or not this holds for the bird has not been determined (Pitts and Korr).

Korr (1939) concluded that the fraction of filtered urea which is reabsorbed is dependent upon the amount of filtered water that is reabsorbed and not upon actual volume of water excreted (urine flow). Reabsorption of urea from tubular urine is believed to be caused by back diffusion rather than active absorption. (See Smith, 1951.)

Uric Acid Clearance

Uric acid is highly concentrated in the urine of birds and constitutes 60 percent or more of the total nitrogen. Since its concentration in the urine is much higher than in plasma, this is considered presumptive evidence of tubular secretion. Uric acid clearance studies by Shannon (1938b) demonstrate that 87 to 93 percent of uric acid of the chicken is excreted by the tubules. The uric acid/inulin clearance ratio at moderate plasma uric acid concentrations (6 to 9 mg. percent) ranges from 7.5 to 15.8. These ratios are about the same as the phenol red/inulin ratios at low plasma levels of the dye. As the plasma level of uric acid is raised, the ratio is depressed until at a plasma uric acid level of 100 mg. percent, the ratios range from 1.8 to 3.2.

The absolute clearance of uric acid at plasma levels of 6 to 9 mg. percent is approximately 30 cc. per kilogram of body weight per minute (Shannon). Gibbs (1928, 1929a, and 1929b) has shown that changes in renal blood flow and pressure, factors affecting filtration rate, do not appreciably affect secretion of uric acid.

Creatinine Clearance

Creatinine is a normal constituent of the urine in mammals, but in birds the amount formed is negligible in relation to the amount of creatine. Clearance studies on birds, man, apes, and certain fish indicate that the tubules of these species secrete creatinine. The creatinine/inulin ratio in the chicken at plasma concentrations of 9 to 12 mg. percent averages 1.54 (Shannon, 1938a). At higher concentrations, the ratio is depressed, and at concentrations of 200 to 230 mg. percent, the ratios are 1.09 and 1.07 respectively. The normal endogenous plasma concentration of creatinine is approximately 1.5 mg. percent (Groebbels, 1932). Phlorizin completely abolishes tubular secretion of creatinine, producing a creatinine /inulin ratio of approximately 1 (Shannon).

Glucose Clearance

Glucose is filtered by the glomeruli and reabsorbed by the kidney tubules so that normally none appears in the urine. Phlorizin, which impairs or inhibits tubular reabsorption, results in a glucose/inulin clearance ratio of 1 in birds and mammals, showing that glucose is filtered but not reabsorbed (Marshall, 1934; Pitts, 1938).

Clearance of Other Substances

Other substances excreted by the tubules of the chicken kidney are hippuric acid, ornithuric acid, *p*-acetylaminobenzoic acid, methyl glucuronide, and phenol sulphuric ester. Benzoic acid, free phenols, *p*-aminobenzoic acid, glucuronic acid, and probably pregnanediol are not excreted by the tubules (Sperber, 1946, 1947, and 1949.)

URINE

Factors Affecting Amount of Urine Voided

The urine and feces of the bird are voided into the cloaca. In order to obtain urine free from fecal matter it is necessary to cannulate the ureter or surgically to exteriorize the opening of the ureter or of the rectum. Uncontaminated urine in the cloaca may also be obtained by plugging the anal opening. Most of the work relating to quantities of urine voided is based on short period collections from which calculations were made on output for 24 hours. Most of those who cannulated the ureters and collected urine for short periods (usually 30 to 100 minutes) estimated the urine output of the adult chicken (weight about 2 kg.) at from 500 to 1000 cc. (Sharpe, 1912; Mayrs, 1924; Davis, 1927; Coulson and Hughes, 1930; Hester, Essex, and Mann, 1940; and others). Short-period collections from exteriorized ureters gave similar estimates (Hester, Essex, and Mann). Thus, the estimates of urine output based on short-period collections are unduly high. An estimated output of 1000 cc. in 24 hours is considerably higher than the water consumption (50 to 250 cc.).

It was demonstrated by Hester, Essex, and Mann (1940) and by Hart and Essex (1942) that such estimates are in error, because they showed that urine output from cannulated ureters for the first 30 minutes averaged 13.9 cc., but during the second 30 minutes averaged only 2.5 cc. Thus, estimates for 24 hours based on first collections gave an output of 667 cc., and on the second period, 120 cc. They concluded that cannulation and handling of the bird causes diuresis, which persists for at least 30 minutes. In later experiments in which urine was collected in bags from exteriorized ureters for 24 hours, the average output was 86.8 cc., with a range of 61 to 123.4 cc. In another experiment, the output was as high as 180 cc.

Diuresis. Administration of water, and particularly water made hypertonic with electrolytes, increases urine output, whereas dehydration decreases urine flow. Certain drugs influence urine flow. Pituitrin or pitressin decreases urine flow (Korr, 1939; Hester, Essex, and Mann, 1940), but ether anesthesia and caffeine increase the flow (Davis, 1927; Hester *et al.;* and others). The effects of ephedrine or adrenaline upon urine flow are inconstant. Mayrs (1924) reported an increase in urine flow, and Hester *et al.*, no effect. Gibbs (1928) and Korr (1939) reported a transient increase in urine flow followed by a slight decrease, but the results were variable. Atropine and pilocarpine have no effect on urine flow according to Gibbs (1929b).

Role of ureters in control of urine flow. The ureters, by peristaltic action, tend to force or milk the urine along. The peristaltic waves move caudally. The pressure exerted by these waves is considerable, and the urine may be forced along against a pressure as high as 30 mm. Hg (Gibbs, 1929c). The ureters, as discussed previously, appear to be under sympathetic control.

Role of the Cloaca in the Absorption of Water

Many of the early investigators believed that water from ureteral urine is absorbed in the cloaca and rectum and that the cloaca serves an important function in the conservation of water (for a review of some of the early work, see Korr, 1939; Hester, Essex, and Mann, 1940; Hart and Essex, 1942). Some of these workers observed an increase in flow of urine collected from cannulated ureters or from the cloaca after plugging the rectum. The urine was thin and watery and had a lower osmotic pressure. In one experiment, in which the rectum was plugged with cotton, approximately 22 cc. of urine were collected from the ureters in 1 hour, as contrasted with 9.8 cc. normally (Korr, 1939; see also Sharpe, 1912). These observations and other considerations led Korr to estimate that from 10 to 30 cc. of ureteral urine may be absorbed from the cloaca per hour. Since the insertion of cannulae into the ureters, plugging of the rectum, handling of the bird, and anesthesia are known to produce diuresis (Hester, Essex, and Mann) during the time of most of the urine collections, these results and estimates are subject to great error and appear unreasonably high.

Sharpe (1923) attempted to measure the amount of water absorbed directly in the cloaca by placing known amounts of solutions in the rectum and the cloaca, which were separated from the ureters. He ligated the rectum just caudal to the ceca, thus forming a blind sac extending from the ceca to the cloaca, into which he introduced the solutions. The solutions introduced were hemoglobin and phenolsulphonephthalen, and changes in their concentration indicated the amount of water absorbed. The amounts absorbed were also determined directly by measuring the amount of introduced solution remaining in the cloaca after a given time. The two methods checked fairly closely, according to the author. From 1 to 3 cc. of water per hour were absorbed from the cloaca and rectum, depending upon the concentration of the solution and the pressure. Isotonic solutions in the cloaca were absorbed more slowly than hypotonic or hypertonic solutions. In some experiments in which phenosulphonephthalen was included in the solution and placed in the cloaca, this was detected in the urine in less than one-half hour, and within $4\frac{1}{2}$ hours, 42 percent of the substance was excreted. It is likely that ligation and manipulation of the rectum and the cloaca influenced the rate of water absorption in these experiments, and the amounts absorbed may not reflect normal absorption.

Later experiments by Hart and Essex (1942), based on long-term urine collections, indicate that some water is reabsorbed in the cloaca, but not in appreciable amounts. The evidence for this conclusion is indirect. They measured water consumption and urine flow in birds in which the ureters were exteriorized, so that there would be no cloacal absorption, and in birds with artificial ani, where the bird retains some ability for water reabsorption. Earlier workers had observed an increase in water consumption following surgical separation of the anus; this suggests that normally water is absorbed in the rectum—hence the smaller water consumption of normal birds. Hart and Essex also reported increased water consumption in their operated birds, but only if no extra salt was added to the diet. When 1 per cent salt was added to the natural diet, which presumably contained enough salt for a normal bird, water consumption was normal and urine output was normal, as follows:

Hen No.	Body weight gm.	Water intake daily	Food intake daily	Urine output	Treatment
1	2,358	242 cc.	87 gm.	129	Artificial anus and 1% salt
2	1,317	231 cc.	106 gm.	—	Normal, no added salt
3	1,255	235 cc.	89 gm.	—*	Exteriorized ureters and 1% salt

* Measured on other birds and ranged from 50 to 180 cc., the same range as for birds with artificial ani.

The birds with artificial ani or exteriorized ureters produced 129 cc. of urine daily, quantities considerably lower than reported by earlier workers. This suggests that normally appreciable quantities of water are not absorbed in the cloaca. Extra salt added to the diet of the operated birds appeared not to affect urine flow, since the figures reported by Hart and Essex are of the same order as those reported earlier by Hester *et al.*, where no extra salt was added to the diet. Withholding drinking water from birds with exteriorized ureters and at the same time not adding salt produced greater dehydration and weight loss than in normal birds and suggests that normally some water is reabsorbed in the cloaca. The effects of withholding drinking water and adding salt to the diet of birds with exteriorized ureters was not determined.

The operated birds without added salt lost weight rapidly. One bird weighing 1500 grams lost 900 grams within a 4-month period, and the blood chlorides dropped from about 400 to 328 mg. percent. The hematocrit increased to 60 per cent, indicating marked dehydration and hemoconcentration. When salt was added, this bird regained the lost weight and a normal blood picture. These data suggest that some sodium chloride is normally reabsorbed in the cloaca and rectum.

It was stated earlier that of the water filtered by the kidney of the bird approximately 98 percent is reabsorbed. Water from the bird's body is lost through vaporization and by way of the kidneys as urine. The amount lost by vaporization is about the same or greater than that lost through the urine (Korr, 1939; Hart and Essex, 1942), averaging 124.7 grams per day per 1864 grams of body weight (Hart and Essex). See also Chapter 8.

Physical Characteristics of Urine

The urine of birds is usually cream-colored and concentrated, contains thick, mucoid material, and is abundant in urates. However, under certain circumstances, such as diuresis, it may be thin and watery. The pH of chicken urine ranges from 6.22 to 6.7, decreasing (more acid) with increasing consistency (Hester *at al.*).

Ureteral urine is usually hypotonic, with an osmotic pressure lower than blood, but under certain conditions it may be hypertonic (Mayrs, 1924; Korr, 1939). The osmotic pressure of ureteral urine of the normally hydrated chicken ranges, in terms of percent sodium chloride, from 0.13 to 1.3 percent, and that of blood, from 0.92 to 0.94 percent (Korr). Abnormal intake of water, which increases urine flow, decreases osmotic pressure; dehydration, which diminishes urine flow, increases osmotic pressure of urine. Korr reported that pitressin decreases urine flow about 10 percent, but it increases urine osmotic pressure from 0.26 to 1.48 percent NaCl. Increasing the osmotic pressure of the blood by injections of sodium chloride or glucose increases urine osmotic pressure (Korr).

The specific gravity of duck urine is 1.0018, and of hen urine, 1.0025 (Groebbels, 1932).

Nitrogenous Constitutents of Urine

The principal differences in the chemical constituents in the urine of birds and of mammals lie in the preponderance of uric acid over urea and of creatine over creatinine in the urine of birds. Creatinine exists only in minute amounts in bird urine (Paton, 1909; Davis, 1927; and others). Some of the nitrogenous chemical constitutents of chicken urine are as follows (in milligrams per 100 ml.):

Species	*Total nitrogen*	*Ammonia nitrogen*	*Uric acid*	*Urea nitrogen*	*Creatine and creatinine nitrogen*[*]	*N, undetermined*	*Author*
Chicken	100.0	17.3	62.9	10.4	8.0	1.4	Davis (1927)

[*] Nearly all as creatine.

Uric acid nitrogen comprises 60 to 80 percent of the total nitrogen of bird's urine (Milroy, 1904; Paton, 1905; Davis, 1927; and others). Uric acid in the blood of birds under normal conditions usually ranges from 5 to 8.0 mg. percent. Adrenaline decreases the percentage of uric acid nitrogen from 77 to 71 mg. percent and increases the ammonia nitrogen in the urine of the goose from 14 to 19 mg. percent (Paton, 1905).

Many investigators have determined the uric acid content of bird excreta, which contain feces and urine. The uric acid, per gram of air-dried excreta, ranges from 53.8 to 89.5 mg., according to Bose (1944), and from 36.6 to 100.7 mg., according to Baker (1946).

About 10 percent of the urates in bird blood is in solution, 18 percent is protein-bound, and about 70 percent exists as an ultra-filterable or colloidial fraction, according to Levine, Wolfson, and Lenel (1947).

The amount of urine water excreted per gram of uric acid varies with the amount of urine produced and ranges from 60 to 100 cc., according to Korr (1939), and from 30 to 165 cc., according to Hart and Essex (1942).

Uric acid is synthesized mainly in the liver of birds, as indicated by Minkowski in 1886 and others since (Milroy, 1904; Folin, Berglund, and Derick, 1924; Benzinger and Krebs in 1933; Edson, Krebs, and Model, 1936; see review of Krebs, 1936). It is now generally agreed that the kidney is also concerned in the synthesis of uric acid. The livers of chickens and pigeons produce hypoxanthine, which is then oxidized to uric acid in the kidney of the pigeon and the liver of chickens by xanthine oxidase. The pigeon kidney, but not the liver, contains xanthine oxidase.

The uric acid content of blood, liver, and kidneys of birds (in milligrams per 100 ml. or 100 grams) is shown as follows:

Species	Whole blood	Muscle	Kidney	Liver	Author
Duck, normal	6.7	1.8	70.5	22.2	Folin *et al.* (1924)
Duck with ligated ureters	224.0	30.2	354.0	101.0	"
Chicken, normal	5.8	—	—	—	Levine *et al.* (1947)
Chicken with ligated ureters	304.0	—	—	—	"

Milroy (1904) revealed that changes in the activity of the liver affect the amounts of uric acid excreted by the duck and goose. Electrical stimulation of the liver increases the excretion and synthesis of uric acid by the liver. Ligation of the ureters of birds causes marked concentration of uric acid in the blood and tissues, but not in the urine. Birds with ligated ureters usually die from uremia within 12 to 24 hours (Folin *et al;* Levine *et al.*).

ABNORMAL KIDNEY FUNCTION

Injury to the ureters, produced by sectioning, may produce renal atrophy, according to Riddle (1930). The pressure developed in the ureters may be higher than the filtration or secretion pressure, according to Gibbs (1929c), and he suggested that spasm of the ureters might well be a cause of renal insufficiency in the bird.

Gross autopsy findings from a number of sources suggest that chronic renal insufficiency accounts for a relatively high percentage of the deaths of adult chickens. The disorder is characterized by hypertrophied kidneys and deposits of urates in the blood and tissues of the body. Filtration and excretion in the kidneys of such birds have not been studied.

Disturbances in renal structure and function of the chicken (nephrosclerosis) have been produced by large doses of desoxycorticosterone acetate (Selye, 1942) or excess sodium chloride (Selye, 1943).

The disease of chickens known variously as pullet's disease, blue comb disease, and monocytosis produces marked abnormalities in the structure and function of the kidney. The glomeruli and the convoluted tubules are involved. Clinically, the disease resembles uremia (Jungherr, 1948). The blood uric acid and nonprotein nitrogen are abnormally high, and calcium may be low. Urine analysis usually reveals glycosuria, which may be due to hyperglycemia or to defective reabsorption of glucose by the damaged tubules.

REFERENCES

Baker, C. J. L.   1946   A note on the estimation of the uric acid radical in avian excreta. Poultry Sci. 25:593.

Benoit, J.   1950   Traité de Zoologie, edited by P. P. Grassé. Tome XV: Oiseaux, p. 341. Masson & Co., Paris.

Bose, S.   1944   An iodometric estimation of uric acid in poultry excreta. Poultry Sci. 23:130.

Bradley, O. C., and T. Grahame   1950   The Structure of the Fowl. J. P. Lippincott Co., Philadelphia.

Chambers, R., and R. T. Kempton   1933   Indications of function of the chick mesonephros in tissue culture with phenol red. J. Cell. & Comp. Physiol. 3:131.

Coulson, E. J., and J. H. Hughes   1930   Collection and analysis of chicken urine. Poultry Sci. 10:53.

Davis, R. E.   1927   The nitrogenous constituents of hen's urine. J. Biol. Chem. 74:509.

Edson, N. L., H. A. Krebs, and A. Model 1936 The synthesis of uric acid in the avian organism: Hypoxanthine as an intermediary metabolite. Biochem. J. 36:1380.

Folin, O., H. Berglund, and C. Derick 1924 The uric acid problem: An experimental study on animals and man, including gouty subjects. J. Biol. Chem. 60:361.

Gibbs, O. S. 1928 The renal blood flow of the bird. J. Pharm. & Exp. Thera. 34:277.

Gibbs, O. S. 1929a The secretion of uric acid by the fowl. Am. J. Physiol. 88:87.

Gibbs, O. S. 1929b The effects of drugs on the secretion of uric acid in the fowl. J. Pharm. & Exp. Thera. 35:49.

Gibbs, O. S. 1929c The function of the fowl's ureters. Am. J. Physiol. 87:594.

Gordeuk, S., Jr., and M. L. Grundy 1950 Observations on circulation in the avian kidney. Am. J. Vet. Res. 11:256.

Groebbels, F. 1932 Der Vogel. Erster Band: Atmungswelt und Nahrungswelt, Kot und Harn, p. 676. Verlag von Gebrüder Borntraeger, Berlin.

Hart, W. M., and H. E. Essex 1942 Water metabolism of the chicken with special reference to the role of the cloaca. Am. J. Physiol. 136:657.

Hester, H. R., H. E. Essex, and F. C. Mann 1940 Secretion of urine in the chicken. Am. J. Physiol. 128:592.

Houssay, B. A., J. T. Lewis, O. Orias, E. B. Menendez, E. Hug, V. G. Foglia, and L. F. Leloir 1951 Human Physiology. McGraw-Hill Book Co., Inc., New York.

Jungherr, E. 1948 Avian monocytosis, Chapter 29 in H. E. Biester and L. H. Schwarte, Diseases of Poultry. Iowa State College Press, Ames.

Korr, I. M. 1939 The osmotic function of the chicken kidney. J. Cell & Comp. Physiol. 13:175.

Krebs, H. A. 1936 Metabolism of amino acids and related substances. Ann. Rev. Biochem. 5:247.

Lambert, P. 1945 Étude comparée de l'élimination de l'inuline, de la créatinine, de l'uro-selectan B, par le rein des oiseaux. Arch. Intern. Pharm. Therap. 71:313.

Levine, R., W. Q. Wolfson, and R. Lenel 1947 Concentration and transport of true urate in the plasma of the azotemic chicken. Am. J. Physiol. 151:186.

Marshall, E. K. 1934 Comparative physiology of vertebrate kidney. Physiol. Rev. 14:133.

Mayrs, E. B.   1924   Secretion as a factor in elimination by the kidneys. J. Physiol. 58:276.

Milroy, T. H.   1904   The formation of uric acid in birds. J. Physiol. 30: 47.

Moller, E., J. F. McIntosh, and D. D. Van Slyke   1928   Studies of urea excretion. II: Relationship between urine volume and rate of urea excretion by normal adults. J. Clin. Invest. 6:427.

Paton, N.   1905   The effect of adrenaline on sugar and nitrogen excretion in the urine of birds. J. Physiol. 32:59.

Paton, N.   1909   Creatine excretion in the bird and its significance. J. Physiol. 39:485.

Pitts, R. F.   1938   The excretion of phenol red by chickens. J. Cell. & Comp. Physiol. 11:99.

Pitts, R. F., and I. M. Korr   1938   The excretion of urea by the bird. J. Cell. & Comp. Physiol. 11:117.

Portmann, A.   1950   Traité de Zoologie, edited by P. P. Grassé. Tome XV: Oiseaux, chapter on Système nerveux, p. 185. Masson & Co., Paris.

Riddle, O.   1930   Complete atrophy of kidney in pigeons following section of the ureter. Proc. Soc. Exp. Biol. & Med. 27:1022.

Selye, H.   1942   Production of nephrosclerosis by overdosage with desoxycorticosterone acetate. Canadian Med. Assoc. J. 47:515.

Selye, H.   1943   Production of nephrosclerosis in the fowl by NaCl. J. Am. Vet. Med. Assoc. 103:140.

Shannon, J. A.   1938a   The excretion of exogenous creatinine by the chicken. J. Cell. & Comp. Physiol. 11:135.

Shannon, J. A.   1938b   The excretion of uric acid by the chicken. J. Cell & Comp. Physiol. 11:135.

Sharpe, N. C.   1912   On the secretion of urine in birds. Am. J. Physiol. 31:75.

Sharpe, N. C.   1923   On absorption from the cloaca in birds. Am. J. Physiol. 66:209.

Smith, H. W.   1951   The Physiology of the Kidney. Oxford University Press, New York.

Spanner, R.   1925   Der Pfortaderkreislauf in der Vogelniere. Morph. Jahrb. 54:560.

Sperber, I.   1946   A new method for the study of renal tubular excretion in birds. Nature 158:131.

Sperber, I.   1947   The mechanism of renal excretion of some detoxication products in the chicken. 17th Intern. Physiol. Congr. 217.

Sperber, I.   1949   The excretion of some organic bases and some phenols and phenol derivatives. Scand. J. Clin. Lab. Invest. 1:345.

CHAPTER 14

The Special Senses

The Eye and Vision

STRUCTURE OF THE EYE

THE eye of the bird has all of the structural components of the reptilian eye and differs principally from the mammalian eye in that it has a pecten. These parts include the eyeball, the optic nerve, and such accessory structures as eyelids, conjunctiva, lachrymal glands, and ocular muscles. The eyeball consists of the cornea, lens, anterior chamber containing aqueous humor, vitreous humor, iris and pupil, ciliary body, pecten, sclera, choroid, and retina and its connection with the optic nerve. (See Figure 41.)

The bird has an upper and lower eyelid and an additional or third eyelid, the nictitating membrane, which is usually concealed when not in use. In most birds, this membrane alone blinks, and the upper and lower lids close only in sleep. The blinking movements keep the cornea and inner eyelids clean (Walls, 1942). It is believed that this membrane covers the cornea during flight and prevents drying of the eye by the wind.

The lachrymal glands, from which tears are secreted, lie above and to the lateral side of the eyeball. The movements of the eyeball are effected by four straight and two oblique muscles (Bradley and Grahame, 1950).

Cornea and lens. The cornea, which is transparent, is histologically similar to that of mammals except that Bowman's membrane is not always differentiated (Walls, 1942). The size of the cornea varies with the species, being relatively small in underwater swimmers and large in nocturnal birds.

The lens is the biconvex body suspended immediately behind the iris by the fibers from the ciliary body. As in most vertebrates,

229

the anterior surface is less sharply curved than the posterior surface. The lens tends to be flattest in diurnal birds and roundest in
nocturnal ones. It is as highly refractive as in mammals or more so
(Walls).

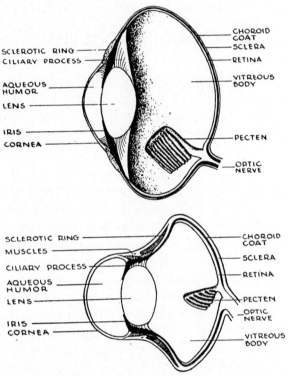

Figure 41. Diagram of sections through the eyeball of
a pigeon (upper), which has a flat eye, and of an owl
(lower), which has a tubular eye. (From Atwood, *A Concise Comparative Anatomy*, C. V. Mosby Co., St. Louis,
1947.)

Choroid, ciliary body, and iris. The choroid is the highly vascular,
pigmented layer between the retina and sclera, and it nourishes
the rods and cones of the retina. It is relatively thicker in birds
than in reptiles or mammals. The ciliary body is the thickened and
radially folded anterior part of the choroid. Associated with it are
the ciliary muscles. Continuous with the choroid is the iris, a pigmented diaphragm pierced by the pupil. The iris functions as does

the diaphragm of a camera to control the amount of light striking the lens.

Aqueous and vitreous humors. Between the cornea and lens is the anterior chamber, which contains aqueous humor, a proteinaceous substance. A similar substance, the vitreous humor, is found in the interior of the eye; it is more refractive than the aqueous humor. These fluids serve to keep the eyeball distended, and they change the refractive index of light passing through the eye. Changes in pressure in these fluids may cause disturbances in vision. Increased pressure may cause glaucoma and blindness.

Sclera. This is the outermost layer of the eyeball. It is dense and contains cartilage which is like the sclera of reptiles, but unlike that of mammals.

Pecten. The pecten projects into the vitreous humor in the ventral half of the eye from the head of the optic nerve, with which its base roughly coincides (Figure 41). It is a vascular, pigmented membranaceous structure arising from the retina. It is made up of laminae and is folded fanwise, or arranged like a folded accordion. The number of folds varies with the different species and ranges in the majority from 14 to 27 (Walls).

The function of the pecten is not understood; however, 30 or more functions have been ascribed to it (Walls, 1942; Prosser *et al.*, 1951). Some believe that it nourishes the eye, but the many variations in size and shape among the species suggest that this is not an important function (Walls). Menner (1938) claimed that the pecten casts a shadow on the retina which results in the production of discontinuous images on localized areas of the retina, thus aiding in the perception of moving objects. An object moving very fast may be seen as a blur, and when not moving, it may not be seen at all. Rapidly moving objects which appear blurred may sometimes be seen distinctly by blinking the eyes and thus producing discontinuous images.

Walls (1942) believed that the pecten has no ulterior function, and he discusses in detail his and other views on its function.

Retina. The retina is the innermost layer of the eyeball (Figures 41 and 42). The retina of the bird is essentially like that of all vertebrates. (For details on the histology of the bird retina, see Polyak,

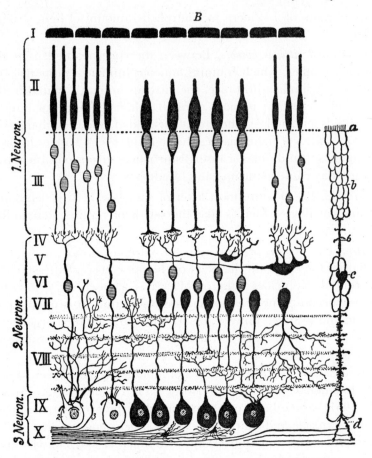

Figure 42. Schematic diagram of structure of the vertebrate retina.
I, pigment layer; II and III, rod and cone cells extending into outer
nuclear layer (III); IV, outer plexiform layer; V to VII, inner nuclear
layer; V, horizontal correlation neurons; VI, bipolar cells; VII, amacrine cells (solid black); VIII, inner plexiform layer; IX, ganglion cells;
X, axons of ganglion cells entering optic nerve. (After Greef, from *Ful-
ton's Textbook of Physiology*, 16th ed., W. B. Saunders Co., Philadelphia,
1950.)

1941; Walls, 1942; and Rochon-Duvigneaud, 1950). It consists of
the pigmented epithelium, rods and cones, outer nuclear area,
inner nuclear layer, Muller fibers, amacrine cells, and the ganglion
layer (Figure 42). The rods and cones are the photoreceptors which

pick up the stimulus and transmit it to the bipolar cells, and these connect with the ganglion cells. The latter, in turn, transmit the impulses by way of the optic nerve to the brain, which records and interprets the impulses and forms the visual image. The photo-receptors of all vertebrate eyes, including man, are essentially the same, but the final image produced depends upon the state of de-

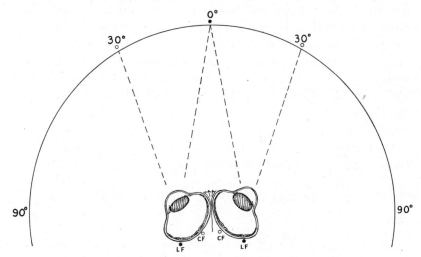

Figure 43. Foveal line of vision in falcon (*Falco tinnunculus*).

CF, central fovea and line of vision (30°); LF, lateral fovea and lines of vision (to 0°). The central foveas focus on two different objects simultaneously (monocular vision). The lateral foveas focus on one object (binocular vision). The four foveas can focus on three different objects at the same time. (Modified from A. Rochon-Duvigneaud, in *Traité de Zoologie*, edited by P. P. Grassé, Tome XV, Figure 184, Masson & Co., Paris, 1950.)

velopment of the brain centers and how these centers handle the stimulus.

The rod bipolar cells connect with the nuclei of three or four cones, and the cone bipolars with only one cone. Each ganglion cell gives off a slender axon which courses along the inner surface of the retina. These then converge at the back of the eye and pass out through the optic nerve. One ganglion cell may synapse with one or more than one bipolar cell (Walls). The amacrine cells are abundant in the bird retina and lie in the inner nuclear layer. Their fibers run horizontally and synapse with the ganglion cells.

In certain areas, the retina is thinner and contains cone cells with few or no rods; at these points visual acuity is greatest. In some species of birds, the area is very thin and depressed, forming a pit or fovea (Figure 43). Most mammals have one area or fovea. In some birds, there may be two or three differentiated areas in the retina (Polyak). Diurnal birds of prey and songbirds possess the deepest foveas. Eagles and hawks have two foveas in each eye, a nasal or central fovea and a lateral or temporal one. The eyes of the hawk and falcon are so directed that each of the two central foveas may be focused to one side on different objects (monocular vision) and the lateral or temporal fovea are focused straight ahead on one object (binocular vision). See Figure 43. The eyes of the chicken and turkey have only central foveas (Rochon-Duvigneaud, 1950).

Where the optic nerve enters the retina, there are no rods and cones, and this is called the blind spot.

FORMATION OF THE IMAGE

Refraction

As light enters the eye, it is refracted by the cornea, the aqueous humor, the lens, and the vitreous humor. The convex lens of the eye conveys the light rays to a point on the opposite side of the retina; there an image is formed, which is inverted. The lens of the eye acts as does the lens on a camera. The distance between the lens and the point of focus (the principal focus) is the focal length of the lens. This length is determined by the curvature and refractive index of the lens and is expressed by the diopter (D), which is the reciprocal of the focal length. Thus, a lens of 1 D has a focal length of 1 meter, and one of 2 D, a focal length of 0.5 meter.

Accommodation

The range or distance over which the lens can change the focus of the eye is known as the accommodation range. In birds, mammals, and most reptiles, accommodation is effected by changing the curvature of the lens through movements of the ciliary muscles.

When distant images are focused on the retina, the condition is known as emmetropia. When the image is focused in front of the retina, the condition is called myopia or nearsightedness; when focused behind the retina, hypermetropia or farsightedness. In humans, such errors of refraction are corrected by spectacles. The accommodation range is greater in young than in old people, and the decrease in the latter is due to hardening of the lens. Most birds are emmetropic or slightly hypermetropic, but the wingless kiwi is myopic (Walls, 1942; see also Rochon-Duvigneaud, 1950).

Certain nocturnal birds such as the owl have an accommodation range of 2 to 4 diopters, while the domestic chicken and pigeon have ranges of 8 to 12 diopters (Walls).

Visual Field

The angle or field through which the bird can see without moving its head is the visual field. This is affected by the position of the eyes in the head and shape of the eyes. Birds with flat eyes, for example the chicken and the pigeon, have wider visual fields than those with globose, or elongated, tubular eyes, such as the eagle and the owl (Figures 41 and 43). When the eyes are laterally situated (wide divergence of optic axis), as in the pigeon, the hen, and song-birds, the visual field for both eyes is approximately 300 degrees. Where the eyes are more frontally located, as in hawks, owls, and eagles, the visual field is less, averaging about 220 degrees in some owls (Prosser *et al.*, 1950) and 160 degrees for the screech owl, *Strix flammea* (Rochon-Duvigneaud, 1950).

Monocular and Binocular Vision

The focusing of one eye on one object is called monocular vision. Binocular vision results when both eyes are focused on one object. Most birds have binocular vision; the penguin is an exception.

The size of the binocular field of vision is also influenced by the shape of the head and position of the eyes in the head. In species with laterally placed eyes, the binocular field is less than that for birds with frontally located eyes. The homing pigeon, with flat, lateral eyes, has a binocular field of 24 degrees (Walls), while owls and hawks (frontal-tubular eyes) have binocular fields of 60 to 70 degrees. The parrot has the smallest field measured.

In most birds, the eyes fit tightly in the orbits, and there is little eye movement. Moving objects are followed by moving the head and neck.

Visual Acuity

The sensitivity of the eye refers to its ability to respond to weak stimuli, or its capacity for continuing to respond to light as the light is slowly dimmed. Visual acuity refers to the ability to continue to see, separately and unblurred, the details of the visual object as those details are made smaller and closer together. Visual acuity involves resolving power.

The acuity or resolving power of the retina depends upon the structure of the rods and cones, their spacing and concentration, and the number connected with each optic nerve fiber. The high resolving power of the bird eye is based upon its large size and the relatively large image cast on the retina, the dense concentration of cones, and the high ratio of optic nerve fibers to the visual cells (Walls).

The concentration of cones in the sparrow's fovea averages 400,000 or more per square millimeter. In the hawk, the fovea may contain one million cones per square millimeter. Even outside the fovea, the hawk retina has nearly twice the number of cones and resolving power as the human fovea. The resolving power of the hawk fovea is eight times that of man (Walls).

DUPLICITY THEORY

Schultze had long observed that the relative number of rods and cones in the retina of different species of birds and animals is related to their habits. Nocturnal and diurnal species showed a preponderance of rods and cones respectively in their retinas. Schultze in 1866 therefore suggested that the rods are receptors of dim light (scotopic vision) and the cones are receptors of bright light (photopic vision). (See Walls, 1942, for review.) Thus, the rods are believed to be responsible for the hazy, crude, achromatic images seen in dim light and the cones for sharp images seen in bright light.

The factors, however, which make rod vision indistinct but sensitive and cone vision sharp are not the same as those which make rod vision achromatic and cone vision chromatic. This is discussed later.

Scotopic and Photopic Vision

The eye is adaptable to wide variations in illumination. In changing suddenly from bright light to dim light or darkness, there is a short time when there is no vision; then the eye becomes adapted to the low illumination and there is vision, even though the image may be hazy and indistinct. This adaptation to darkness (scotopic vision) is effected mainly by an increase in the sensitivity of the retina and also by the dilation of the pupil which allows more light to enter. The increased retinal sensitivity is due to the synthesis of rhodopsin or visual purple in the outer segments of the rods. The greater the concentration of this pigment in the rods, the more light that is absorbed. Rhodopsin is destroyed by light and is synthesized in dim light or darkness. The rods of all birds contain rhodopsin, but in many diurnal species, only a few rods are present (Walls).

Rhodopsin is a chromoprotein consisting of a protein nucleus and several chromophoric groups. The colored portion, retenine, is related to carotene, and the synthesis of vitamin A is necessary for its formation.

The dark-adapted, rod-stimulated human eye responds maximally to green light, at a wave length of about 510 mμ. (millimicrons). The light-adapted eye responds maximally at 560 mμ., or to yellow-green light. The light-adapted eye therefore sees better in light of a longer wave length than does the dark-adapted eye. This shift or change in response is known as the Purkinje phenomenon. Spectrophotometric studies of rhodopsin reveal that its absorption curve corresponds very closely with the luminosity curve for the dark-adapted eye.

The bird eye also shows the Purkinje phenomenon. The eye of the pigeon, subjected to darkness for at least 45 minutes, becomes dark adapted and responds maximally to light at 534 mμ. and up to 664.5 mμ. The spectral range for the light-adapted eye is 424 to 704, with the maximum response at 564 (Laurens, see Walls).

Electroretinograms. When the retina is stimulated by light, electrical potentials are generated which can be recorded by placing one electrode on the outer surface and the other on the inner surface of the retina (see Granit, 1947). These potentials are different in the dark-adapted and light-adapted eyes. Granit has recorded the electro-retinograms of a number of species, including the bird.

Color Vision

When light of a known wave length strikes the retina, the cones are stimulated and color is perceived. The color perceived depends upon the wave length involved and mixtures of these. The colors of the visible spectrum are red, orange, yellow, green, blue, and violet. The wave length of red is greatest (about 750 mμ.), and that of violet the least (about 390 mμ.). White is a mixture of different wave lengths. Some objects reflect all light and are white, and others absorb all light and are black. Some objects may absorb certain wave lengths and reflect others, thus producing color.

It can be shown experimentally that three colors, red, green, and violet, when combined in varying proportions can produce 160 or more different colors or hues. Since the sensations of all hues can be evoked by appropriate mixtures of red, green, and violet, human vision is said to be trichromatic. Evidence for and against the trichromatic theory is not within the scope of this discussion. For details, see book by Walls (1942) or by Granit (1947).

In birds. Most of the discussion on color vision which follows is taken from Walls. It is experimentally difficult to determine the extent of color perception in animals and birds, because it is necessary to train them to distinguish colors and usually no more than two colors at a time. They then have to be retrained to distinguish another pair.

For years, it was believed that diurnal birds experienced color vision, but that birds are blind to violet and blue. The work of Hess in 1912 appeared to have established this fact. He sprinkled grains on a spectrum projected on a white floor and found that the birds ate the grains from the red end of the spectrum up to the junction of green and blue, but would not eat grains in the blue or violet lights. Later work by Honigmann (1921), Hahn, and others did not confirm the results of Hess. By staining rice grains different colors or by illuminating them with different colors, it was shown that the birds (chickens) did eat the blue and violet colored grains, but less avidly than those of other colors.

More careful studies by Watson and Lashley indicated the chick's spectral limits to be from wave lengths of 700 mμ. to 715 at one end of the spectrum and 395 to 405 mμ. at the other end. Thus, the spectral limits of the chick are similar to those of man, except that the chick is more sensitive to red. Lashley was able to train bantam cocks to distinguish red (650 mμ.), yellow (588 and 565 mμ.), green (520 mμ.), and blue-green (500 mμ.) lights and to discriminate each of these from other colored and white lights. The hen's color vision is therefore trichromatic and essentially like man's except that the presence of oil droplets in the bird retina, which have a filtering effect, may modify the situation somewhat.

There are three types of these droplets in the retinas of chickens and pigeons, namely red, yellow-green, and orange (Wald and Zussman, 1937). All of these are present in the eye of the hatched chick, but apparently in greater density in the adult chicken, because Honigmann (1921) demonstrated that the maximum sensitivity of the chick eye is at 560 mμ. and for the adult eye 580. This shift toward the red end of the spectrum was believed to be due to an increase with age in density of oil droplets. Thus, the abundance of red oil droplets in the retinas of pigeons, chickens, and songbirds causes these species to see blue and violet poorly and red better. Hawks, woodpeckers, and parrots, which have few or no red droplets, however, have practically the same spectral range as man and see blues and violets as well as man.

Hearing

STRUCTURE OF THE EAR

The ear of the bird is essentially like that of reptiles. It consists of an inner ear, a middle ear, and an external auditory meatus or canal, but no pinna like that of man. (See Figure 44.) The auditory canal leads to the eardrum or tympanic membrane, which is the boundary between the outer and middle ear. Attached to the inner surface of this membrane is the rod-shaped bone, the columella, which extends through the tympanic cavity and joins the stapes, a bone that fits into the membranous oval window or opening (fenestra) of the inner ear. The cavity of the middle ear is connected to the oral cavity by the Eustachian tube, whose function is to equilibrate the air pressure of the middle ear with that of the environment and to serve as a drainage canal.

The inner ear is a fluid-filled structure housed in a complex system of cavities and tunnels, known as the bony labyrinth. This labyrinth consists of an irregular central cavity, or vestibule, from which proceed three membranous semicircular canals (which aid

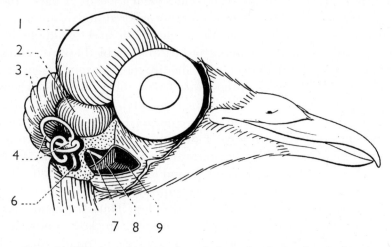

Figure 44. Diagram of lateral view of pigeon head, showing the location and parts of the ear.

1, cerebral hemisphere; 2, optic lobe; 3, cerebellum; 4, semicircular canals; 6 lagena; 7, middle ear and columella; 8, tympanic membrane; 9, external auditory meatus. (From Portmann, in *Traité de Zoologie*, edited by P. P. Grassé, Tome XV, Figure 153, Masson & Co., Paris, 1950, after Krause.)

in maintaining balance), the utriculus, the sacculus, and the lagena or part corresponding to the cochlea of mammals. The lagena is short and only slightly curved, instead of coiled as is the cochlea in mammals. (See Figures 44 and 45.) The cavity of the membranous labyrinth is filled with fluid (endolymph), and the space between the bony and membranous labyrinths is filled with perilymph.

The histology of the lagena of birds is similar to that of the cochlea of mammals, but there are differences. (See Portmann, 1950, for details.) The lagena is not as large as the cochlea in mammals, and the organ of Corti, which consists of sensory and supportive cells, is not as well developed.

The basement membrane of the organ of Corti contains a number of hair cells whose free ends have stiff cilia. The hair cells are the structures by which sound waves are converted into nerve impulses. The number of these cells in the bird ear is considerably less than in man, averaging about 1200 (Portmann) or 3000 (Prosser *et al.*, 1950). A figure of 24,000 for man is reported by Prosser *et al.*

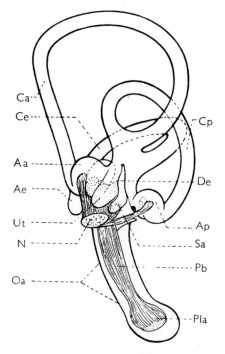

Figure 45. Diagram of inner ear of bird.

Aa and Ca, ampulla and anterior semicircular canal; Ae and Ce, ampulla and lateral semicircular canal; Ap and Cp, ampulla and posterior semicircular canal; De, endolymph duct; N, auditory nerve; Oa, papilla basilaris; Pb, basilar membrane; Pla, lagena; Sa, sacculus; Ut, utriculus. (From Portmann, in *Traité de Zoologie*, edited by P. P. Grassé, Tome XV, Figure 154, Masson & Co., Paris, 1950, after Satoh.)

MECHANISM OF HEARING

The external auditory canal picks up sounds and transmits these to the tympanic membrane, where vibrations are set in motion which are then transmitted by way of the columella and stapes to the inner ear through the fenestra. The hair cells of the basement membrane are next activated, and this stimulates the sensory cells. The nervous impulses thus evoked are transmitted to the central nervous system, which is able to detect differences in loudness, pitch, and quality of sound. The manner in which this is accomplished is not known, but a number of theories have been presented (see Wever, 1949).

Physical Characteristics of Sound

Sound waves are vibratory disturbances in physical media. Sounds vary in frequency, intensity or loudness, and wave form or quality. Frequency refers to the number of vibrations per second and largely determines pitch, but intensity also influences pitch.

Table 34. Range of sounds (frequencies) audible to the ear of birds

Species	Frequency range Cycles per second	Author
Starling	700–15,000	Brand & Kellogg (1939a)
English sparrows	675–11,500	"
Horned owl	60– 7,000	"
Horned lark	350– 7,600	Edwards (1943)
Snow bunting	400– 7,200	"
Canary	1,100–10,000	Brand & Kellogg (1939b)
Pigeon	200– 7,500	Brand & Kellogg (1939a)
"	65– 1,303	Wassiljew (1933; see Wever & Bray, 1936)
"	652– 1,740	Wada (Wever & Bray)
"	100–10,000*	Wever & Bray
Parrots & crossbills	40–14,000	Knecht (1939)

* Microphonic effect—based on electrical potentials recorded in lagena.

Quality refers to the presence or absence of overtones. Sounds may have the same frequency and intensity, but differ in quality.

Hearing in Birds

In order to determine what sounds are audible to birds and how they discriminate different pitches or frequencies, it is necessary to train or condition them. There are several ways of doing this. One method is to subject the bird to sound and at the same time electrically shock it. The bird responds to the shock by moving or jumping. After repeated trials, the bird responds to sound alone.

The range of sounds or different frequencies which are audible to various bird species is shown in Table 34. The upper limit of audibility for most birds is about 10,000 cycles per second, with cycles of 14,000 and 15,000 being the highest reported. The lower limits of the range vary from 40 to 400 cycles for most birds. The ear of birds cannot detect as wide a range of sounds as the ear of certain mammals, such as man, whose range is 16,000 to 20,000 cycles; the dog, 35,000 upper limit; the cat, 50,000 upper limit; and the bat, 98,000 upper limit (Prosser *et al.*, 1950).

The discrimination of frequencies within the range for birds appears to be about equal to man (Prosser *et al.*). Trained pigeons are able to discriminate between frequencies of 300 and 365, 387.5 and 500, 800 and 1000 cycles per second (See Wever and Bray, 1936). Turtledoves and parrots appear to be equally discriminatory (Jellinek, 1926a and 1926b; Knecht, 1939). Electrical potentials of the lagena indicate that the pigeon is less sensitive to loudness than the mammal (Wever and Bray, 1936).

Taste

TASTE BUDS

The end organs of the sense of taste are the taste buds. The histology of the taste buds of birds is very much like that of mammals. They are located mainly on the tongue of birds, but some may be found in the soft palate, according to some workers. The greatest concentration of buds is found in the dorsocaudal part of the tongue, approximating 70 percent of the total number in the pigeon. They may also be found on the lateral, ventral, or medial surfaces of the tongue. The maximum number found on the pigeon tongue is 59 and the minimum 27, with an average of 37 (Moore and Elliot, 1946). Among birds, the parrots have the largest numbers of taste buds. The number of taste buds is much lower than in mammals, where the number approaches 9000 in man and 35,000 in cattle (Moncrieff, 1946).

SENSE OF TASTE (GUSTATION)

Few controlled experiments have been conducted on the sense of taste in birds. It is generally believed that gustation in them is rudimentary and probably resembles a common chemical sense more than true taste (Moncrieff, 1946).

The presence of asafetida, anise, oil of lavender, or camphor has no effect upon the selection of food by turkeys, according to Hill (1905). The hen has a poorly developed gustatory sense and cannot distinguish between sodium chloride and hydrochloric acid, hydrochloric acid and acetic acid, or glycerol and magnesium, but she is capable of tasting, and this ability is influenced by the concentration of the substances. In each case, the bird prefers the more dilute solution, regardless of the substance. The hen is able to distinguish between magnesium chloride and acid, magnesium chloride and sodium chloride, and magnesium chloride and saccharin (Engelmann, 1937). Bitter or sweet substances, however, do not affect the selection of food among herring gulls (Prosser *et al.*, 1950).

Since odor also affects taste, some of the experiments just described may be a measure of olfaction as well as taste.

Smell

OLFACTORY ORGANS

The olfactory organs of the bird consist of the paired external nares which open at each side at the base of the beak, the internal nares which open into the mouth, the turbinate bones, and the olfactory epithelium. There are two turbinate bones, or conchae, in some birds, three in most birds. These are the anterior, median, and superior conchae. There is a division of the nasal passage into a respiratory and olfactory chamber, but only the superior conch of many birds has olfactory epithelium. However, some birds have well-developed olfactory organs, such as the kiwi.

SENSE OF SMELL

The sense of smell is believed to be poorly developed in most birds, but relatively few controlled experiments have been conducted to determine the extent of development of this sense. It has been suggested that vultures find carrion by sense of smell, but Audubon (1835) and Darwin (1834) reportedly disproved this.

Beebe (1909), claimed, however, that the turkey vulture can definitely smell tainted meat.

Walter (1943) concluded that olfaction in pigeons, ducks, and some other species is very poorly developed, and Strong (1911) reported that pigeons can smell oil of bergamot, but not certain other substances which he tested. Similar results were reported by Zahn (1933). Turkeys cannot discriminate odors of asafetida, camphor, chloroform, and oil of lavender, according to Hill (1905).

The kiwi, however, is believed to possess a keen sense of smell because it has a very-well-developed olfactory organ. Its vision is so poor, however, that it must rely on olfaction to survive (Portmann, 1950).

REFERENCES

Atwood, W. H.   1947   A Concise Comparative Anatomy. C. V. Mosby Co., St. Louis.

Audubon, J. J.   1835   Ornithological Bibliography. 2:33.

Beebe, C. W.   1909   New World Vultures. Part II. Zool. Soc. Bull., New York, No. 32, p. 465.

Bradley, O. C., and T. Grahame   1950   The Structure of the Fowl. J. B. Lippincott Co., Philadelphia.

Brand, A. R., and P. P. Kellogg   1939a   Auditory Responses of Starlings English Sparrows, and Domestic Pigeons. Wilson Bulletin, Vol. LI, No. 1.

Brand, A. R., and P. P. Kellogg   1939b   The range of hearing of canaries. Science 90:354.

Darwin, C.   1834   Naturalist's Voyage around the World. D. Appleton and Co., New York.

Edwards, E. P.   1943   Hearing ranges of four species of birds. Auk 60: 239.

Engelmann, C.   1937   Weitere Versuche über den Geschmackssinn des Huhns. Z. vergl. Physiol. 24:451.

Granit, R.   1947   Sensory Mechanisms of the Retina. Oxford University Press, New York.

Hill, A.   1905   Can birds smell? Nature 71:318.

Honigmann, H.   1921   Untersuchungen über Lichtemfindlichkeit und Adaptierung des Vogelauges. Arch. ges. Physiol. (Pflügers) 189:1–72.

Jellinek, A.   1926a   Versuche über das Gehör der Vögel. I: Dressurversuche an Tauben mit akustischen Reizen. Arch. ges. Physiol (Pflügers, 211:64. Cited by Wever and Bray, 1936.

Jellinek, A.   1926b   Versuche über das Gehör der Vögel. II: Gehörprü-fungen an Tauben nach Exstirpation des Mittelohres. Arch. ges. Physiol (Pflügers) 211:73. Cited by Wever and Bray, 1936.

Knecht, S.   1939   Über den Gehörsinn und die Musikalität der Vögel. Z. vergl. Physiol. 27:169.

Menner, E.   1938   Die Bedeutung des Pecten im Auge des Vogels für die Wahrnehmung von Bewegungen: nebst Bemerkungen über seine Ontogenie und Histologie. Zool. Jarhb. Abt. f. allg. Zool. u. Physiol. d. Tiere. 58:481–538. Cited by Walls, 1942.

Moncrieff, R. W.   1946   The Chemical Senses. John Wiley & Sons, Inc., New York.

Moore, C. A., and R. Elliot   1946   Numerical and regional distribution of taste buds on the tongue of the bird. J. Comp. Neurol. 84:119.

Polyak, S. S.   1941   The Retina. University of Chicago Press, Chicago.

Portmann, A.   1950   Traité de Zoologie, edited by P. P. Grassé. Tome XV: Oiseaux, p. 205. Masson & Co., Paris.

Prosser, C. L., D. W. Bishop, F. A. Brown, T. L. Jahn, and V. L. Wulff   1950   Comparative Animal Physiology. W. B. Saunders Co., Phila-delphia.

Rochon-Duvigneaud, A.   1950   Traité de Zoologie, edited by P. P. Grassé. Tome XV: Oiseaux, p. 221. Masson & Co., Paris.

Strong, R. M.   1911   On the olfactory organs and sense of smell in birds. J. Morph. 22:619.

Wald, G., and H. Zussman   1937   Carotenoids of the chicken retina. J. Biol. Chem. 122:445.

Walls, G. L.   1942   The Vertebrate Eye. Cranbrook Institute of Science, Bloomfield Hills, Mich.

Walter, W. G.   1943   Some experiments on the sense of smell in birds, studied by the method of conditioned reflexes. Arch. Néerland, Phy-siol. Homme et Anim. 27.

Wassiljew, M. P.   1933   Über das Unterscheidungsvermögen der Vögel für die hohen Töne. Z. vergl. Physiol. 19:424. Cited by Wever & Bray, 1936.

Wever, E. G.   1949   Theory of Hearing. John Wiley and Sons, New York.

Wever, E. G., and C. W. Bray   1936   Hearing in the pigeon as studied by the electrical responses of the inner ear. J. Comp. Psychol. 22:353.

Zahn, W.   1933   Über den Geruchsinn einiger Vögel. Z. vergl. Physiol. 19:785.

CHAPTER 15

Reproduction in the Female and Egg Formation

ANATOMY AND HISTOLOGY OF THE FEMALE REPRODUCTIVE SYSTEM

Ovary

THE ovary, or female gonad, is situated on the left side of the body at the cephalic end of the kidneys and is attached to the body wall by the mesovarian ligament. The ovary consists of an outer cortex, made up of follicles containing ova, and an inner medulla. Before maturity the ovary of the chicken consists of a mass of small ova. Pearl and Schoppe (1921) counted 1906 ova (the average of 24 birds) which were visible to the naked eye and about 12,000 in one bird which were microscopic in size. Others have estimated that the number of oöcytes in the chicks may run into the millions (see Hutt, 1949). Only a few of these, however, reach maturity and are ovulated. At sexual maturity the individual follicles enlarge and attain a diameter of approximately 40 mm. before ovulation (Figure 46).

During embryonic development a right gonad and oviduct are formed, but these usually degenerate, and only rudiments persist when the chick is hatched. In some cases, the right ovary and oviduct may persist. Crew (1931) reported a persistent right ovary, and Quinn, Burrows, and McNally (1939) and Bryant (1944) described a right ovary and oviduct in the chicken, but they were not functional. Webster (1948) also observed in the chicken a large

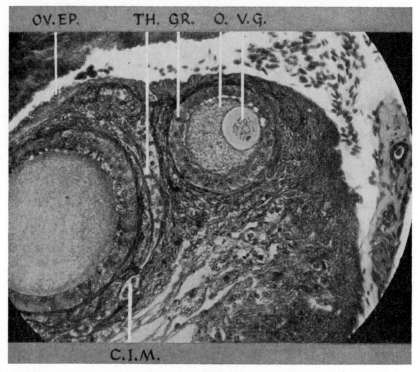

Figure 46. Cross section of ovary of chicken at two months of age.
OV.EP., ovarian epithelium; TH., theca; GR., granulosa; O., oöcyte; V.G., germinal vesicle; C.I.M., interstitial cells of medulla. (From Benoit, in *Traité de Zoologie*, edited by P. P. Grassé, Tome XV, Figure 279, Masson & Co., Paris, 1950.)

apparently functional right oviduct with a small right ovary. A functional right ovary and right oviduct were reported in the duck by Chappelier (1913); the bird laid two eggs per day.

Most of the ovarian follicle is highly vascular except for the stigma; this to the naked eye appears avascular, but microscopic examination shows that small arteries and veins extend across it, according to Nalbandov and James (1949; see Figure 47). The ovary receives its blood supply from the short ovarian artery which arises usually from the left renolumbar artery, but which may branch directly from the dorsal aorta (Figure 48; see Nalbandov and James for details). The ovarian artery divides into many branches, and usually two to four separate arterial branches lead

Figure 47. Mature ovarian follicle of the hen. A, arteries; V, veins; S, stigma. (From Nalbandov and James, *Am. J. Anat.*, 1949.)

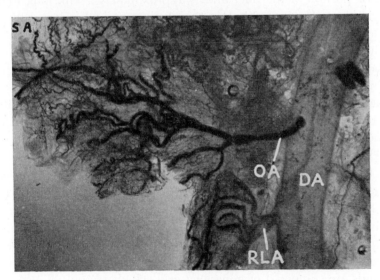

Figure 48. Arterial supply to ovary of hen.
DA, dorsal aorta; OA, ovarian artery; RLA, renolumbar artery; SA, spiral artery. (From Nalbandov and James, *Am. J. Anat.*, 1949.)

to a single follicular stalk. A few arteries immediately surround the ovum and, after branching, pass through the theca, become arterioles, and form a capillary network peripheral to the basement membrane.

The venous system of the follicle is more prominent than the arterial system and forms three layers or beds: the innermost, located in the theca; a middle layer; and the outer or peripheral layer consisting of a few large veins which encircle the follicle and leave via the stalk. Eventually all the veins from the ovary unite into the two main, anterior and posterior veins, which empty into the posterior vena cava.

Structure of Oviduct and Movement of Egg

The oviduct is the long, convoluted duct or tube through which the ovum is moved and in which the albumen, shell membranes, and shell are formed. The oviduct consists of five distinct areas or parts (Figure 49).

Infundibulum. The infundibulum is the funnel-shaped, most anterior portion of the duct and is approximately 9 cm. long in the laying hen. The infundibulum engulfs the ovum when it is ovulated into the body cavity. The activity of the funnel is conditioned or initiated by the ovum; it is normally quiescent until the ovum is liberated. If a foreign body is placed in the abdominal cavity at the time of ovulation and the ovum is removed, the infundibulum will engulf the foreign body. If this is done sometime before or after ovulation, the funnel remains inactive. The ovum remains in the funnel, on the average, about 18 minutes (Warren and Scott, 1935).

Magnum. The ovum passes to the magnum, which is the largest single portion of the oviduct (hence its name) and measures 33 cm. in length. Here, most of the protein of the egg (albumen) is formed. Histological studies by a number of workers reveal that the magnum is highly glandular and contains two types of glands, tubular and unicellular (see Romanoff and Romanoff, 1949). The tubular glands are composed of nongoblet cells which are not ciliated, but the unicellular glands are goblet in nature. Most observers believe that the goblet cells secrete mucin which is responsible for the thick white albumen and that the tubular glands secrete the material that forms the thin albumen. The ovum remains in the magnum an average of 2 hours and 54 minutes (Warren and Scott, 1935). Details on the formation of the various layers of albumen will be discussed later.

Isthmus. The peristaltic movements of the magnum force the ovum into the isthmus. In the laying female this region is approximately 10 cm. in length, and the line of demarcation between it and the magnum is distinct; the folds of the glands in the isthmus are not as large and numerous as in the magnum (Figure 49). The inner and outer shell membranes are formed in the isthmus, and some workers, notably Pearl and Curtis (1912) and McNally (1934), believe that some albumen is added to the egg here, but the data of other workers suggest that no albumen and insignificant amounts of water are added (details will be given later). The ovum remains in the isthmus 1 hour and 14 minutes and then moves into the uterus. Thus, the time elapsing from the engulfing of the ovum by the funnel until it

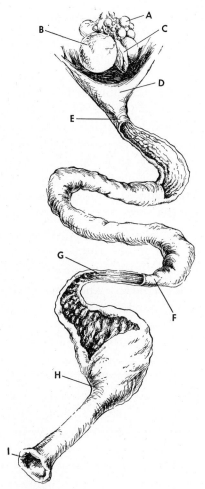

Figure 49. Reproductive tract of the laying hen.

A, immature ovum of ovary; B, mature ovum; C, ruptured ovarian follicle; D, infundibulum or funnel or oviduct; E, beginning of albumen-secreting region or magnum; F, end of magnum and beginning of isthmus; G, end of isthmus and beginning of uterus; H, end of uterus and beginning of vagina; I, opening of oviduct into cloaca.

reaches the uterus is, on the average, 4 hours and 26 minutes.

Uterus. The uterus is the pouchlike portion of the oviduct and is approximately 10 to 12 cm. long in the laying hen. Its walls are thick and muscular. It contains tubular and unicellular glands, but the function of these glands is unknown. It is presumed that they form the watery uterine fluid which is added to the albumen through the shell membranes. The manner in which these glands are concerned in shell formation is unknown. The ovum remains in the uterus 18 to 20 hours (Warren and Scott, 1935); there it receives the shell, and water and salts are added to the albumen. The pigment of the shell is also formed in the uterus in the last 5 hours before laying (Warren and Conrad, 1942).

Vagina. The vagina, which is about 12 cm. in length, is the part of the oviduct leading from the uterus to the cloaca, but it takes no part in the formation of the egg.

Blood supply. The oviduct receives its blood supply from three main sources, according to Mauger (1941). The infundibulum is supplied by a branch of the left renal artery, the magnum and isthmus by a branch of the left sciatic artery, and the uterus and cloaca by a branch of the left internal iliac artery.

Little is known concerning the innervation of the ovary and oviduct. Mauger described a number of autonomic ganglia whose fibers could be traced to various parts of the tract. He made no distinction, however, between sympathetic and parasympathetic ganglia.

The pH of the areas of the oviduct are, according to Buckner and Martin (1929), as follows: infundibulum, 6.4; magnum, 6.4; isthmus and uterus, 5.8 and vagina, 5.9.

OVIPOSITION AND LAYING AND BROODING
HABITS OF BIRDS

Birds vary widely in their laying and brooding habits. They vary in (1) the number of eggs laid in a given time, (2) the sequence in which the eggs are laid, (3) the interval between breaks or interruptions in the sequence, and (4) whether or not they incubate their eggs.

Wild birds usually lay one or more eggs in sequence and then stop laying and sit on them (clutches). The number of clutches and the number of eggs in the clutch vary with the species and seasons. Some birds, such as the auk and the penguin, lay only one egg before sitting; the pigeon usually lays two and the partridge as many as 12 to 20 eggs before sitting (Romanoff and Romanoff, 1949). Removal of eggs from the nests of many wild birds prolongs laying time and delays the onset of broodiness. Egg production may be doubled in the pigeon by this means.

The interval between successively laid eggs of the pigeon is 40 to 44 hours, but the number of clutches and the interval between clutches varies with season (Levi, 1941). Records from the New Jersey Pigeon Test (Platt, 1946) show that the number of clutches laid by pigeons averages eight per year, and the interval between clutches is approximately 45 days in the fall and winter and 30 to 32 days in the spring and early summer. The interval may be shortened by removing eggs from the nest or by increasing the amount of light (artificially) in the winter.

Laying Cycle and Rate of Laying

Many of the domesticated species, notably the chicken and duck, lay a number of eggs on successive days (a sequence), and then the sequence is interrupted for one or more days before laying is resumed; such birds usually do not incubate their eggs. The terms cycle and clutch have been used to designate such behavior, but the Romanoffs (1949) state that only wild birds which incubate their eggs lay in clutches and that nonsitters lay in cycles. Neither of these terms, however, adequately describes the rate and rhythm of laying of domesticated birds. A cycle means a regularly recurring succession of events, and when applied to laying, it involves sequence and the time intervals of interruption in the sequence. Strictly speaking, a hen laying a three-egg cycle would have to lay three eggs on successive days before skipping a day or more and then repeat the performance. According to the terminology of Romanoff and Romanoff, this is a regular cycle. For most chickens, however, the laying sequence and interruption in the sequence are not constant and regular, and such behavior constitutes an irregular cycle, according to these authors.

Illustration of some of the variations in rhythm or pattern of laying exhibited by chickens follows:

xx-xx-xx-   Two-egg cycle
xxx-xxx-xxx-   Three-egg cycle
xxx-xxx-xxx---Regular sequence; irregular skip
xx-xxx-x-   Irregular sequence; regular skip
xx-xxx-x----   Irregular sequence; irregular skip
xxxxxxxxxx   Long sequence

The rate of lay, or laying frequency, represents the number of eggs laid in a given period of time, without regard to the pattern or rhythm of laying. Thus, a hen laying 15 eggs in 30 days lays at a rate of 50 percent.

In better-bred flocks of chickens, 5 to 10 percent of the birds may lay 300 or more eggs in a year. Selected hens of the better laying breeds entered in the American Egg Laying Contests lay, on the average, about 240 eggs per bird per year. The number of successively laid eggs for most good laying hens ranges from four to six, but some birds may lay for many days without interruption in the sequence.

The interval between eggs laid on successive days ranges from 24 to 28 hours for most hens, depending on the length of the sequence (Warren and Scott, 1935; Scott and Warren, 1936; Heywang, 1938). This is illustrated in Figure 50, which shows the delay or lag in hours between successively laid eggs in a cycle. Thus, the lag or the interval between eggs is greater in short than in long sequences, and the interval between the first two eggs and between the last two eggs of the sequence is greater than that between intervening eggs, regardless of cycle length. This difference in interval between eggs and the rhythm of lay of birds represents mainly differences in time of ovulation, because the lag between ovulations parallels fairly closely the lag between laid eggs, except for the interval between the first two and the last two ovulations in the sequence, which is usually less than that between the same laid eggs of the cycle, according to Fraps (in press). This difference might suggest that the terminal egg and possibly the second egg of the cycle, in some cases, are held in the oviduct slightly longer before laying than are other eggs of the sequence.

The actual time of day when eggs are laid depends on the length of the sequence and position of the egg in the sequence and also on the length of the day (hours of daylight). Although hens may lay eggs during any of the daylight hours, most of them lay in the forenoon, and they tend to lay earlier when the days are longer.

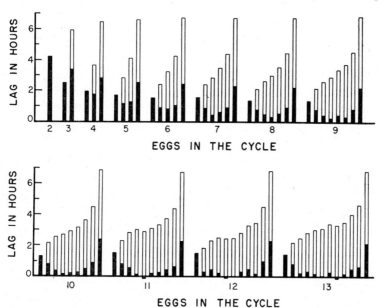

Figure 50. The delay or lag in hours between the laying of successive eggs in a cycle.

A 2-egg cycle is represented by 1 bar; a 3-egg cycle by 2 bars, etc. A lag of 0 hours means an interval of 24 hours between eggs. A lag of 4.2 hours occurs between the laying of the first and second egg of a 2-egg cycle (black bar). For the 3-egg cycle, the lag between the first and second egg is about 2.5 hours, and between the second and third, about 3.4 hours (second black bar). The cumulative lag (white bar) is about 5.9 hours. In a sequence, the lag between the last egg and the preceding one is always greatest. (Courtesy of Dr. R. M. Fraps, based on data of Heywang, *Poultry Sci.*, 1938.)

Birds laying three to four eggs in the sequence lay nearly all of them before noon, and most of them between the hours of 8 and 9:30 A.M. For birds laying one and two eggs in sequence, most of the eggs are laid between the hours of 11 A.M. and 1:30 P.M. and between 9 and 10:30 A.M. respectively (Heywang, 1938).

The differences observed in the laying and brooding habits among different species of birds suggest temporal differences in the release of pituitary hormones concerned in the growth and maturation of the follicles, in ovulation and broodiness. These are discussed later in this chapter and in Chapter 17.

Control of Oviposition

The egg remains in the uterus of the hen 18 to 20 hours, after which time the uterus contracts and forces the egg out through the vagina and cloaca. Little is known concerning the factors which normally initiate uterine contraction and oviposition, but there is evidence which shows that the time of laying is influenced by the ruptured follicle from which the egg is ovulated (Rothchild and Fraps, 1944a and 1944b).

The most recently ruptured follicle influences laying time most, but older ruptured follicles and even unovulated ones also influence this time. Surgical removal of the recently ruptured and all unovulated follicles retards oviposition for 9 to 36 hours. This might suggest that the ruptured follicle elaborates a hormone which normally initiates the process of laying, but attempts to isolate such a hormone from the follicles have thus far been unsuccessful (Fraps, unpublished).

That light is not the main factor involved in the time of laying was demonstrated by McNally (1947) and by Fraps, Neher, and Rothchild (1947). Hens placed on a day of 14 hours of light and then on continuous lighting continue to lay out their cycles normally. When the birds on continuous lighting were fed from 8 A.M. through 4 P.M., most of the eggs were laid from 6 A.M. to 6 P.M. When, however, the hens were then fed from 8 P.M. to 4 A.M. under continuous lighting, time of laying for most birds was during the hours of feeding. Body temperature also was highest during the feeding periods. These workers concluded that photoperiodicity is not a necessary factor in the regulation of time of lay and ovulation.

Posterior pituitary preparations containing the pressor and the oxytocic fractions, particularly the latter, cause premature laying in the pigeon and chicken (Riddle, 1921; Burrows and Byerly, 1942; Burrows and Fraps, 1942). Obstetrical pituitrin (containing mainly oxytocin) injected at the rate of 0.1 to 0.2 cc. intravenously is effective in most birds within three to four minutes. That pituitrin causes contraction of the uterus was demonstrated in uterine strips *in vitro* by McKenney, Essex, and Mann (1932) and by Morash and Gibbs (1929) in the opened bird. The latter workers also demonstrated that histamine, acetylcholine, and ergotoxine produce contraction and that epinephrine produces relaxation of the uterus. Atropine abolishes the effects of acetylcholine. Acetylcholine and histamine cause premature oviposition, and ephedrine retards laying from 4 to 24 hours in the intact hen, and these results suggest that the uterus of the hen is innervated by sympathetic inhibitory and parasympathetic stimulatory fibers (Weiss and Sturkie, 1952). Progesterone, desoxycorticosterone acetate, and certain estrogens and androgens may retard oviposition in the pigeon and dove, particularly if administered in large amounts (Dunham and Riddle, 1942).

Orientation of Egg in Oviduct

The orientation of the egg in the oviduct and its movement and rotation have been subjects of controversy. Early workers, including Purkinje in 1825 and Von Baer in 1828 and others since (see Bradfield, 1951, for review), observed that the egg in the uterus of the opened hen lay with its pointed end caudad. However, a number of investigators observed that the blunt end of the egg emerged first (caudad) when the egg was laid (Aristotle, Nathusius, Wickmann, Bartlemez; see Bradfield). Olsen and Byerly (1932), however, in an extensive study, observed that the pointed end appeared first in 66 to 82 percent of the eggs laid. Their method of study was to wait until the bird rose to its feet, apparently to lay, and then either to remove the bird from the nest and let it lay in the observer's hand or else to place one hand under the cloaca and grasp the egg as it emerged. Bradfield, by fluoroscopic examinations of the egg in the uterus of the bird, without disturbance, showed that, of the 18 to 20 hours which the egg remains in the uterus, most of this time it remained in the same position, with the pointed end directed caudally, but that, just prior to laying, the egg is rotated through 180° and is laid with the blunt end caudad.

FORMATION AND GROWTH OF OVA

As the female approaches sexual maturity, the immature ova begin growing at a rapid rate and reach maturity within 9 to 10 days (see Figure 51). The weight of the yolk during the 7 days

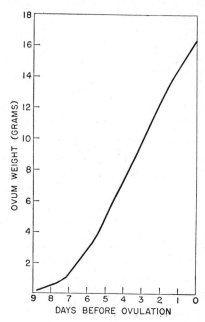

preceding maturity and ovulation increases approximately 16-fold and in a regular and straight-line fashion. During the growth period, the yolk material is laid down in concentric rings (Figure 52). The rate of growth and the amount of yolk deposited in a given time can be determined by feeding or injecting Sudan III, a fat dye which leaves marks on the yolk.

The growth and maturation of the ovarian follicles are caused by the action of the follicle-stimulating hormone, released from the pituitary (see Chapter 17). The growing follicles and the medulla of the ovary then elaborate the gonadal hormones, estrogen and androgen, which produce pronounced changes in the oviduct, comb, and blood chemistry of the

Figure 51. Changes in weight of the ovum of the chicken during the nine days preceding ovulation. (From Warren and Conrad, *J. Agric. Res.*, 1939.)

laying bird (see Chapter 18).

The mature ovum may consist of alternate layers or rings of yellow and white yolk, and the yellow layer is wider than the white. Riddle (1911) believed that these bands were formed as a result of diurnal variation in metabolic rate, but Conrad and Warren (1939) showed that the alternate white and yellow bands are not formed when the birds are fed a uniform diet *ad libitum,* but are produced when the birds are supplied at irregular intervals with feeds differing in xanthophyl content.

Factors Affecting Size of Ova

The rate of growth of the ovum is not related to rate of laying or ovulation (Warren and Conrad, 1939). The yolk size of the first egg of a sequence is larger than succeeding ones, but this is not due to differences in rate of ovum growth, but apparently to a difference in the period of growth (Warren and Conrad) or to differences in the time and amounts of the ovulating and follicular-stimulating hormones released from the pituitary.

The administration of certain drugs, hormones, and chemicals is known to reduce yolk size. Among these are quinine sulfate (Riddle and Anderson, 1918), alcohol (Riddle and Basset, 1916), the vermifuge, kamala (Maw, 1934), and thyroxine (Asmundson and Pinsky, 1935). High environmental temperature also decreases yolk size.

OVULATION

Mechanics

Ovulation is the release of the ovum from the ovarian follicle and normally occurs within 15 to 75 minutes after laying in the chicken and 4 to 5 hours after laying of the first egg by the pigeon. Successive ovulations in a cycle are of about the same

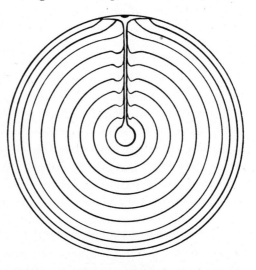

Figure 52. Diagram illustrating the growth and development of egg yolk.

The concentric rings represent daily growth of yolk, and their positions were determined by injecting into the hens a dye, Sudan III, which stains fat. (From Warren and Conrad, *J. Agric. Res.,* 1939.)

magnitude as that between laid eggs, with certain exceptions discussed previously. The mechanics of ovulation in the chicken has been studied in detail by Warren and Scott (1934), and reviewed by Phillips and Warren (1937), and Warren (1949). Rupture of the follicle takes place at the stigma, which is relatively avascular. The immediate causes and factors concerned in the rupture have been discussed by Phillips and Warren. They concluded that ovulation appears to be independent of stimuli from the ovary or other organs of the hen. Clamping the follicular stalk just prior to ovulation or complete excision of the follicle from the ovary does not prevent ovulation. They suggested that tension of the fibers of the follicular membrane may cause ovulation. Olsen and Neher (1948) demonstrated that excised ova can be made to ovulate *in vitro* by placing them in Ringer's solution at a temperature of 107° F. The ova ovulated within one hour.

Fraps and co-workers, in a series of reports, demonstrated that ovulation is induced by the cyclic release of the luteinizing hormone (LH) from the pituitary (see also Chapter 17). Ovulation can be induced prematurely by as much as 17 to 30 hours in some instances by injecting extracts containing LH (Fraps, Olsen, and Neher, 1942; Fraps, Riley, and Olsen, 1942 and later). Further evidence on the behavior of the ovulating hormone was supplied by hypophysectomizing laying hens 3 to 8 hours prior to their normal time of ovulation (Rothchild, 1946; Rothchild and Fraps, 1949). Among those hens operated on 8 or more hours prior to ovulation, all failed to ovulate, but 73 percent of those hypophysectomized 3 to 4 hours before ovulation time ovulated. These data indicate that the ovulating hormone is released by the pituitary 6 to 8 hours prior to time of ovulation, and this is borne out by the fact that injections of LH or of progesterone also induce ovulation within the same period. Very small amounts of progesterone applied directly to the pituitary or to the muscle of the leg are also effective in inducing ovulation (Rothchild, 1949). Progesterone, however, is ineffective in the hypophysectomized chicken, indicating that it normally stimulates the pituitary to release LH (Rothchild and Fraps, 1949). Progesterone may inhibit or retard ovulation in the pigeon and dove, according to Dunham and Riddle (1942). The first ovarian follicle of a sequence is more sensitive to given quantities of ovulating hormone than succeeding ones (Fraps, 1946).

Neher and Fraps (1950) were able to increase, by injecting progesterone or LH, the number of eggs laid in a 12-day period by an average of 2.7 eggs per bird, but the yolk size of the laid eggs was smaller than normal, suggesting that the ova were being ovulated before they were mature (see also Chapter 17).

Time of laying apparently does not influence ovulation time. Premature laying (Warren and Scott, 1935; Sturkie and Williams,

1945) or retarded laying (Weiss and Sturkie, 1952), induced experimentally, has no effect upon time of subsequent ovulations.

Interruption of Ovulation

Ovulation can be inhibited in a number of ways. Subcutaneous injections of such substances as ovalbumin, casein, peptone, desiccated brain, muscle, and other tissues delay ovulation in the fowl from 6 to 10 hours when small dosages are administered, but large doses produce prompt and extensive follicular atresia (Fraps and Neher, 1945). A number of steroids, including progesterone, estradiol benzoate, desoxycorticosterone acetate, and androsterone, delay or inhibit ovulation in the pigeon and dove (Dunham and Riddle, 1942).

Abdominal operations usually cause a temporary cessation of ovulation in the fowl. Rothchild and Fraps (1945) found that the incidence of follicular atresia and time before resumption of ovulation following operations were inversely proportional to the rate of ovulation preceding the operation. Huston and Nalbandov (1953) reported that injury to, or a foreign body in, the oviduct, above the uterus, inhibits ovulation. When such objects as glass beads, pieces of thread, and the like were suspended in the oviduct, ovulation was inhibited, but not the growth or ripening of the follicles. These authors postulated that injury to the oviduct in some way inhibits or alters the release of certain pituitary hormones. It would appear that the release of the luteinizing, but not follicle-stimulating, hormone is inhibited.

Effects of Light on Ovulation

The stimulating effect of light on ovulation and laying is well known and has been reviewed by Romanoff and Romanoff (1949), Benoit (1950), and Bissonnette (1936). It is known that lights cause birds to start laying earlier than usual and cause them to lay more intensely during the fall and early winter months. However, lights do not usually increase average annual egg production.

For many years light was thought to stimulate egg production directly by the increase in hours of daylight and in feeding periods, but ample experimental work has shown that the principal effect of light is its stimulating effect upon the pituitary, which in turn stimulates the ovary (see also Chapter 17). Rowan and others believed that light merely permits birds to remain awake and causes them to exercise and eat more feed and that this is the primary sexually activating stimulus. That time of feeding does have an effect upon time of laying, but does not increase egg production, was discussed previously. Most workers are now agreed that 12 to 14 hours of light are required to produce maximum stimulation of the pituitary and egg production (see Byerly and Moore, 1941; Carver, 1941; and others).

Little work on the different wave lengths of light as they affect ovulation has been reported. Platt (unpublished) reported that red light of a given intensity is more effective in stimulating egg production than white light of the same intensity. Ultraviolet light, in addition to adequate light within the visible spectral range, increases egg production from 10 to 19 percent, even when adequate amounts of vitamin D are already supplied (Barott, Schoenleber, and Campbell, 1951). The authors give no explanation for their results, but it is presumed that the effect is mediated by way of the pituitary.

FORMATION OF ALBUMEN, SHELL MEMBRANES, AND SHELL

The components of the egg are shell, shell membranes, albumen, and yolk. The proportionate part of the total of each of these com-

Table 35. Composition of the hen's egg (Romanoff and Romanoff, 1949)

| | Yolk | Albumen layers | | | | Shell |
		Outer	Middle	Inner	Chalaziferous	
Weight (grams)	18.7	7.6	18.9	5.5	0.9	6.2
Water (percent)	48.7	88.8	87.6	86.4	84.3	1.6
Solids (percent)	51.3	11.2	12.4	13.6	15.7	98.4
			All layers			
Proteins (percent)	16.6		10.6			3.3
Carbohydrates	1.0		0.9			—
Fats	32.6		trace			0.03
Minerals	1.1		0.6			95.10

ponents is shown in Table 35. A number of investigators have studied the formation of the egg components. The subject is reviewed by Warren (1949) and Romanoff and Romanoff (1949).

FORMATION OF ALBUMEN

There are four distinct layers of albumen in the laid egg. These are: (1) the chalaziferous layer attached to the yolk; (2) the inner liquid layer; (3) the middle dense or thick layer; and (4) the outer thin or fluid layer. Approximately one-fourth of the total albumen is found in the outer layer, and one-half in the dense, thick layer. The inner layer comprises 16.8 percent, and the chalaziferous layer 2.7 percent of the total.

An egg taken from the hen just before it enters the isthmus contains only one layer of albumen, thick and jellylike in consistency. At this time, the egg contains approximately one-half the amount of albumen of the laid egg and about twice the amount of protein per given volume (Pearl and Curtis, 1912; McNally, 1934; Scott, Hughes, and Warren, 1937). Thus, the presence of the different strata of albumen and the relative decrease in the proteins and solids of the laid egg suggest that after the egg leaves the magnum mainly water is added to the albumen and that this change, plus other physical changes resulting from rotation and movement of the egg down the oviduct, are responsible for the stratification of the albumen. Evidence for this will be presented later.

Pearl and Curtis (1912) and McNally (1934) concluded from studies of laid eggs and of eggs taken from the isthmus that about 10 percent of the total nitrogen of the albumen is added while the egg is in the isthmus. If this were true, it would mean that the proteins are added before the shell membranes are formed, because it appears physically impossible for the protein molecules to pass through the semipermeable shell membranes. Scott (1938), however, showed no increments of protein (nitrogen) to the egg in the isthmus. Burmester (1940), who studied the volume of albumen of the egg as it entered and left the isthmus, showed that water is added, but in insignificant amounts. Asmundson (1939) also revealed that water is added to turkey eggs in the isthmus. Pearl and Curtis as well as McNally based their conclusions upon nitrogen determinations of the laid egg, which was the first egg of the cycle, and the uterine egg, which was the second egg of the cycle. Scott,

Hughes, and Warren (1937) demonstrated that the second laid egg of the cycle contains about 10 percent less nitrogen than the first egg, due to the fact that the second egg is usually smaller than the first egg, and this could account for the discrepancy in results.

Scott, Hughes, and Warren also compared the nitrogen content of the laid egg (first egg of the cycle) with the uterine egg (second egg) and found that the latter contained 96.2 percent of the nitrogen of the laid egg. The actual amounts of albumen and nitrogen in the uterine and the laid egg are as follows:

	Albumen in gm. (wet)	Nitrogen in gm.
Uterine egg	16.60	0.509
Laid egg	32.84	0.529

Beadle, Conrad, and Scott (1938) determined the chemical composition of uterine fluid and found that it contained only 0.06 percent nitrogen. Their analysis follows:

Solids*	Ash	Protein N	Na	K	Ca	Mg	Cl	HCO₃
1.4	0.90	0.06	0.255	0.098	0.019	0.001	0.255	0.345

* All values in percent.

Thus, it is clear from their studies that little or no nitrogen is added to the egg in the uterus. They also compared the chemical composition of the albumen of the laid egg with the uterine solution and concluded that the principal additions to the albumen are potassium and bicarbonate ions, with smaller amounts of sodium and chloride ions.

Types of Proteins in Albumen

Hughes and Scott (1936) determined the amounts of mucin, globulin, and albumin in the different layers of albumen of laid and oviducal eggs and the percentage of the total nitrogen contributed by the different types as follows (the oviducal eggs had been in the uterus about four to five hours and most of the albumen had been formed by this time):

		Outer thin		Middle thick		Inner thin	
		Laid	Ovi-ducal	Laid	Ovi-ducal	Laid	Ovi-ducal
Mucin,	percent	1.91	2.79	5.11	5.47	1.10	1.47
Globulin	"	3.66	3.13	5.59	5.03	9.59	7.85
Albumin	"	94.43	94.05	89.18	89.48	89.29	90.85

Mucin is highest in the middle thick layer and lowest in the inner thin layer of both laid and oviducal eggs, but is higher in all layers of the oviducal egg than in the laid egg. The amount of mucin is responsible for the higher viscosity of the thick white layer, yet this layer contains slightly more water than the outer thin white. Globulin, however, is higher in all layers of laid eggs than that in oviducal eggs. Globulin is highest in the inner thin and lowest in the outer thin layers. There is little or no difference in the relative amounts of albumin in the laid and oviducal eggs with respect to a given layer of albumen, but the highest amount is found in the outer thin white. The authors state that their analysis of ovomucin was not entirely satisfactory, and later workers (Forsythe and Berquist, 1951) have indicated that present methods of analysis of ovomucin are inadequate. These data suggest, however, that the addition of water and salts to the egg in the uterus results in changes and rearrangements in the types and amounts of proteins in the strata of albumen.

Formation of Chalazae and Inner Thin White

The chalazae are the paired twisted strands of albumen attached at opposite poles of the yolk and parallel to the long axis of the egg. It is a well-known fact that the mucin content of inner thin white is less than thick white, and this suggested to Conrad and Phillips (1938) that the chalazae are formed by the mechanical twisting and segregation of the mucin fibers from the inner layer of albumen, and histological evidence supports this view (Scott and Huang, 1941). That the decrease in mucin was not due to its chemical destruction was determined *in vitro*. The fact that the chalazae are twisted clockwise and counterclockwise at the large and small ends of the egg respectively suggests that the egg is rotated on its long axis, resulting in the twisting of the strands. Conrad and

Phillips were able to produce chalazae artificially by placing isthmian eggs in a mechanical rotater.

Rate of Formation of Albumen Layers

The rate at which fluid is added to the albumen in the isthmus and uterus is shown in Figure 53 (Burmester, 1940), where the total

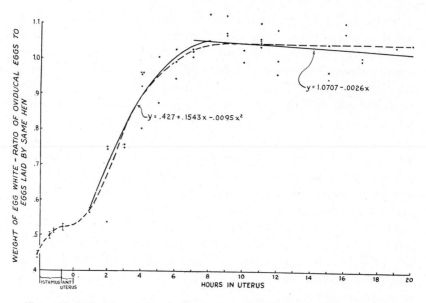

Figure 53. Relative weight of albumen in eggs taken from the isthmus and uterus (oviducal eggs).

The broken line is the curve drawn by freehand which represents the data throughout the whole period. The solid lines between 1 and 8 hours and between 7 and 20 hours represent the functions of the curvilinear and linear regression equations respectively. (From Burmester, *J. Exp. Zool.*, 1940.)

egg albumen of oviducal and laid eggs of the same hen is compared. This graph shows that the weight of albumen of the egg entering the uterus is approximately one-half that of the laid egg. After the first hour in the uterus and up to the sixth or eighth hours, rate of increase in albumen weight is rapid and fairly constant, but not quite a straight-line function. After the eighth hour in the uterus, there is little change in weight, since most of the albumen has been formed.

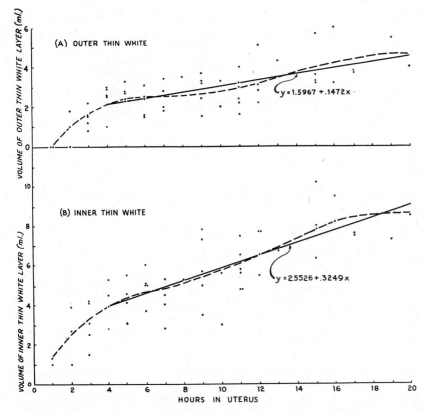

Figure 54. Volume of the outer thin white (A) and inner thin white (B) in eggs from the uterus.

In each graph, the broken line is the curve drawn by freehand which represents the data throughout the whole period, and the solid line between 4 and 20 hours represents the function of the linear regression equation. (From Burmester, *J. Exp. Zool.*, 1940.)

The rates of formation of the inner thin and outer thin white are shown in Figure 54. The slope of the curves for inner and outer thin are similar and reveal that the increase in volume during the first 4 to 5 hours in the uterus is rapid, then slows and is fairly constant up to 18 hours. The graphs show that for the egg held 20 hours in the uterus, or the fresh-laid egg, the volumes of outer and inner thin albumen approximate 5 and 9 cc. respectively. Basing their figures upon a large number of fresh-laid eggs of varying

albumen quality, Sturkie and Weiss (unpublished) found the
weights of the outer and inner albumen to average 5.8 and 7.3
grams respectively.

The curve for the formation of thick white (Figure 55) shows a
rapid decrease in percentage of thick white (volume) during the
first 4 to 6 hours that the egg is in the uterus. There is little change
from 6 to 12 hours; then there is a gradual but persistent decrease
in volume up to 17 hours, after which there is no appreciable

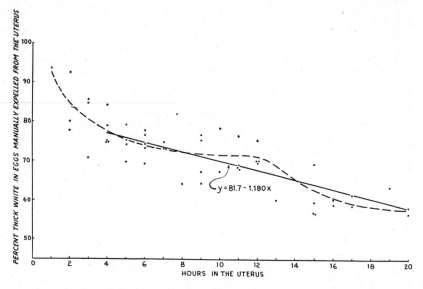

Figure 55. Percentage of thick white in eggs manually expelled from the uterus of
the hen at different periods. (From Burmester, *J. Exp. Zool.*, 1940.)

change. This curve is approximately the reciprocal of the combined
curves for inner and outer thin white. After the egg has spent 20
hours in the uterus, the volume of thick albumen is approximately
58 percent of what it was when the egg left the magnum.

The great decrease in thick albumen occurring during the first
5 to 6 hours in the uterus is due mainly to the addition of water
(see also Figure 56), although the slight but progressive decrease
thereafter, particularly after shell is formed, is caused in large part
by the breakdown of mucin, the constituent which makes albumen
thick. With the addition of water through the shell membranes to

the thick albumen, there is a corresponding decrease in percent solids, mainly protein, during the first 4 to 6 hours, but no change thereafter (Figure 56). The changes in percent solids for the inner thin albumen parallel those for the thick layer.

The decrease in percent solids of the inner thin and thick albumen begins as the egg enters the isthmus. No outer thin albumen

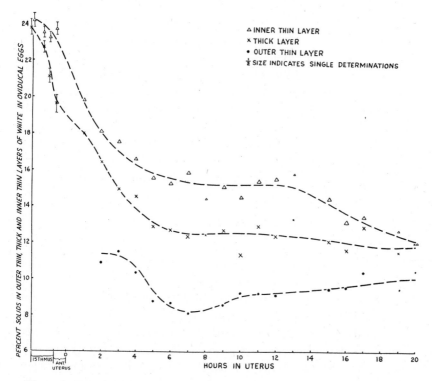

Figure 56. The decrease in percent solids of the inner thin, thick, and outer thin layers of white while the egg is in the isthmus and uterus. (From Burmester, *J. Exp. Zool.*, 1940.)

is formed at this time and is first evident after the egg reaches the isthmus. The percent solids then decrease and reach a low at 7 hours, and the solids then increase continuously but gradually thereafter (Figure 56). An increase in the outer thin layer implies a decrease in the volume of the thick, but such a decrease does not occur until about the 12th hour (see Figure 55). This suggests that while the egg is in the uterus, water is added at a more rapid rate than its diffusion into and through the thick white. The curve for percent solids of the outer thin white is not the reciprocal of the volume curve of the same layer and thus suggests that the relationship between the volume of the layer and protein concentration is not close (Burmester).

Effects of Resection of Magnum on Albumen Formation

Surgical removal of different areas of the magnum by a number of investigators (see Warren, 1949, for review) demonstrates that the amount and quality of albumen formed in the laid egg are reduced. On the basis of such experiments, Asmundson and Burmester (1938) interpreted their results to mean that most of the thick albumen is produced by the posterior half of the magnum. Scott and Burmester (1939) found that the amount of thin albumen was reduced most when the anterior and posterior sections of the magnum were removed. Removal of the middle and posterior areas reduced the amount of thick albumen most.

Mechanical Stimulation of Albumen Formation

Stimulation of the magnum and other parts of the oviduct to elaborate albumen, shell membranes, and shell is believed by many to represent a reflex reaction to the passage of a body or object through the oviduct (Asmundson and Baker, 1940; Asmundson, Baker, and Emlen, 1943). The pressure of the yolk stimulates the magnum to secrete albumen, and the amount formed is believed to be related to the size of the yolk. There are cases on record, however, of isolated loops of oviduct that secrete albumen when an egg passes through the intact portion of the tract and of yolk-less eggs containing albumen (Burmester and Card, 1939 and 1941). Thus, stimuli other than mechanical ones are also concerned in the secretion of albumen.

Nervous Control of, and the Effects of Drugs on, Albumen Formation

That the ovary and oviduct are innervated by the autonomic system has been discussed, but no work on the physiology of these nerves has been conducted. Some of the nerve plexuses described by Mauger (1941) were located in the hen by Sturkie and Weiss (unpublished), but their position and size were such that direct stimulation could be accomplished in the open bird only after considerable manipulation of the viscera. In view of these difficulties, the direct approach was abandoned in favor of the indirect approach, utilizing drugs which mimic the effects of the autonomic nerves. It was hoped that, by using sympathomimetic and parasympathomimetic drugs, information could be obtained concerning the type of innervation and what effect such nerves had upon secretion of albumen. A similar procedure was followed by Riddle and King (1921) on the ringdove. They used atropine, cocaine, pilocarpine, and nicotine. With none of these drugs did they obtain significant changes in albumen secretion. Among the drugs used by Sturkie and Weiss (1950) and Sturkie *et al.* (1953) were ephedrine sulfate (sympathomimetic) and acetylcholine (parasympathomimetic). The drugs were injected, usually subcutaneously in oil, during a four to eight hour period from the time of ovulation and the time when albumen is formed in the magnum. The laid eggs were then broken open, and measurements on volume, viscosity, and total solids were made on the outher thin, inner thin, and thick layers of albumen and compared with control eggs from the same birds.

When the drugs were injected during a four-hour period from the time of ovulation, while the egg is in the magnum, there were slight but no significant changes observed in the albumen. But when the injections were made over the first eight-hour period, which means that the eggs were in the isthmus and uterus for three to four hours of the injection period, significant but not appreciable changes in albumen were observed in most instances.

Acetylcholine increased the viscosity of the outer and thin albumen significantly, but there were no appreciable changes in the volume or the total solids. Since changes in viscosity reflect changes in mucin, the increase is in the mucin content with no changes in water content. Ephedrine usually decreased the viscosity of all albumen layers, and particularly that of the middle thick and inner thin, but other changes were not significant. The viscosity changes were significant in many instances, but not appreciable.

When acetylcholine or ephedrine was injected after the egg left the magnum and was in the uterus, similar changes were produced in the albumen. These results suggest that acetylcholine and ephedrine produce their effects while the egg is in the isthmus and uterus, as well as in the magnum. The effects may be concerned with the rate of breakdown of mucin. Acetylcholine may prevent or retard, and ephedrine may increase, the breakdown of mucin in the uterus. This remains to be proven.

Acetylcholine, epinephrine, and histamine affect the motility of the magnum and oviduct *in vitro* (McKenney, Essex, and Mann, 1932). Acetylcholine and histamine cause contraction of all segments of the oviduct, and epinephrine produces contraction of short duration in the magnum and infundibulum, but relaxation of the uterus.

These results suggest that the magnum is innervated by sympathetic and parasympathetic nerves which govern its motility, but the insignificant effects of these drugs on the secretion of albumen indicate that these nerves play a minor role in the formation of albumen in the magnum.

Effects of Diseases, Environment, and Heredity on Formation and Deterioration of Albumen

High environmental temperature decreases the amount and viscosity of the albumen of laid eggs (Bennion and Warren, 1933; Lorenz and Almquist, 1936; and others). Respiratory diseases such as Newcastle and bronchitis cause deterioration of the thick albumen in laid eggs.

Heredity also influences the amount of thick white in the egg. Strains of chickens have been developed, by selective breeding, that differ markedly in the amount of thick and thin white produced in the egg (see Hutt, 1949, for review). Cole (1938) reported that the goblet cells of the magnum, which are believed to secrete mucin, are significantly larger and taller in birds laying eggs containing more viscous albumen. These results suggest that the qualitative differences in albumen of laid eggs is due principally to the relative amounts of thick and thin albumen secreted in the magnum. Results from experiments involving surgical removal of different parts of the magnum tend to support this view.

Conrad and Scott (1942), however, found only slight and insignificant differences in the development and height of the goblet cells in the magnum of hens laying eggs of poor or of good quality albumen. It is well known that the thick albumen of normal freshly laid eggs deteriorates with age, length of storage, temperature, and other factors. This suggests that freshly laid eggs containing albumen of low viscosity (thin, watery albumen) may result also from the breakdown of mucin in the isthmus and uterus. Results of Sturkie and Polin (1953) support this view. Eggs from hens which normally laid eggs with thin, watery albumen or with thick, upstanding albumen were removed from the oviduct within two hours after the eggs entered the uterus. The eggs intercepted from hens normally laying eggs of poor quality albumen showed more deterioration of the thick albumen than eggs from hens laying eggs of good quality albumen, but the difference was not great. The data indicate that, while decreased secretion of mucin in the magnum may account for some of the differences observed in the albumen quality of laid eggs, breakdown of mucin in the uterus accounts for much of it.

Formation of Avidin by the Magnum

The albumen of eggs contains a factor, avidin, which when fed to chickens or rats produces a biotin deficiency, since it inactivates the biotin. Avidin is produced by the oviducts of birds and amphibia (Hertz and Sebrell, 1942) and by the magnum only of the laying hen (Fraps, Hertz, and Sebrell, 1943). The magna of nonlaying hens with atrophic ovaries do not contain avidin, indicating that avidin production is correlated closely with ovarian and oviducal function. Avidin formation, however, can be induced in the nonlaying hen or immature female by administration of stilbestrol and progesterone (Hertz, Fraps, and Sebrell, 1943).

FORMATION OF SHELL MEMBRANES

There are two shell membranes, inner and outer. The inner membrane is about one-third as thick as the outer (Hays and Sumbardo, 1927). The membranes are made up of a network of protein fibers, keratin (Calvery, 1933). The inner membrane is formed first. An egg partly extending into the isthmus is observed to have the membrane (inner) formed on that part of the egg. By the time that all of the egg is in the isthmus, the outer membrane is believed to be formed (Richardson, 1935). Data from other sources tend to support this view.

The amount of membrane formed in relation to the time the egg moves into and remains in the isthmus has been studied by a number of workers. The relation of rate of formation of the protein in the membranes to the distance that the center of the egg has traversed in the isthmus is a linear one, according to Burmester (1940).

FORMATION OF THE SHELL

The shell is a porous structure consisting of an organic framework, or matrix, and an inorganic portion, containing minerals. The shell is composed of approximately 94 percent $CaCO_3$, 1 percent $MgCO_3$, 1 percent $Ca_3(PO_4)_2$, and 3 to 4 percent of organic matter, chiefly protein.

Rate of Calcium Deposition

Little calcium is deposited on the shell during the first three to five hours that the egg is in the uterus, but thereafter it is deposited at a fairly rapid and constant rate. See Figure 57 and also reports by Burmester, Scott, and Card (1939), Burmester (1940), and Warren and Conrad (1942). These results were confirmed by Bradfield (1951), who studied calcium deposition by means of frequent fluoroscopic examinations of the egg in the uterus.

Sources of Calcium for Shell Formation

Most of the calcium for shell formation comes from that ingested, but some comes from the body stores. Comar and Driggers (1949) and Driggers and Comar (1949), using radioactive Ca^{45} as a tracer, calculated that from 60 to 75 percent of the Ca in the shell comes from ingested calcium and the remainder from the body stores. The roles of estrogen and the parathyroids in the mobilization of calcium are discussed in Chapters 18 and 20 respectively.

The calcium content of venous blood from the intestines of laying hens, where ingested calcium is absorbed, is about 25 percent higher than that in arterial blood (Buckner, Martin, and Hall, 1930). There is no difference in nonlaying birds.

Calcium is not stored in the uterus of the hen, but the quantity stored in the bones during the prelaying period is sufficient for about six eggs (Common, 1938). On low calcium rations, hens are in negative calcium balance, but they can mobilize about 25 percent of their bone calcium for eggs. On high calcium rations, the birds are in positive calcium balance and store the extra calcium in the bones. A study of bone composition indicates that usually

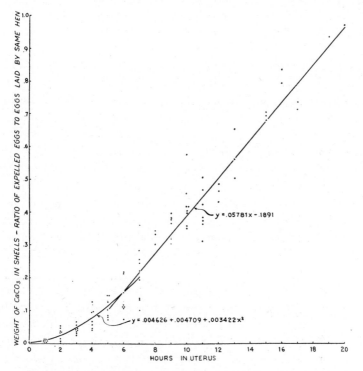

$$y = .05781x - .1891$$

$$y = .004626 + .004709 + .003422x^2$$

Figure 57. Rate of calcium carbonate deposition on the egg in the uterus of the hen.

The curved and straight lines represent the functions of the curvilinear and linear regression equations respectively. (From Burmester, *J. Exp. Zool.*, 1940.)

with increasing drain on the bones for calcium there is a decrease in the ratios of Ca/P, of carbonate Ca to total Ca, of residual Ca to total Ca, of residual Ca to carbonate Ca, and of Ca to magnesium. These results suggest that bone from which Ca is mobilized for shell formation has a much higher Ca to P *ratio* than average bone (Common, 1938).

Physiology of Calcium Deposition

The blood calcium of the laying hen is approximately twice that of the nonlaying bird, and most of the increase is in the non-diffusible fraction, which is bound to protein, or exists in a colloidal form (see Chapters 2 and 18). One might expect total blood calcium to be higher in the laying hen at the time when calcium is being deposited on the egg, and experiments by Knowles, Hart, and Halpin (1935) suggested that this was the case; but later some of these same investigators (Deobald, Lease, Hart, and Halpin, 1936) could not confirm this. They found that total blood calcium level varied only slightly with the presence or absence of an egg in the tract.

Since the calcium of the shell is in the form of $CaCO_3$, and about 60 percent of the calcium of the blood of laying hens is bound, how is the latter dissociated into free calcium and deposited on the egg? This has not been determined, but there is some evidence to suggest that certain enzymes are somehow concerned in the process. The serum alkaline phosphatase of high laying hens is higher than that of nonlayers or of poor layers, but there is no difference in the uterus (Gutowska, Parkhurst, Parrott, and Verburg, 1943).

The enzyme carbonic anhydrase is also involved in the calcification of the shell. Uterine tissue of hens contains more of the enzyme than other oviducal tissues (Common, 1941a). Gutowska and Mitchell (1945) found the carbonic anhydrase content of the uterus, but not the blood, much higher in high laying hens which laid eggs with good shell texture than in poor layers and nonlayers. Injection of birds with sulfanilamide caused them to lay soft-shelled eggs, not because the calcium content of the blood was changed (this was not affected), but because the carbonic anhydrase in the shell gland was inactivated. These workers consider the enzyme necessary for shell formation.

According to Gutowska and Mitchell (1945), carbonic anhydrase (CA.) could catalyze the decomposition of H_2CO_3 in the secreting cells of the uterus, in the reaction as follows:

$$2HCO_3^- \rightleftharpoons H_2CO_3 + CO_3^{--}$$
$$\Updownarrow \; CA.$$
$$H_2O + CO_2$$

The bicarbonate ions in the uterus are obtained from the blood and could react to form carbonic acid and carbonic ions. This is an equilibrium reaction in which the accumulation of carbonic acid would limit the formation of the necessary number of carbonate ions needed for the $CaCO_3$ of the shell. These workers propose that the uterus absorbs calcium proteinate from the blood and dissociates it into carbonate ions in accordance with the principle of Donnan's equilibrium.

Factors Affecting Shell Deposition

The thickness and texture of the shell of the egg are manifestations of the hen's efficiency of calcium metabolism. There are numerous factors which may affect the metabolism and deposition of calcium on the shell. Among these are nutrition (amount of calcium, phosphorus, manganese, and vitamin D ingested), season, age of the hen, environmental temperature, physiological efficiency, and hereditary constitution. These are discussed in detail by Romanoff and Romanoff (1949).

The shell of the egg tends to become thinner with advancing age of the bird. Hereditary constitution, no doubt, plays an important role in determining the physiological efficiency with which individual hens convert ingested calcium into shell. Poultry breeders have long known that certain individuals and families of chickens produce thin-shelled eggs. Taylor and Lerner (1939) established, by breeding, two strains of chickens each laying preponderantly thin-shelled and thick-shelled eggs respectively. Certain diseases, notably Newcastle and bronchitis, cause hens to lay thin-shelled eggs. High environmental temperatures decrease the amount of calcium deposited on the egg (Warren and Schnepel, 1940) and the amount of blood calcium (Conrad, 1939).

Hypothermia causes hens to expell their eggs prematurely and prevents calcium deposition (Sturkie, 1946). When the cloacas of hypothermic hens are stitched in order to prevent expuslion of the egg from the uterus, no calcium is laid down, even though the body temperature may be normal for 8 to 10 hours before laying time (birds warmed). Whether or not the hypothermia inactivates carbonic anhydrase in the uterus has not been determined. That it does appears unlikely, judging from the report of Meldrum and Roughton (1934), which showed that the enzyme is stable at temperatures as low as 68° F., lower than those induced in the hypothermic birds.

Administration of certain sulfonamides affects calcium deposition. Sulfanilamide causes hens to lay thin-shelled or soft-shelled eggs, depending on the dosage (Hinshaw and McNeil, 1943; Scott, Jungherr, and Matterson, 1944), because carbonic anhydrase is inactivated (Gutowska and Mitchell, 1945). Sulfonamides of the R-SO$_2$NH$_2$ group inactivate carbonic anhydrase, but others not of this group, such as sulfapyradine, sulfathiazole, and sulfaguanidine, do not, according to Keilen and Mann (1940). Thus, the latter drugs should not affect calcium deposition, and do not, according to Benesch, Barron, and Mawson (1944). Sulfapyradine does produce thin-shelled eggs, according to Bernard and Genest (1945).

The steroid hormones, progesterone, desoxycorticosterone acetate, and large doses of dehydroandrosterone tend to inhibit shell formation when injected into pigeons and doves (Dunham and Riddle, 1942).

REFERENCES

Asmundson, V. S.   1939   The formation of the egg in the oviduct of the turkey (Meleagris gallopavo). J. Exp. Zool. 82:287.

Asmundson, V. S., and G. A. Baker   1940   The percentage of shell as a function of shell thickness, egg volume, and egg weight. Poultry Sci. 19:227.

Asmundson, V. S., G. A. Baker, and J. T. Emlen   1943   Certain relations between the parts of birds' eggs. Auk 60:34.

Asmundson, V. S., and B. R. Burmester   1936   The secretory activity of the parts of the hen's oviduct. J. Exp. Zool. 72:225.

Asmundson, V. S., and B. R. Burmester   1938   The effect of resecting a part of the uterus on the formation of the hen's egg. Poultry Sci. 17:126.

Asmundson, V. S., and P. Pinsky   1935   The effect of the thyroid on the formation of the hen's egg. Poultry Sci. 14:99.

Barott, H. G., L. G. Schoenleber, and L. E. Campbell   1951   The effect of ultraviolet radiation on egg production of hens. Poultry Sci. 30:409.

Beadle, B. W., R. M. Conrad, and H. M. Scott   1938   Composition of uterine secretion of the domestic fowl. Poultry Sci. 17:498.

Benesch, R., N. S. Barron, and C. A. Mawson 1944 Carbonic anhydrase, sulphonamides, and shell formation in the domestic fowl. Nature 153:138.

Bennion, N. L., and D. C. Warren 1933 Temperature and its effect on egg size in the domestic fowl. Poultry Sci. 12:69.

Benoit, J. 1950 Traité de Zoologie, edited by P. P. Grassé. Tome XV: Oiseaux, p. 459. Masson & Co., Paris.

Bernard, R., and P. Genest 1945 Sulfonamides and egg shell formation in the domestic fowl. Science 101:617.

Bissonnette, T. H. 1936 Sexual photoperiodicity. Quart. Rev. Biol. 11:371.

Bradfield, J. R. G. 1951 Radiographic studies on the formation of the hen's egg shell. J. Exp. Biol. 28:125.

Bryant, R. L. 1944 A single comb White Leghorn pullet with two ovaries and oviducts. Poultry Sci. 23:77.

Buckner, G. D., and J. H. Martin 1929 The hydrogen ion concentration of the reproductive organs of the White Leghorn. Am. J. Physiol. 89:164.

Buckner, G. D., J. H. Martin, and F. E. Hall 1930 Distribution of blood calcium in the circulation of laying hens. Am. J. Physiol. 93:86.

Burmester, B. R. 1940 A study of the physical and chemical changes of the egg during its passage through the isthmus and uterus of the hen's oviduct. J. Exp. Zool. 84:445.

Burmester, B. R., and L. E. Card 1939 The effect of resecting the so-called "chalaziferous region" of the hen's oviduct on the formation of subsequent eggs. Poultry Sci. 28:138.

Burmester, B. R., and L. E. Card 1941 Experiments on the physiology of egg white secretion. Poultry Sci. 20:224.

Burmester, B. R., H. M. Scott, and L. E. Card 1939 Rate of egg shell formation in the hen. Proc. Seventh World's Poultry Congr., p. 99.

Burrows, W. H., and T. C. Byerly 1942 Premature expulsion of eggs by hens following injection of whole posterior pituitary preparations. Poultry Sci. 21:416.

Burrows, W. H., and R. M. Fraps 1942 Action of vasopressin and oxytocin in causing premature oviposition by domestic fowl. Endocrinol. 30:702.

Byerly, T. C., and O. K. Moore 1941 Clutch length in relation to period of illumination in the domestic fowl. Poultry Sci. 20:387.

Calvery, H. O. 1933 Some analyses of egg shell keratin. J. Biol. Chem. 100:183.

Carver, J. S. 1941 Light requirements of laying hens. Fiftieth Annual Report Wash. Agr. Exp. Sta. (Abs).

Chappelier, A. 1913 Persistence et développement des organes génitaux droits chez les femelles adultes des oiseaux. Bull. Sci. France Belg. 47:361.

Cole, R. K. 1938 Histology of the oviduct of the fowl in relation to variations in the condition of the firm egg albumen. Anat. Rec. 71:349.

Comar, C. L., and J. C. Driggers 1949 Secretion of radioactive Ca in the hen's egg. Science 109:282.

Common, R. H. 1938 Observations on the mineral metabolism of pullets. J. Agric. Sci. 28:347.

Common, R. H. 1941a The carbonic anhydrase activity of the hen's oviduct. J. Agric. Sci. 31:412.

Common, R. H. 1941b Observations on the mineral metabolism of pullets. V: Acid base equilibrium and reproductive activity. J. Agric. Sci. 31:281.

Conrad, R. M. 1939 The effect of high temperature on the blood calcium of the laying hen. Poultry Sci. 18:327.

Conrad, R. M., and R. E. Phillips 1938 The formation of the chalazae and inner white in the hen's egg. Poultry Sci. 17:143.

Conrad, R. M., and H. M. Scott 1938 The formation of the egg of the domestic fowl. Physiol. Rev. 18:481.

Conrad, R. M., and H. M. Scott 1942 Differences between high and low quality fresh eggs. Poultry Sci. 21:77.

Conrad, R. M., and D. C. Warren 1939 The alternate white and yellow layers of yolk in the hen's ova. Poultry Sci. 18:220.

Crew, F. A. E. 1931 Paired oviducts in the fowl. J. Anat. 66:100.

Deobald, H. J., E. J. Lease, E. B. Hart, and J. G. Halpin 1936 Studies on calcium metabolism of laying hens. Poultry Sci. 15:179.

Driggers, J. C., and C. L. Comar 1949 The secretion of radioactive calcium (Ca[45]) in the hen's egg. Poultry Sci. 28:420.

Dunham, H. H., and O. Riddle 1942 Effects of a series of steroids on ovulation and reproduction in pigeons. Physiol. Zool. 15:383.

Forsythe, R. S., and D. H. Berquist 1951 The effects of physical treatments on some properties of egg white. Poultry Sci. 30:302.

Fraps, R. M. 1946 Differential ovulatory reaction of first and subsequent follicles of the hen's clutch. Anat. Rec. 96:573.

Fraps, R. M., R. Hertz, and W. H. Sebrell 1943 Relation between ovarian function and avidin content in the oviduct of the hen. Proc. Soc. Exp. Biol. & Med. 52:140.

Fraps, R. M., and B. H. Neher 1945 Interruption of ovulation in the hen by subcutaneously administered non-specific substances. Endocrinol. 37:407.

Fraps, R. M., B. H. Neher, and I. Rothchild 1947 The imposition of diurnal ovulatory and temperature rhythms of periodic feeding of hens maintained under continuous light. Endocrinol. 40:241.

Fraps, R. M., M. W. Olsen, and B. H. Neher 1942 Forced ovulation of normal ovarian follicles in the domestic fowl. Proc. Soc. Exp. Biol. & Med. 50:308.

Fraps, R. M., G. M. Riley, and M. W. Olsen 1942 Time required for induction of ovulation following intravenous injection of hormone preparations in the fowl. Proc. Soc. Exp. Biol. & Med. 50:313.

Gutowska, M. S., and C. A. Mitchell 1945 Carbonic anhydrase in the calcification of the egg shell. Poultry Sci. 24:159.

Gutowska, M. S., R. T. Parkhurst, E. M. Parrott, and R. M. Verburg 1943 Alkaline phosphatase and egg formation. Poultry Sci. 22:195.

Hays, F. A., and A. H. Sumbardo 1927 Physical characters of eggs in relation to hatchability. Poultry Sci. 6:196.

Hertz, R., R. M. Fraps, and W. H. Sebrell 1943 Induction of avidin formation in the avian oviduct by stilbestrol and progesterone. Proc. Soc. Exp. Biol. & Med. 52:142.

Hertz, R., and W. H. Sebrell 1942 Occurrence of avidin in the oviduct and secretions of the genital tract of several species. Science 96:257.

Heywang, B. W. 1938 The time factor in egg production. Poultry Sci. 17:240.

Hinshaw, W. R., and E. McNeil 1943 Experiments with sulfanilamide for turkeys. Poultry Sci. 22:291.

Hughes, J. S., and H. M. Scott 1936 The change in the concentration of ovoglobulin in egg white during egg formation. Poultry Sci. 15:349.

Huston, T. M., and A. V. Nalbandov 1953 Neurohumoral control of the pituitary in the fowl. Endocrinol. 52:149.

Hutt, F. B. 1949 Genetics of the Fowl. McGraw-Hill Book Co., Inc., New York.

Keilen, D., and T. Mann 1940 Sulfanilamide as a specific inhibitor of carbonic anhydrase. Nature 146:164.

Knowles, H. R., E. B. Hart, and J. G. Halpin 1935 The variation in the calcium level of the blood of the domestic fowl. Poultry Sci. 14:83.

Levi, W. M. 1941 The Pigeon. R. L. Bryan Co., Columbia, S.C.

Lorenz, F. W., and H. J. Almquist 1936 Seasonal variations in egg quality. Poultry Sci. 15:14.

McKenney, F. D., H. E. Essex, and F. C. Mann 1932 The action of certain drugs on the oviduct of the domestic fowl. J. Pharm. & Exp. Thera. 45:113.

McNally, E. H. 1934 Passage of ovoglobulins through the shell membrane. Proc. Soc. Exp. Biol. & Med. 31:946.

McNally, E. H. 1947 Some factors that effect oviposition in the domestic fowl. Poultry Sci. 26:396.

Mauger, H. M., Jr. 1941 The autonomic innervation of the female genitalia in the domestic fowl and its correlation with the aortic branchings. Am. J. Vet. Res. 2:447.

Maw, A. J. G. 1934 The effect of kamala on egg production and egg weight. Poultry Sci. 13:131.

Meldrum, N. U., and F. J. W. Roughton 1934 Carbonic anhydrase: Its preparation and properties. J. Physiol. 80:8.

Morash, R., and O. S. Gibbs 1929 The effect of pituitary on the bird. J. Pharm. & Exp. Thera. 37:475.

Nalbandov, A. V., and M. F. James 1949 The blood-vascular system of the chicken ovary. Am. J. Anat. 85:347.

Neher, B. H., and R. M. Fraps 1950 The addition of eggs to the hen's clutch by repeated injections of ovulation-inducing hormones. Endocrinol. 46:482.

Olsen, M. W., and T. C. Byerly 1932 Orientation of the hen's egg in the uterus and during laying. Poultry Sci. 11:266.

Olsen, M. W., and B. H. Neher 1948 The site of fertilization in the domestic fowl. J. Exp. Zool. 109:355.

Pearl, R., and M. R. Curtis 1912 Studies on the physiology of reproduction in the domestic fowl. V: Data regarding the physiology of the oviduct. J. Exp. Zool. 12:99.

Pearl, R., and W. F. Schoppe 1921 Studies on the physiology of reproduction in the domestic fowl. XVIII: Further observations on the anatomical basis of fecundity. J. Exp. Zool. 34:101.

Phillips, R. E., and D. C. Warren 1937 Observations concerning the mechanics of ovulation in the fowl. J. Exp. Zool. 76:117.

Platt, C. S. 1946 Report of the New Jersey Pigeon Breeding Test, Millville, New Jersey.

Quinn, J. P., W. H. Burrows, and E. H. McNally 1939 A Rhode Island Red pullet with two oviducts. Poultry Sci. 28:381.

Richardson, K. C. 1935 The secretory phenomena in the oviduct of the fowl, including the process of shell formation examined by the micro-incineration technique. Phil. Trans. Roy. Soc. London, Series B, 225:149.

Riddle, O. 1911 On the formation, significance, and chemistry of the white and yellow yolk of ova. J. Morph. 22:455.

Riddle, O. 1921 A simple method of obtaining premature eggs from birds. Science 54:664.

Riddle, O., and C. E. Anderson 1918 Studies on the physiology of reproduction in birds. VIII: The effects of quinine on the production of egg yolk and egg albumen. Am. J. Physiol. 47:92.

Riddle, O., and G. C. Basset 1916 The effect of alcohol on the size of the yolk of the pigeon's egg. Am. J. Physiol. 41:425.

Riddle, O., and C. V. King 1921 Studies on the physiology of reproduction in birds. XII: The relation of nerve stimuli to oviducal secretions as indicated by effects of atropine and other alkaloids. Am. J. Physiol. 57:275.

Romanoff, A. L., and A. J. Romanoff 1949 The Avian Egg. John Wiley & Sons, Inc., New York.

Rothchild, I. 1946 The time of release of the ovulating hormone from anterior pituitary of domestic hen. Anat. Rec. 96:542 (Abs.).

Rothchild, I. 1949 An indication that the ovulating hormone release inducing action of progesterone is an indirect one. Fed. Proc. 8:135.

Rothchild, I., and R. M. Fraps 1944a Relation between light-dark rhythms and hour of lay of eggs experimentally retained in the hen. Endocrinol. 35:355.

Rothchild, I., and R. M. Fraps 1944b On the function of the ruptured ovarian follicle of the domestic fowl. Proc. Soc. Exp. Biol. & Med. 56:79.

Rothchild, I., and R. M. Fraps 1945 The relation between ovulation frequency and the incidence of follicular atresia following surgical operation in the domestic fowl. Endocrinol. 37:415.

Rothchild, I., and R. M. Fraps 1949 The induction of ovulating hormone release from the pituitary of the domestic fowl by means of progesterone. Endocrinol. 44:141.

Scott, H. M. 1938 The physiology of egg size in the domestic fowl. Thesis. University of Illinois.

Scott, H. M., and B. R. Burmester 1939 Effect of resection of the albumen tube on secretion of egg white. Proc. Seventh World's Poultry Congr., p. 102.

Scott, H. M., and W. Huang 1941 Histological observations on the formation of the chalaza in the hen's egg. Poultry Sci. 20:402.

Scott, H. M., J. S. Hughes, and D. C. Warren 1937 Augmentation of nitrogen to the egg white after the formation of the shell membranes in the fowl. Poultry Sci. 16:53.

Scott, H. M., E. Jungherr, and L. D. Matterson 1944 The effect of feeding sulfanilamide to the laying fowl. Poultry Sci. 23:446.

Scott, H. M., and D. C. Warren 1936 Influence of ovulation rate on the tendency of the fowl to produce eggs in clutches. Poultry Sci. 15:381.

Sturkie, P. D. 1946 The effects of hypothermia upon the reproductive tract of the hen. Poultry Sci. 25:369.

Sturkie, P. D., and D. Polin 1953 Role of the magnum and uterus in the determination of albumen quality of laid eggs. Poultry Sci. (in press).

Sturkie, P. D., and H. S. Weiss 1950 The effects of sympathomimetic and parasympathomimetic drugs upon egg formation. Poultry Sci. 29:781 (Abs.).

Sturkie, P. D., H. S. Weiss, and R. K. Ringer 1953 Effects of injections of acetylcholine and ephedrine upon the components of the hen's egg. Poultry Sci. (in press).

Sturkie, P. D., and A. G. Williams 1945 Studies on pregastrular development, early embryonic development, and hatchability of prematurely laid eggs of the hen. Poultry Sci. 24:546.

Taylor, L. W., and I. M. Lerner 1939 Inheritance of egg-shell thickness in White Leghorn pullets. J. Agric. Res. 58:386.

Warren, D. C. 1949 Formation of the hen's egg, Chapter II in L. W. Taylor, Fertility and Hatchability of Chicken and Turkey Eggs. John Wiley & Sons, Inc., New York.

Warren, D. C., and R. M. Conrad 1939 Growth of the hen's ovum. J. Agric. Res. 58:875.

Warren, D. C., and R. M. Conrad 1942 Time of pigment deposition in brown-shelled hen eggs and in turkey eggs. Poultry Sci. 21:515.

Warren, D. C., and R. Schnepel 1940 The effect of air temperature on egg-shell thickness in the fowl. Poultry Sci. 19:67.

Warren, D. C., and H. M. Scott 1934 Ovulation in the domestic hen. Science 80:461.

Warren, D. C., and H. M. Scott 1935 The time factor in egg production. Poultry Sci. 14:195.

Webster, H. D. 1948 The right oviduct in chickens. J. Am. Vet. Med. Assoc. March, p. 221.

Weiss, H. S., and P. D. Sturkie 1952 Time of oviposition as affected by neuromimetic drugs. Poultry Sci. 31:227.

CHAPTER 16

Reproduction in the Male, Fertilization, and Early Embryonic Development

ANATOMY AND HISTOLOGY OF THE MALE
REPRODUCTIVE SYSTEM

THE reproductive system of the male consists of paired testes, the epididymi, the vasa deferentia (which transport the spermatozoa to the penis), and the penis (See Figure 58.) The testes are near the cephalic end of the kidneys and ventral to them. The weight of the testes comprises about 1 percent of the total body weight (Parker, 1949). The epididymi in birds are small in comparison to those in mammals. The penis in some species of birds is well developed (ducks and geese), but in the chicken it is rudimentary (Benoit, 1950).

Mature spermatozoa of birds vary in size and shape, depending on the species. In the chicken, the spermatozoon has a long headpiece with a pointed acrosome and a short midpiece, to which is attached the long tail (Figure 59).

The testes are composed of seminiferous tubules and intertubular tissue (Figure 60). In the prepuberal state, the seminiferous tubules are small and lined with a single layer of cells (Figure 60A). The mature testis has a multilayered epithelium representing the various stages of spermatogenesis. From the wall of the tubule to the lumen may be found spermatogonia, primary spermatocytes, secondary spermatocytes, spermatids, the nutritive cells (cells of Sertoli) to which the spermatids are attached, and the spermatozoa.

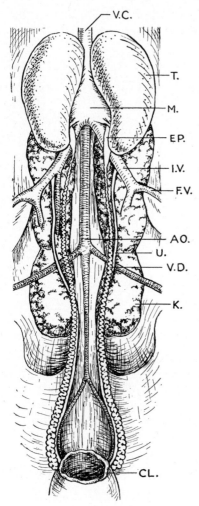

The connective tissue stroma between the tubules contains the interstitial cells (Leydig) and blood vessels. The follicle-stimulating hormone from the pituitary, FSH, is responsible for the growth of the tubules. The interstitial-cell-stimulating hormone (ICSH) stimulates the growth and development of the Leydig cells, and the luteinizing hormone (LH) causes these cells to secrete androgen (see Chapters 17 and 18).

Development of the Testes and Spermatogenesis

The growth and development of the testes and spermatogenesis have been studied in detail by a number of workers (see reviews by Parker, 1949, and Benoit, 1950). Kumaran and Turner (1949a and 1949b), who studied the histology of the testes of White Plymouth Rock males at various ages (see also Blivaiss, 1947), reported their observations as follows. During the first 5 weeks, the tubules are organized, and multiplication of the basal layer of cells, the spermatogonia, occurs. The primary spermatocytes begin to appear about the sixth week. During the next 2 or 3 weeks, growth of the primary spermato-

Figure 58. Urogenital system of the male chicken.

V.C., posterior vena cava; T, testes; M, mesorchium; EP., epididymis; I.V., iliac vein; F.V., femoral vein; AO., aorta; U, ureter; V.D., vas deferens; K, kidney; CL., cloaca.

cytes takes precedence over the further multiplication of the spermatogonial layer.

The secondary spermatocytes begin to appear at about 10 weeks of age as a result of the reduction division of the primary spermatocytes (Figure 60B). Spermatids (immature spermatozoa) begin to appear in the seminiferous tubules at about 12 weeks of age, and by the 20th week are usually present in all the tubules (Figure 60C). The weight of the testes of the Plymouth Rock cockerels averaged 9.13 grams at 20 weeks and 2.7 grams at 16 weeks.

In White Leghorns, which are more precocious sexually, average weight of the testes at 20 weeks is 16.7 grams (Jones and Lamoreux, 1942). In older males, testes weight may reach 30 grams. Although histologically the testes may show spermatozoa at 16 to 20 weeks, and in Leghorn cockerels even at 12 weeks, fertility is not good until the males are 24 to 26 weeks of age (Hogue and Schnetzler, 1937; Parker, McKenzie, and Kempster, 1942). In the absence of the thyroid gland, the development of the testes is subnormal, and spermatogenesis does not proceed beyond the formation of secondary spermatocytes (Blivaiss, 1947).

Maturing of Spermatozoa

Munro (1938a) demonstrated that spermatozoa of the chicken

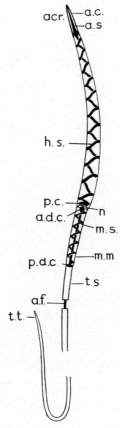

Figure 59. Diagram of the spermatozoon of the chicken.

a.c., apical cap; acr., acrosome; a.d.c., anterior distal centriole; a.f., axial filament; a.s., apical spine; h.s., headspiral; m.m., midpiece membrane; m.s., midpiece spiral; n, neck; p.c., proximal centriole; p.d.c., posterior distal centriole; t.s., tail sheath; t.t., tip of tail. (Modified slightly from Grigg, *Proc. Ninth World's Poultry Congr.*, 1951.)

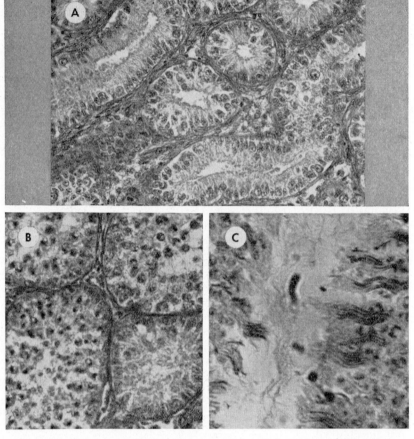

Figure 60. Cross sections of testes of cockerels at 42 days of age (A), at 70 days of age (B), and at six months of age (C), showing different stages of spermatogenesis.

A shows beginning of formation of primary spermatocytes in some tubules. In many areas, however, there is one layer of cells. In B, primary and secondary spermatocytes are abundant. In C, spermatids, spermatozoa, and Sertoli cells are present. Between the tubules are the interstitial cells. (Figures A and B from Kumaran and Turner, *Poultry Sci.*, 1949. Figure C from Blivaiss, *Physiol. Zool.*, 1947.)

must be ripened or matured in the epididymis before they are capable of fertilization. Spermatozoa taken directly from the testes do not fertilize ova, and those taken from the epididymis fertilized only 13 percent of the females inseminated. When semen was taken from the lower vas deferens, 74 percent of the females inseminated laid fertile eggs. The motility of the spermatozoa from these sites was directly proportional to their fertilizing capacity. The duration of the ripening period apparently is not long, because it was shown that spermatozoa could pass from the testes through the vas deferens to the cloaca within 24 hours. Since ligation of the vas deferens or castration had no effect upon the spermatozoa in the vas deferens, Munro (1938b) believed that hormones from the testes were not concerned in the process of maturing.

Site of Production of Androgen

The consensus is that the Leydig cells produce androgen (see review by Taber, 1951). Kumaran and Turner (1949a), Benoit (in 1922 and later), and others have demonstrated that the great increase in interstitial tissue coincides with the growth and development of the comb, an indication of androgenic activity. Kumaran and Turner (1949b) observed birefringence material in the testes of young cockerels first at 12 to 16 weeks of age, when comb growth begins. This material was observed only in the interstitial cells. The birefringence technique is a means of identifying androgen and other steroid hormones.

Breneman (1936), who believed that the tubules of the testes secreted androgen, based his conclusions on the fact that injections of follicule-stimulating hormone (FSH) produced comb growth, but luteinizing hormone (LH) did not. More recent work by Nalbandov, Meyer, and McShan (1946), who studied the growth of the comb and testes of hypophysectomized males following injections of a number of pituitary preparations containing FSH and LH, leaves little doubt that the Leydig cells are the principal, if not the whole, source of androgen. They found that pituitary preparations absolutely free of LH (pure FSH) did not cause growth of the comb of hypophysectomized males, but did cause growth of the testes. Pure LH produced both comb and testes growth. There is a synergistic effect between FSH and LH. FSH contaminated with minute amounts of LH stimulates both comb and testes growth. Some of the pituitary preparations which were tested by these workers and which were reputedly free of LH gave comb growth, indicating the presence of LH. It is possible that the preparations used by Breneman were impure, and this may have influenced his results.

X-rays, which destroy practically all tubular tissue, have no effect upon interstitial tissue, except possibly to increase it (Benoit, 1924; Essenberg and Karrasch, 1940). Sturkie, Pino, Weatherwax, Donnelly, and Dorrance (1949) demonstrated that sterilizing doses of X-rays, 2100 to 5600 roentgen units, do not affect comb growth or sexual libido of males, even though testis size is decreased considerably.

FACTORS AFFECTING FERTILITY IN THE MALE

Number of Spermatozoa and Amount of Semen Produced

Semen from the cock is usually white and opaque, but may be clear and watery, particularly when the concentration of spermatozoa is low. The pH of cock semen is 7.04 according to Wheeler and Andrews (1943) and 7.27 according to Parker, McKenzie, and Kempster (1942).

The volume of semen of a given ejaculation has been determined by a number of workers, and some of the variation reported may be attributable to the methods of collection. Some have collected the semen from the cloaca of the hen after a normal mating, and some have collected it directly from the male by massaging the abdomen according to the technique of Burrows and Quinn (1937, and 1939).

Parker (1949), who reviewed the subject, compiled the results of a number of investigators, including his own. The volumes reported (averages) range from 0.11 cc. (collected from the cloaca of the hen) to 1 cc. (collected from the male directly). Spermatozoa per cubic millimeter of semen average about 3.5 million. Thus, in a given ejaculate (0.5 to 1 cc. volume) the number of spermatozoa ranges from 1.7 to 3.5 billion.

There is little correlation between the concentration of spermatozoa and fertility when the semen contains from 825 thousand to 7 million spermatozoa per cubic millimeter, according to Hutt (1929). A minimum of 100 million spermatozoa must be inseminated to obtain optimum fertility (Munro, 1938c; Parker, McKenzie, and Kempster, 1942). Abnormal spermatozoa may cause sterility, but apparently very few males produce sufficient numbers of abnormal spermatozoa to cause sterility (Sampson and Warren, 1939).

The number of matings or ejaculations per day influences the volume of semen produced and the concentration of spermatozoa. Both decrease with the frequency of mating, and after three to four successive ejaculations, concentration of spermatozoa is very low in some males (Parker, McKenzie, and Kempster, 1940).

The number of times a male chicken mates per day may range as high as 25 to 41, according to Heuser (1916) and Philips (1918). More recent work by Guhl (1951) suggests that males may mate more frequently than is indicated by the figures given above. Guhl made studies on individual males placed in pens with 30 to 40 females, and mating behavior was observed for 21 minutes per day for periods as long as 84 days. The observations were based on the first 21 minutes after the males were placed in the pens with the females. The actual observation time was 29 hours and 24 minutes. The number of treadings during this period for three males were 410, 788, and 853, or 13.9, 26.7, and 29.0 matings respectively per hour. It was shown, however, that when males are first introduced into a pen, they mate most frequently during the first 3 to 6 minutes. Guhl, Collias, and Allee (1945) and Guhl and Warren (1946) demonstrated that the social order or "peck order" of the hens to which males are introduced affects their mating behavior. Males, regardless of their social standing, tend to mate most frequently not with the highest or lowest ranking hens, but with the "middle-class hens." When three or more males are introduced together into a pen of females, the frequency of matings and fertility are highest for the top-ranking male. The lowest-ranking male mates with few females because of interference from the higher-ranking males.

There is a diurnal variation in the production of spermatozoa by the fowl, with the greatest spermatogenic activity at 3 A.M., according to Riley (1940), and at midnight, according to Macartney (1942).

Other factors affecting the production of semen and fertility of the male and female are age, season, amount of light, state of nutrition and health, and hormones. It is generally conceded that fertility declines in males and females in the second and third years of life. Male chickens vary in their production of semen and fertility with season (Parker and McSpadden, 1943; Wheeler and Andrews, 1943). The investigators found that the amount of semen and number of spermatozoa increase from December through April and then decline and reach a low in July and August. Fertility also declines in the summer.

Effects of Light

It is well known that light stimulates the pituitary to elaborate FSH and LH, which in turn activate the gonads (see Chapter 17). When young cockerels receive 12 or more hours of light, growth of testes and semen production are maximal. Maximum response to light is observed in about one month. With less than 9 hours of light, stimulation is at a minimum (Lamoreux, 1943).

Different wave lengths of light vary in their stimulating effect on the testes of birds (Bissonnette, 1936; Benoit and Ott, 1938; Burger, 1943; Benoit, Walter, and Assenmacher 1950.) Only that portion of the spectrum visible to man, between 4000 and 7000 angstroms, has a stimulating effect on spermatogenesis in the starling (Burger). Red light is slightly more effective than white, and blue-green light is least effective. Benoit and Ott (1938) reported the order of effectiveness of colored lights in stimulating the pituitary and testes of ducks as follows: (1) red, (2) orange, (3) yellow, (4) green, (5) blue. Blue had a slight stimulating effect, and infrared was ineffective.

More recent experiments by Benoit, Walter, and Assenmacher (1950), in which the heads of ducks were exposed to lights where the wave lengths covered a narrower and more specific spectral range, show that only red and orange (708 and 617 mμ.) are very effective stimulators of the pituitary and gonads. Stimulation begins with yellow (577 mμ.) and reaches a maximum at 617 to 708 mμ. and decreases at 740 mμ.

Flashing light may also activate the testes. Burger, Bissonnette, and Doolittle (1942) subjected starlings to uninterrupted light, but not enough to be sexually activating, in addition to flashing light. Both types of light equaled 14 hours. They found that, to be effective, the interval of light must be more than 0.9 seconds, and the interval of darkness must be less than 15 seconds.

Storage of Semen

Attempts at storing chicken semen for subsequent use, without impairing fertility, have been generally unsuccessful. Burrows and Quinn (1939), who stored semen at 4.4° C. or lower, found that spermatozoa lost their fertilizing capacity in a short time. Semen can be stored at −79° C. for 14 months, and then thawed, but fertility is very poor, according to Shaffner, Henderson, and Card (1941). The length of life of spermatozoa in the unfrozen state is greatest at 0 to 1° C. Semen can be quick-frozen to a solid state at −6° C. and then thawed immediately at 42° to 45° C. without apparent damage to motility and fertility. But if it is stored for more than one minute after quick freezing, fertility decreases greatly.

Artificial Insemination

Burrows and Quinn (1937 and 1939) and Parker (1939) developed a technique for obtaining semen artificially from the male. It is thus possible to dilute semen as much as 10 times and inseminate a large number of females, provided at least 100 million sperm are introduced at a given insemination. To insure good fertility, inseminations should be made every fourth or fifth day in the chicken, according to Warren and Gish (1943). They revealed that fertility declines rapidly after the fourth day following insemination. Turkey hens remain fertile after matings much longer than chickens. Burrows and Marsden (1938) obtained good fertility in turkeys (83 percent) when the hens were inseminated every 30 days.

Fertility and Time of Mating

The time elapsing between copulation and the first fertile egg obtained in chickens has been reported by many investigators (see review of Parker, 1949). The time averages about 72 hours, but may be as low as 19.5 hours, according to one report. The latter figure, if correct, means that the egg may be fertilized while it is in the magnum or isthmus.

Mimura (1939) studied the movement of spermatozoa through the oviduct of the fowl and showed that when spermatozoa are introduced into the uterus, they reached the upper part of the oviduct or ovary within as short a time as 26 minutes. Under normal conditions, with an egg in the oviduct, the time may be different.

A number of workers have studied the relationship of time of insemination to fertility. Moore and Byerly (1942) reported that when females are inseminated at the time a hard-shelled egg is present in the uterus, fertility is lowest; it is highest when inseminations are made after the egg has been laid.

Other workers have reported that fertility is significantly higher if inseminations or matings are restricted to the afternoon, when usually a soft-shell egg is in the uterus (Gracewski and Scott, 1943; Malmstrom, 1943; Parker, 1945). When matings were restricted to the afternoon, fertility was 80.9 percent, as compared to 54.8 percent with morning matings and 71 and 74 percent with unrestricted matings (Gracewski and Scott).

Later work by Parker (1950), however, showed only a slight and probably insignificant difference in fertility between matings restricted to the morning (91.0 percent) and the afternoon (93.7 percent). Unrestricted matings produced fertility of 94.8 percent.

Maximum fertility in chickens is usually obtained at about 2 to 3 days after matings. Good fertility is obtained as long as 5 to 6 days after the last mating, and then declines rapidly, but a few fertile eggs may be obtained as late as 30 days after the last mating. Seventy-two hours after the last mating, however, spermatozoa are found only in the infundibulum, according to Van Drimmelen (1945 and 1951). This finding was based upon mucous scrapings of various parts of the oviduct.

FERTILIZATION AND EARLY EMBRYONIC DEVELOPMENT

Site of Fertilization

Ivanoff (1924) and Walton and Whetham (1933) washed out the oviduct of the hen with a spermicide and still obtained fertile eggs. Ivanoff therefore concluded that fertilization occurs in the ovary before ovulation. Because of the numerous folds and crypts in the

oviduct, it is probable that the spermicide did not reach all spermatozoa in the oviduct (Walton and Whetham).

Olsen and Neher (1948) proved conclusively that fertilization
occurs after ovulation and before the egg reaches the magnum.
They removed mature ovarian follicles from the ovaries of sterile
nonmated hens just before ovulation. These follicles then ovulated
in vitro and were transferred to the oviducts of fertile, mated hens.
Eighty-two percent of the eggs laid subsequently were fertile.

The investigators also removed ovarian follicles from fertile females, and after ovulation *in vitro*, these were transferred to the
oviducts of sterile, nonmated hens. All of these eggs were sterile.
These workers as well as Van Drimmelen (1951) also reported that
ova could be fertilized by placing fresh semen in the infundibulum
of the abdominal cavity.

Maturation, Cleavage, and Gastrulation

Approximately 24 hours before ovulation the walls of the germinal vesicle of the hen's ovum begins to disintegrate and the inner
surface of the vesicle becomes flattened (Olsen, 1942). The first
maturation division and the formation of the first polar body occur
while the ovum is still attached to the ovary. The spindle for the
second maturation division is then formed, after which ovulation
occurs.

The egg is then fertilized, usually within 15 minutes after ovulation. Three to four spermatozoa normally enter the egg at the
time of fertilization, but the female pronucleus is fertilized by only
one spermatozoon. The second polar body is extruded following
the penetration of the spermatozoa and before or simultaneously
with the fusion of the male and female pronuclei. The first cleavage
division occurs as the egg enters the isthmus, approximately 5
hours after ovulation. Within 20 minutes, the second division
occurs. The 4-cell and 8-cell cleavage stages occur while the egg is
in the isthmus. Within 4 hours after the egg has entered the uterus,
cleavage of the bastodisc has progressed from the 16-cell to approximately the 256-cell stage.

The maturation changes in the ovum can be induced prematurely with the ovulating hormone, suggesting that this hormone
normally initiates the growth and maturation division of the ovum
(Olsen and Fraps, 1950). Neher and Fraps (1946) studied the

effects of premature ovulation upon subsequent fertility and embryonic development. They forced hens to ovulate 6, 14, 22, and 30 hours prematurely, by intravenous injections of male chicken anterior pituitary extract. There was practically no difference in the fertility and hatchability of normally ovulated eggs and those ovulated 6 and 14 hours prematurely. When the ovulations were 22 hours premature, 9 out of 13 eggs were fertile.

Gastrulation in the pigeon occurs about 5 to 7 hours before laying, according to Patterson (1909). It has been assumed that the chicken egg has reached the gastrula stage by the time it is laid. However, Butler (1935), Jacobson (1948), and Sturkie and Williams (1945) have shown that this is not necessarily true. Many of the eggs have not reached the gastrula stage.

On the basis of work by Stockard (1921), it has been assumed that twinning and monstrosities in chicks are due to an interruption of development in eggs which had not reached the gastrula stage when they were laid. Sturkie and Williams believe that this assumption has little foundation. They removed eggs from the hen 5 to 10 hours before such eggs would have been laid normally and cooled them. After cooling for several hours (development interrupted long before gastrulation), the eggs were incubated. The percentage of duplicate embryos obtained was higher than the normal incidence, but was still very low (1.5 percent).

Sturkie (1946) showed that twinning and duplicity could be produced in 8 percent of the embryos when normal development was interrupted during the very early cleavage stages by lowering the body temperature of the hens.

REFERENCES

Benoit, J.   1924   Action des rayons X sur le testicule du coq domestique. Comp. Rend. Soc. Biol. 90:802.

Benoit, J.   1950   Traité de Zoologie, edited by P. P. Grassé. Tome XV: Oiseaux, p. 350. Masson & Co., Paris.

Benoit, J., and L. Ott   1938   Action de lumières de différentes longeurs d'onde sur la gonadostimulation chez le canard impubère. Comp. Rend. Soc. Biol. 127:906.

Benoit, J., F. X. Walter, and I. Assenmacher   1950   Contribution à l'étude du réflexe opto-hypophysaire gonadostimulant chez le canard soumis à des radiations lumineuses de diverses longeurs d'onde. Journal de Physiologie (Bordeaux) 42:537–541.

Bissonnette, T. H. 1936 Sexual photoperiodicity. Quart. Rev. Biol. 11:371.

Blivaiss, B. B. 1947 Interrelationships of thyroid and gonad in the development of plumage and other sex characters in Brown Leghorn roosters. Physiol. Zool. 20:67.

Breneman, W. R. 1936 The effect on the chick of some gonadotrophic hormones. Anat. Rec. 64:211.

Burger, J. W. 1943 Some effects of colored illumination on the sexual activation of the male starling. J. Exp. Zool. 94:161.

Burger, J. W., T. H. Bissonnette, and H. D. Doolittle 1942 Some effects of flashing light on testicular activation in the male starling. J. Exp. Zool. 90:73.

Burrows, W. H., and S. J. Marsden 1938 Artificial breeding of turkeys. Poultry Sci. 17:408.

Burrows, W. H., and J. P. Quinn 1937 The collection of spermatozoa from the domestic fowl and turkey. Poultry Sci. 16:19.

Burrows, W. H., and J. P. Quinn 1939 Artificial insemination of chickens and turkeys. U.S. Dept. of Agr. Cir. 525.

Butler, E. 1935 The developmental capacity of the unincubated chick blastoderm. J. Exp. Zool. 70:357.

Essenberg, J. M., and R. J. Karrasch 1940 An experimental study of the effects of roentgen rays on the gonads of the sexually mature domestic fowl. Radiology 34:358.

Gracewski, J. J., and H. M. Scott 1943 The influence of time of mating on fertility. Poultry Sci. 22:264.

Grigg, G. W. 1951 The morphology of fowl spermatozoa. Proc. Ninth World's Poultry Congr. 3:142.

Guhl, A. M. 1951 Measurable differences in mating behavior of cocks. Poultry Sci. 30:687.

Guhl, A. M., N. E. Collias, and W. C. Allee 1945 Mating behavior and the social hierarchy in small flocks of White Leghorns. Physiol. Zool. 18:365.

Guhl, A. M., and D. C. Warren 1946 Number of offspring sired by cockerels related to social dominance in chickens. Poultry Sci. 25:460.

Heuser, G. F. 1916 A study of the mating behavior of the domestic fowl. Thesis. Cornell University.

Hogue, R. L., and E. E. Schnetzler 1937 Development of fertility in young Barred Rock males. Poultry Sci. 16:62.

Hutt, F. B. 1929 On the relation of fertility in fowls to the amount of testicular material and density of sperm suspension. Proc. Roy. Soc. Edinburgh 49:102.

Ivanoff, E.   1924   Recherches expérimentales à propos du processus de la fécondation chez les poules. Comp. Rend. Soc. Biol. 91:54.

Jacobson, W.   1948   The early development of the avian embryo. I: Endoderm formation. J. Morph. 62:415.

Jones, D. G., and W. F. Lamoreux   1942   Semen production of White Leghorn males from strains selected for high and low fecundity. Poultry Sci. 21:173.

Kumaran, J. D. S., and C. W. Turner   1949a   The normal development of the testes in the White Plymouth Rock. Poultry Sci. 28:511.

Kumaran, J. D. S., and C. W. Turner   1949b   Endocrine activity of the testes of the White Plymouth Rock. Poultry Sci. 28:636.

Lamoreux, W. F.   1943   The influence of different amounts of illumination upon the production of semen in the fowl. J. Exp. Zool. 94:73.

Macartney, E. L.   1942   Diurnal rhythm of mitotic activity in the seminiferous tubules of the domestic fowl. Poultry Sci. 21:130.

Malmstrom, M. V.   1943   Factors influencing fertility in the domestic fowl. Master's thesis. University of Connecticut.

Mimura, H.   1939   On the mechanism of travel of spermatozoa through the oviduct in the domestic fowl, with special reference to artificial insemination. Sonderabdruck aus Okajimas Folia Anatomica Japonica, Band 17, Heft 5 (January, 1939). Trans. by Moore and Byerly, 1942.

Moore, O. K., and T. C. Byerly   1942   Relation of time of insemination to percent fertility. Poultry Sci. 21:253.

Munro, S. S.   1938a   Functional changes in fowl sperm during their passage through the excurrent ducts of the male. J. Exp. Zool. 79:71.

Munro, S. S.   1938b   The effect of testis hormone on the preservation of sperm life in the vas deferens of the fowl. J. Exp. Biol 15:186.

Munro, S. S.   1938c   The effect of dilution and density on the fertilizing capacity of fowl sperm suspensions. Canadian J. Res., D, 16:281.

Nalbandov, A. V., R. K. Meyer, and W. H. McShan   1946   Effect of purified gonadotrophes on the androgen secreting ability of testes of hypophysectomized cocks. Endocrinol. 39:91.

Neher, B. H., and R. M. Fraps   1946   Fertility and hatchability of the prematurely ovulated hen's egg. J. Exp. Zool. 101:83.

Olsen, M. W.   1942   Maturation, fertilization, and early cleavage in the hen's egg. J. Morph. 70:513.

Olsen, M. W., and R. M. Fraps   1950   Maturation changes in the hen's ovum. J. Exp. Zool. 114:475.

Olsen, M. W., and B. H. Neher 1948 The site of fertilization in the domestic fowl. J. Exp. Zool. 109:355.

Parker, J. E. 1939 An avian semen collector. Poultry Sci. 18:455.

Parker, J. E. 1945 Relation of time of day of artificial insemination to fertility and hatchability of hen's eggs. Poultry Sci. 24:314.

Parker, J. E. 1949 Fertility in chickens and turkeys, Chapter III in L. W. Taylor, Fertility and Hatchability of Chicken and Turkey Eggs. John Wiley & Sons, Inc., New York.

Parker, J. E. 1950 The effect of restricted matings in flocks of New Hampshire chickens on fertility and hatchability of eggs. Poultry Sci. 29:268.

Parker, J. E., F. F. McKenzie, and H. L. Kempster 1940 Observations on the sexual behavior of New Hampshire males. Poultry Sci. 19:191.

Parker, J. E., F. F. McKenzie, and H. L. Kempster 1942 Fertility in the male domestic fowl. Mo. Agr. Exp. Sta. Res. Bull. 347.

Parker, J. E., and B. J. McSpadden 1943 Seasonal variation in semen production in domestic fowls. Poultry Sci. 22:142.

Patterson, J. T. 1909 Gastrulation in the pigeon's egg: A morphological and experimental study. J. Morph. 20:65.

Philips, A. G. 1918 A brief study of the mating habits of fowls with a test of the value of a single mating. J. Am. Inst. and Invest. Poultry Husb. 4:30.

Riley, G. M. 1940 Diurnal variations in spermatogenic activity in the domestic fowl. Poultry Sci. 19:360.

Sampson, F. R., and D. C. Warren 1939 Density of suspension and morphology of sperm in relation to fertility in the fowl. Poultry Sci. 18:301.

Shaffner, C. S. 1942 Longevity of fowl spermatozoa in frozen condition. Science 96:337.

Shaffner, C. S., E. W. Henderson, and C. G. Card 1941 Viability of spermatozoa of the chicken under various environmental conditions. Poultry Sci. 20:259.

Stockard, C. R. 1921 Developmental rate and structural expression: An experimental study of twins, double monsters, and single defomrities and the interaction among embryonic organs during their origin and development. Am. J. Anat. 28:115.

Sturkie, P. D. 1946 The production of twins in Gallus domesticus. J. Exp. Zool. 101:51.

Sturkie, P. D., J. A. Pino, J. S. Weatherwax, A. J. Donnelly, and G. M. Dorrance 1949 Effect of X-rays on fertility in White Leghorn male chickens treated before puberty. Radiology 52:112.

Sturkie, P. D., and A. G. Williams 1945 Studies on pregastrular development, early embryonic development, and hatchability of prematurely laid eggs of the hen. Poultry Sci. 24:546.

Taber, E. 1951 Androgen secretion in the fowl. Endocrinol. 48:6.

Van Drimmelen, G. C. 1945 The location of spermatozoa in the hen by means of capillary attraction. J. S. Afr. Vet. Med. Assoc. 16:97 (Abs.).

Van Drimmelen, G. C. 1951 Artificial insemination of birds by the intraperitoneal route. A study in sex physiology of pigeons and fowls with reports upon a modified technique of semen collection, and a new technique of insemination, and observations on the spermatozoa in the genital organs of the fowl. Onderstepoort J. Vet. Res., Supp. N. 1:212 pp.

Walton, A., and E. O. Whetham 1933 The survival of the spermatozoon of the domestic fowl. J. Exp. Biol. 10:204.

Warren, D. C., and C. L. Gish 1943 The value of artificial insemination in poultry breeding work. Poultry Sci. 22:108.

Wheeler, N. C., and F. N. Andrews 1943 The influence of season on semen production in the domestic fowl. Poultry Sci. 22:361.

CHAPTER 17

Hypophysis

INTRODUCTION

THE endocrine organs secrete substances which have important physiological effects upon certain organs and processes of the body. These glands are ductless and discharge their hormones into the blood stream, where they are transported to the organs concerned. Some of the endocrine glands of the body produce only hormones (internal secretions), and others elaborate hormones and other substances (external secretions).

The endocrine glands or organs of the bird are: (1) hypophysis or pituitary; (2) thyroids; (3) parathyroids; (4) adrenals; (5) pancreas; (6) testes and ovary (gonads); and (7) the intestine. The first four of these are strictly endocrine organs, but the last three exhibit both endocrine and exocrine functions. The thymus and pineal bodies, which are sometimes classified as endocrine organs, are present in the bird, but their functions are not clear.

The hypophysis is the master endocrine organ because it elaborates a number of hormones which in turn stimulate other glands to secrete hormones. The testes and ovary secrete androgen and estrogen respectively, and these are discussed in the chapters on reproduction in the female and the male (Chapters 15 and 16) and in Chapter 18 (gonadal hormones). The hormones of the thyroids, parathyroids and pancreas, and adrenals are considered in Chapters 19, 20, and 21 respectively. A brief account of the intestinal hormone, secretin, is given in Chapter 11.

ANATOMY OF HYPOPHYSIS

The hypophysis, or pituitary gland, is situated in the saddlelike depression of the sphenoid bone (sella turcica), just posterior to the optic chiasma at the floor of the diencephalon. The gland comprises an anterior lobe (which consists of two distinct areas cytologically) and a posterior lobe, but no intermediate lobe, which is present in mammals. There is, as in mammals, a pars tuberalis. (See Atwell, 1939; Rahn and Painter, 1941; and Green, 1951 for review; see also Figures 61, 62, and 63.) The anterior lobe or glandular part is separated from the posterior lobe or nervous portion (infundibu-

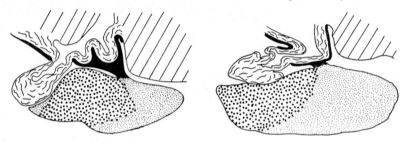

Figure 61. Diagrams of the pituitaries of the chicken (left) and duck (right); sagittal sections.

Large dots and small dots represent caudal and cephalic areas respectively of the anterior lobe. Solid black area, pars tuberalis; wavy lines, posterior lobe; parallel lines, area of third ventricle of brain. (From Rahn and Painter, *Anat. Rec.*, 1941.)

lum) by a distinct connective tissue sheath. The infundibulum and stalk communicate with the third ventricle of the brain. The anterior lobe, which is derived from Rathke's pouch as it is in mammals, and the posterior lobe are ectodermal in origin.

Nerve and Blood Supply

Drager (1945) stated that the bundle of nerve fibers comprising the pituitary stalk, the hypothalamico-hypophyseal fasciculus in the chicken, can be traced from the hypothalamus to the posterior lobe, with a few fibers leading to the pars tuberalis, but none to the anterior lobe (Figure 62). Prominent vascular channels, however, extend from the pars tuberalis into the anterior lobe of the hypophysis.

Detailed studies on the blood vessels of the bird and mammalian hypophyses have recently been made by Green (1951; see Figure 63). Similar studies concerning the duck hypophysis have been made by Benoit and Assenmacher (1951).

Green's account of the blood supply in the chicken gland is summarized as follows. The superior hypophyseal arteries supply the primary capillary net on the median eminence. The portal

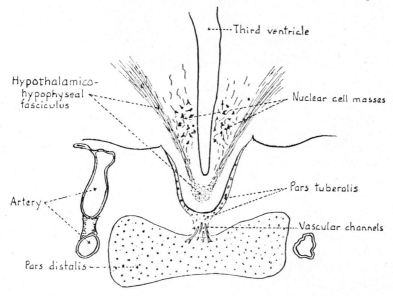

Figure 62. A composite drawing constructed from frontal sections of the chicken hypophysis, showing innervation. (From Drager, *Endocrinol.*, 1945.)

vessels collect the blood from this plexus and pass downward to the anterior lobe. On reaching the latter, they fan out in all directions (see secondary capillary network) and drain into the venous sinuses surrounding the gland. The neural lobe receives an independent blood supply from a superficial plexus of vessels which penetrates it in the form of regular arcades. These vessels project inward toward the infundibular recess. In all of the birds studied by Green, the carotid arteries anastomosed behind the anterior lobe, indenting its caudal end.

Size. The anterior lobe of birds is small. Kumaran and Turner (1949) found the anterior lobe of White Plymouth cockerels to

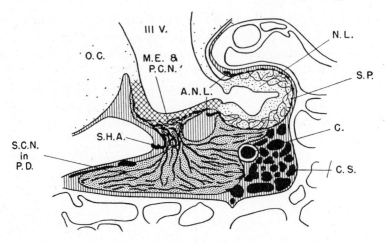

Figure 63. Pituitary of *Gallus domesticus* showing blood supply.
N.L., neural lobe; M.E., median eminence; P.C.N., primary capillary
net of portal vessels; S.H.A., superior hypophyseal artery; S.C.N., second-
ary capillary net of portal vessels; III V., third ventricle; P.D., pars distalis;
O.C., optic chiasma; A.N.L., artery of neural lobe; C.S., cavernous sinus;
C, carotid artery; S.P., superficial plexus. (From Green, *Am. J. Anat.*, 1951.)

range from 2.6 mg. at 6 weeks of age to 9.9 mg. at 20 weeks (or
near maturity). The pituitary weights of White Leghorn cockerels
at different ages are shown in Figure 64. There appears to be no
difference in the gland weights of normal males and females of
comparable body weights, at least up to 120 days of age (Oakberg,
1951). The data from Oakberg follow:

Sex and age	No.	Body weight gm.	Pituitary weights mg.	$\dfrac{Organ\ wt.}{Body\ wt.} \times 100$
White Leghorn males 120 days	59	1672	10.3	0.00063
White Leghorn females 120 days	99	1226	8.4	0.00062

HISTOLOGY

Cytologically, there are two distinct areas in the anterior lobe of
the bird pituitary. These are similar in all of the species (18) studied (Rahn and Painter, 1941). The chicken anterior lobe contains

three cell types: chromophobes, acidophils, and basophils. There are two types of acidophils; those occupying the caudal region are designated as A_1 cells, and those in the cephalic area are A_2 cells (Rahn, 1939; Payne, 1942). The cells of the caudal area are cytologically like those of the anterior lobe of mammals. The A_2 cells are usually smaller and less granular. The granules of the A_2

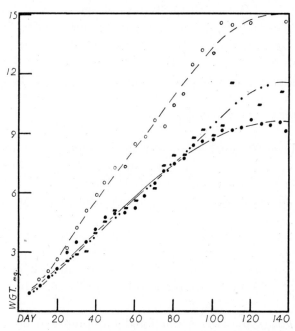

Figure 64. Anterior pituitary weights of White Leghorn cockerels and capons.

Solid line with dots, cockerels; dash-dot line with rectangles, unilaterally castrated males; broken line with circles, capons. (From Breneman, *J. Exp. Zool.*, 1950.)

cells are scarlet when stained with acid-fuchsin and methyl green, while the A_1 cells contain red or orange granules.

The time at which the cell types of the anterior lobe differentiate is controversial. Granular acidophils have been reported present in the embryonic hypophysis at either 10 days (Rahn, 1939) or 17 days (Payne, 1942). The basophils develop more slowly but appear as early as 10 days and increase in number with age of the bird, according to Payne. Rahn, however, feels that fully differentiated basophils do not appear until the bird reaches sexual maturity.

Male hypophysis. Payne (1946) studied the chicken hypophysis from the early embryonic stages to old age in both sexes. Between 10 and 30 days the weight of the male gland more than doubles, and many chromophobes change into basophils and acidophils during this time. From 30 to 50 days of age or later, there is an increase in number and size of basophils and a considerable increase in size of the testes. Breneman (1944 and 1945) reported a doubling in weight of testes and a fourfold increase in the gonadotrophic content of the pituitary during this period. All these changes are evidences of an actively growing and secreting gland. The basophils increase in number and are distributed throughout the gland. They are large and appear to be functionally active (Payne). From 90 days on, there is little change in the male pituitary except an increase in size to sexual maturity, and little change occurs after this time to one year of age. In males six to eight years old, basophils have decreased in number, but many are still functional (Payne).

From 10 days of age to sexual maturity, the acidophils become less conspicuous, because their increase is slow. Following sexual maturity, functional acidophils are still present, but in old cocks (six to eight years) they are reduced in number according to Payne (1946).

Female hypophysis. Large functional basophils are present at 10 days of age, but they are not as numerous or as large as in the male gland. From 10 days to sexual maturity, the development of the basophils fall into three periods (Payne, 1946). (1) From 10 to 40 days of age, large functional basophils continue to increase in size and number. The cells have the appearance of being highly active. (2) From 40 to 85 days, the basophils continue to increase in number, but they remain small and are not secreting at the high rate that they were at an earlier stage. (3) After 85 days, the numbers increase rapidly until at 115 days and older the pituitary is male-like in appearance. The basophils are functioning at a maximum, and this condition persists while the bird is laying.

From 10 to 115 days, the acidophils are more numerous in the female than in the male, and after sexual maturity, there is little difference. The significance of the greater number in the female is not known.

During periods of broodiness, basophils practically disappear from the pituitary and are replaced largely by small acidophils, which Payne (1943) calls "broody cells." Castration cells, which are found in the pituitaries of some castrated mammals, are not present in the castrated chicken pituitary, but are present in normal male and female chicks from 30 days to maturity (Payne, 1940 and 1947).

It is generally agreed by most workers that the basophils produce the gonadotrophic hormones. The function of the acidophils is not clearly defined. Schooley and Riddle (1938) stated that the increase and development of the acidophils in the pigeon coincide with the period of greatest growth and prolactin production. Rahn (1939) also believed that the acidophils produced prolactin and the growth hormone.

HORMONES OF THE ANTERIOR LOBE

The anterior lobe of the bird pituitary produces all of the known hormones found in the pituitaries of mammals except possibly the growth hormone, which has not yet been demonstrated. These are the adrenocorticotrophic (ACTH), thyrotrophic (TSH), follicle-stimulating (FSH), and luteinizing (LH) hormones, and prolactin. The exact units per gland of all of these have not been determined. There is evidence that the chicken pituitary produces an additional hormone, the interstitial-cell-stimulating hormone (ICSH), which is discussed later.

Three general techniques are used to determine the presence and action of pituitary hormones: (1) administration of hormones to the intact animal; (2) ablation of pituitary (hypophysectomy); and (3) replacement therapy. The hypophysis is surgically removed, and the effects on the various organs and physiological behavior are observed. Replacement therapy can follow several lines. The normal or hypophysectomized animal can be implanted or injected with whole pituitaries, pituitary extracts, or separate fractions from the glands of the same or other species, and the response of the animal observed. Quantitative estimation of the potency of the glands can be made in this way, providing the preparation of the extracts is standardized.

Considerable work has been done in assaying bird pituitaries in other animals, particularly the gonadotrophic hormones. Fractionation of the gland into specific hormones can be accomplished in the chicken by the same procedure as in mammals (Fraps, Fevold, and Neher, 1947). The major difficulty is to obtain enough glandular material to make extraction profitable. Some of the effects of the pituitary hormones have been discussed under the organs affected.

Adrenocorticotrophic Hormone (ACTH)

ACTH stimulates the growth and development of cortical tissue and the elaboration of cortical hormones of the adrenal. The bird pituitary, like that of mammals, contains ACTH, but exact amounts or potencies have not been established. ACTH is present in the hypophysis of the chick embryo by the 16th day of development and increases thereafter to hatching time. Pituitary extracts of 16-day to 18-day chick embryos injected into rabbits increase adrenal size (Moszkowski, 1949). Decapitation of chick embryos in the early stages has no appreciable effect upon adrenal size prior to 16 days of age, but thereafter there is a pronounced decrease in adrenal size and cortical tissue. That the changes in the adrenal are caused by the lack of ACTH was demonstrated by injections of ACTH which partially restored adrenal size of the decapitated embryos (Case, 1951).

The depressed adrenal weight of hypophysectomized rats can be restored to normal with fresh chicken pituitary (500 mg.) or extracts (Herbert, 1939). Early death from hypophysectomy in chickens and pigeons can be prevented by injections of extracts containing ACTH or adrenal cortical extracts (Hill and Parkes, 1934; Schooley, Riddle, and Bates, 1941; Nalbandov and Card, 1943).

In some mammals, administration of ACTH, or epinephrine which causes the pituitary to release ACTH, results in the stimulation of the adrenal cortex, which, in turn, elaborates cortical hormones. Such stimulation usually produces a depletion of ad-

renal ascorbic acid and cholesterol, and lymphopenia or eosinopenia, but this is not the case for birds. Injections of ACTH and
epinephrine into chicks (Jailer and Boas, 1950) and quails (Baldini
and Zarrow, 1951) and epinephrine into ducks (Zarrow and Zarrow, 1950) do not deplete the adrenals of ascorbic acid, but cause
adrenal hypertrophy. The effects upon the lymphocytes of the blood
were not studied. Thus, in birds the decrease of adrenal ascorbic
acid is not a necessary concomitant to the release of corticosteroids
(Jailer and Boas). In preliminary tests, ACTH injected into the chick
did not produce lymphopenia or eosinopenia (Stamler, Bolene,
Katz, Harris, and Pick, 1950).

The chick has been used as an assay animal for ACTH of mammalian origin (Bates, Riddle, and Miller, 1940). Two-day-old
chicks were injected with pituitary extracts three times daily for
five days. Increased adrenal weight served as the end point. A
straight-line response between dosage and adrenal weight was obtained. The authors described the unit of ACTH as that amount
in milligrams which produces a 25 percent increase in weight of
the adrenal during a five-day period. It was not considered necessary to hypophysectomize the chicks because they reported, contrary to others, that many nonpituitary substances which are known
to cause an increased secretion of ACTH in mammals had no effect
upon the chick (see Chapter 21).

ACTH has been isolated in pure form by Li, Evans, and Simpson (1943). It is a protein of high molecular weight (about 20,000),
and the isoelectric point is 4.7.

Thyrotrophic Hormone (TSH)

Martindale (1941) demonstrated the presence of thyrotrophic
hormones in the 11-day chick embryo by transplanting chick embryo pituitaries into the hypophysectomized chick, which restored
thyroid size. Fowl pituitary material stimulates thyroid growth in
mammalian species, and conversely the chick and pigeon thyroid
can be stimulated by pituitary extracts of mammalian origin
(Adams, 1946). Further evidence for the presence of TSH in the
bird pituitary is the decrease in size of the thyroid which follows
hypophysectomy (Mitchell, 1929; Nalbandov and Card, 1943) and
the appearance of "T" cells in the chicken pituitary following thy-

roidectomy (Payne, 1944)—effects which are duplicated in the mammal. The exact function of these T cells is not known, but Payne postulated that the normal thyroid holds their production in check just as the gonads prevent the castrate cells from forming. The thyrotrophic potency of the pituitaries containing the T cells should be higher than normal, but this has not been reported. It would appear, then, that in the fowl the thyrotrophic hormone may be elaborated by cells other than the acidophils (Payne). The chicken pituitary rates below that of the frog, rat, mouse, duck, and pig in potency of TSH, according to Adams (1946), but the chick thyroid is more sensitive in its response to TSH than glands of most animal species and is admirably suitable for assaying TSH (see Chapter 19). Winchester (1940) found the TSH content of hens' pituitaries to be highest in February and lowest in the summer.

Prolactin

Prolactin, the hormone which produces milk secretion in mammals and crop-sac secretion in pigeons, causes broodiness in chickens. It was isolated from the mammalian pituitary by Riddle, Bates, and Dykshorn (1932), who named it, and was crystallized by White, Catchpole, and Long (1937). Exact potencies of the bird pituitary for prolactin are unknown, but the glands of broody chickens contain more prolactin than nonbroody ones (Burrows and Byerly, 1936; Byerly and Burrows, 1936). This was determined by implanting chicken pituitaries on the crop sacs of pigeons and observing visually the change in thickness and proliferation of the crop-sac epithelium. Riddle, Bates,, and Lahr (1935) first demonstrated that prolactin when injected into hens causes broodiness and that the full expression of broodiness (clucking and nesting) is induced only in those breeds showing a natural tendency to go broody. Nonbroody hens clucked, but did not set, when injected.

Nalbandov and Card (1942) working with the chicken and Riddle and Bates (1939) with the pigeon showed that different breeds and strains vary in the response to prolactin. Leghorn males (a nonbroody breed) require four to five times as much prolactin to produce broodiness as the Cornish, a naturally broody breed.

The crop-sac method has been widely used in assays for prolactin. There are a number of techniques, but all are based on stimulation and growth of the gland. Three of these methods are (1) the gross weight, (2) minimum stimulation, and (3) local stimulation (see Riddle and Bates, 1939, for review).

The first is an objective method. The second is a subjective method based upon observed changes in the excised crop as examined by transmitted light. Positive stimulation is indicated by the presence of parallel strands of thickened mucosa, according to McShan and Turner, 1936. The pigeon unit is defined by them as the total amount of hormone injected (in pectoral muscles) during a period of four days which will cause a minimum, but definite, proliferation of the crop glands of 50 percent of 20 common pigeons.

In the local stimulation method (Lyons and Page, 1935), prolactin is injected intracutaneously over the crop sac, and only that small area at the site of the injection is affected. A single injection is made, and the birds are autopsied after 48 hours. The excised crop is examined as in the minimum stimulation method. This method is very sensitive. As little as 0.1 microgram of the hormone produces a response. There are also modifications of this method.

Prolactin is effective in stimulating the crop sac of pigeons in the absence of the pituitary, adrenals, thyroids, or testes, according to Riddle and Dykshorn (1932) and Schooley, Riddle, and Bates (1937).

The antigonadal action of prolactin has been demonstrated in pigeons (Riddle and Bates, 1939) and chickens (Nalbandov, Hockhauser, and Dugas, 1945). The testes and ovaries of sexually mature pigeons regress following prolactin administration, but the change can be prevented by simultaneous administration of FSH. Thus, prolactin acts by suppressing the output of FSH, which is necessary for gonad stimulation.

Riddle and Lahr (1944) induced broodiness in pigeons and doves by administration of testosterone or progesterone. These hormones caused the pituitary to release prolactin, according to these workers.

That broodiness in chickens can be terminated by estrogen administration is discussed in Chapter 18 and suggests that this hormone prevents the release of prolactin by the pituitary.

For the effects of prolactin on blood sugar, see Chapter 12.

Growth Hormone

The presence of the growth hormone in the pituitaries of birds has not been demonstrated. Results on hypophysectomy indicate that growth is retarded, but this does not indicate that the retardation is specifically due to absence of the growth hormone. Schooley, Riddle, and Bates (1941) claim to have obtained adequate growth in hypophysectomized pigeons with prolactin. Bates, Loones, and Riddle (1935) showed that prolactin increased growth in dwarf rats. Mammalian or chicken pituitary material containing the growth fraction has not been used on hypophysectomized chickens.

Gonadotrophic Hormones

The gonadotrophic hormones of the hypophysis stimulate the growth and development of the male and female gonads (Chapters 15 and 16). The pituitary of the bird, like that of mammals, produces the ovarian follicle-stimulating hormone (FSH), the luteinizing hormone (LH), and also ICSH. FSH and possibly LH are present in the pituitary of the chick embryo by 18 days of development (Moszkowski, 1949). Although the bird ovary does not produce corpora lutea, which in mammals are developed as a result of LH, both FSH and LH have been shown to exist in the chicken and duck by implants or injections of pituitary material from these species into the immature hypophysectomized mouse or rat (Benoit, 1937; Leonard, 1937; Gorbman, 1941; Riley and Fraps, 1942b; Fraps, Fevold, and Neher, 1947). Hypophysectomy results in gonad degeneration in birds (Nalbandov and Card, 1942 and 1943; Benoit, 1950). FSH stimulates tubular growth of the testes and spermatogenesis in the male and ovarian-follicle growth in the female bird, as in the mammal (Jaap, 1935; Breneman, 1936; Nalbandov and Card, 1946; and others). LH is generally agreed to be concerned with ovulation in the female and stimulation of the interstitial cells of the testes in the male of mammals.

Recent evidence by Nalbandov, Meyer, and McShan (1951) indicates that the chicken hypophysis contains either a third gonadotrophic hormone, avian ICSH, or a luteinizing hormone possessing properties different from mammalian LH. Their conclusion is based on results summarized as follows. The combs of male chickens which atrophy after hypophysectomy can be made to grow for 10 to 12 days by administering mammalian LH, but regression of comb size ensues thereafter in spite of continued administration of LH. Continuous comb growth, however, can be produced by administering chicken pituitary material. This and histological results support the contention that avian ICSH or a part of avian LH causes the metamorphosis of precursor cells into secretory Leydig cells which secrete androgen when stimulated by mammalian or avian LH.

Release of LH from the chicken pituitary occurs six to eight hours before ovulation. This was demonstrated by injecting pituitary extracts and also by hypophysectomizing laying birds prior to ovulation (Chapter 16). LH of mammalian origin is also effective in inducing ovulation in the fowl. The pituitaries of sexually mature males are considerably more potent in FSH and LH than in females, and those of nonlaying females are more potent than those of laying hens (Riley and Fraps, 1942a and b; Fraps, 1943). Male pituitaries contain 11 times as much FSH as those of laying hens and 7 times as much as those of nonlaying hens. The LH potencies in terms of ovulating units are 200, 25, and 17 units respectively for the pituitaries of males, nonlaying hens, and laying hens (Fraps, 1943). The ovulating unit is the least amount of dry pituitary tissue required to produce ovulation in 50 percent of the females treated. These results suggest that, as in mammals, estrogen secreted by the active ovary of the hen cuts down on the production of gonadotrophins by the pituitary.

Phillips (1942) assayed unfractionated pituitaries of birds of different ages and conditions for gonadotrophins. He used the rat as the assay animal and determined the effects of the extracts upon ovarian growth and epithelial changes in the vagina. He ranked these chickens in descending order of pituitary potency as follows: (1) capons; (2) springers, 2.5 to 3.5 pounds; (3) roasters, 3.5 to 6 pounds; (4) pullets approaching sexual maturity; (5) laying hens, poor to medium production; and (6) laying hens, good production.

A deficiency of vitamin E in the diet of male chickens decreases testis size and spermatogenesis and reduces the gonadotrophic potency of the pituitary (Herrick, Eide, and Snow, 1952). Nalbandov and Card (1946) concluded that in the immature chicken FSH

alone is incapable of inducing maturation of ova and that probably other hormones which mobilize calcium and yolk material
are also necessary.

The gonadotrophic potency of the serum of immature males,
immature females, and nonlaying hens is about the same and is
higher than in laying females and adult males, according to Bailey
and Phillips (1952). One cubic centimeter of the serum of nonlaying hens contains 0.1 rat unit.

Gonadotrophins and egg production. Various attempts have been
made to increase egg production in chickens by administration of
anterior pituitary hormones, but most of the results were unsuccessful or questionable. Koch (1935) and Eufinger (1939) claim to
have stimulated egg production in birds that had almost stopped
laying by administering anterior pituitary extracts (prolan). Nalbandov and Card (1946) found that FSH and LH caused pullets
to start laying about two weeks earlier than untreated birds. Very
poor or nonlaying birds laid a few more eggs, but good laying
hens stopped laying when FSH was administered. Egg production
in birds laying at a low but regular rate can be increased tempo-
rarily with progesterone or unfractionated chicken pituitary extracts, according to Neher and Fraps (Chapter 16). The injections
were made on the days that the birds normally would have not ovulated. After a number of eggs were added to the laying cycle (induced), the yolks became progressively smaller and laying eventually ceased. These workers presumed that the hen's pituitary failed
to secrete sufficient FSH to bring the follicles to maturity as rapidly
as they were ovulated.

HYPOPHYSECTOMY

Hypophysectomy has been performed in the pigeon, duck, and
chicken (Mitchell, 1929; Hill and Parkes, 1934; Schooley, 1939;
Nalbandov and Card, 1943; Rothchild, 1948a and 1948b; Benoit,
1950). There are two principal approaches to the hypophysis;
through the orbit, which entails removal of the eye (Benoit), and
through the roof of the mouth and pharynx. Some have made the
incision through the floor and roof of the mouth with beak and
mouth closed (transbuccal); others have made the incision only
through the roof of the mouth, with mouth opened and beak pulled

backward (oral approach, Rothchild). The mortality following the operation is usually higher when the transbuccal approach is employed. The injury to the lower beak and mandible makes eating difficult and increases the chances for infection. These complications are avoided or minimized by employing the oral, or parapharyngeal, approach (Schooley, 1939). With this approach, the incision is made below the mouth, around the trachea, and through the palate. After the incision is made, the area is exposed and preparations are made for drilling through the bone. Burrs of suitable size and a drill are necessary. After the gland is exposed, it may be removed by suction or destroyed by cautery. Nalbandov and Card (1943) first removed the gland by suction and then cauterized the opening. It would appear that great care must be exercised in the use of the cautery in order to avoid injury to the posterior lobe or the hypothalamus. Rothchild and also Schooley used only suction in removing the gland. In these experiments, only the anterior lobe was removed. Removal of the posterior lobe was attempted by Rothchild (unpublished), who destroyed it with the cautery.

Effects of Hypophysectomy on Mortality

The mortality rates of chickens hypophysectomized by the transbuccal and oral routes, without replacement therapy, are shown in percents, as follows (Rothchild, 1948b):

Weeks after operation	1	2	3	4	6	8	10
Oral method (42 birds)	12	14	45	62	83	90	95
Transbuccal method (130 birds)	40	48	56	62	74	81	93

The mortality for those receiving the oral operation was considerably less during the first and second weeks (less trauma), but from the third week on, there was little or no difference in the two groups of birds. Mitchell (1929) stated that none of his birds survived longer than 11 days after the operation. For growing chicks completely hypophysectomized at 60 days of age, the mortality is 70 percent 30 days after the operation (Nalbandov and Card, 1943).

Hill, Corkill, and Parkes (1934), using the transbuccal technique, reported that 24 out of 30 birds died within 48 hours after the operation. Schooley (1939) reported an early mortality of only 2 percent from the operation in pigeons.

Effects of Hypophysectomy on Growth

Data relating to growth and hypophysectomy are meager, mainly because of the excessive early mortality reported by some workers and because most of the operations on chickens were performed on the adult.

Nalbandov and Card (1943 and earlier) found that, when the gland is completely removed in growing chicks, body weight continues to increase for as long as 60 days or more, even above that of the control birds. However, the increase in weight is due to abnormal deposition of fat (from five to seven times that found in the controls), rather than true growth. Increase in length of the bones, particularly the metatarsals, in the operated birds is only 10 percent, as compared to 50 percent in the control birds during the same period. The extreme obesity observed in the birds of these investigators, who used cautery in the operation, suggests that the hypothalamus was injured, but the authors did not think so. The obesity was not associated with lipemia, as the blood lipids were of the same order as normal birds.

Rothchild (1948b) reported that hypophysectomized hens did not develop obesity or undergo marked changes in body weight. During the first 3 weeks, postoperative, body weight dropped from 10 to 15 percent and remained at this level until the 9th or 10th weeks; at this time, body weight increased to about 110 percent of the original weight and remained at this point until death at 52 weeks.

Immature hypophysectomized pigeons lose weight rapidly following the operation, approximately 20 percent during the first 10 days (Schooley, 1939). Part of this loss is due to loss of appetite, since fasted pigeons lose as much weight as the operated birds. It was shown that when the hypophysectomized birds were force-fed they maintained normal body weight.

Ablation of the pituitary in chickens decreases food consumption 50 to 70 percent and metabolic rate 20 to 40 percent (Nalbandov and Card, 1942). Restriction of food intake in normal birds reduces metabolic rate to about the same level.

Hypophysectomy and Organ Weights

It has been amply demonstrated that hypophysectomy decreases the size of many of the endocrine organs, such as the thyroids, adrenals, and gonads, and some nonendocrine organs. The effects upon the endocrine organs are as expected and have been discussed in detail under the organs concerned. Hypophysectomy in pigeons reduced the length of the intestines 20 percent. Weights of organs were reduced as follows: liver, 18 percent; pancreatic tissue, 54 percent; crop sac, 14 percent; adrenals, 27 percent; thyroids, 50 percent; and testes, 66 percent (Schooley, Riddle, and Bates, 1941).

POSTERIOR LOBE OF HYPOPHYSIS

The posterior lobe contains the pressor, oxytocic, and antidiuretic factors, according to DeLawder, Tarr, and Geiling (1934), but the amounts or units of these have not been determined. These authors state that the cephalic portion of the anterior lobe also contains these factors, but in considerably smaller quantities than the posterior lobe.

Pituitrin or pitocin, which is a commercial preparation containing mainly the oxytocic factor, produces contraction of the uterine muscles in mammals, chickens, and pigeons and causes birds to expell their eggs prematurely (Chapter 15). Effects of the pressor factor are discussed in Chapter 3.

INTERMEDIN

The chicken pituitary has no intermediate lobe, but the presence of intermedin in the anterior lobe has been demonstrated (Kleinholz and Rahn, 1940). The cephalic portion of the lobe is considerably more potent than the caudal portion (20 times). Chen, Oldham, and Geiling (1940) report that this hormone is present in the chick's hypophysis as early as the fifth day of embryonic development; they used the hypophysectomized frog as the assay animal. Intermedin causes an expansion of melanophores in the skin of the frog, chameleon, lizard, and fish. Kleinholz and Rahn used the hypophysectomized lizard, *Anolis carolinensis*, to assay the potencies of the pituitaries of several species for intermedin. They found that the cephalic portion of the anterior lobe of chickens is more potent in intermedin than equal weights of pituitary from the intermediate lobes of cattle.

CONTROL OF PITUITARY SECRETION

The manner in which the pituitary is stimulated to elaborate its hormones has been a subject of controversy and numerous researches. Although the anterior lobes of the pituitaries of mammals and birds are not directly innervated, according to most observers, some think that the gland may be activated by nerve fibers through the infundibular stalk.

Sectioning of the stalk usually produces damage to, and a hypofunctioning, pituitary (Greep and Barrnett, 1951), but the results obtained depend, in part, on the type and completeness of the operation (see also Harris, 1948a, 1948b, and 1949; Everett, Sawyer, and Markee, 1949; Everett and Sawyer, 1950; Green, 1951). In some cases, pituitary function is normal after the operation (Harris, 1949). The results of Greep and Barrnett indicate that the initial damage to the pituitary attendant upon stalk sectioning is due to impairment of the blood supply of the stalk, rather than to the blocking of nervous impulses through the stalk, which some have considered essential for activation of the hypophysis.

Direct electrical stimulation of the anterior lobe of the rabbit does not usually produce ovulation, a species in which ovulation is induced normally by coitus, but stimulation of the hypothalamus causes ovulation (Markee, Sawyer, and Hollinshead, 1946; Harris, 1948a and 1948b). Later, Harris and DeGroot (1950) showed that electrical stimulation of the hypothalamus, but not the anterior lobe, causes the rabbit's pituitary to elaborate ACTH. ACTH secretion was evidenced by a marked drop in the number of lymphocytes in the blood (lymphopenia). Harris concluded that secretion of the anterior pituitary hormones is under neural control by way of the hypothalamus and the hypophyseal portal blood vessels of the pituitary stalk. Thus, stimulation of the hypothalamus causes the elaboration of a substance which gets to the anterior lobe by way of the blood vessels and stimulates it. Further evidence for the neurohumoral control of the mammalian pituitary is found in reports by Sawyer *et al.* (1949a and 1949b). See review by Green (1951).

Benoit and co-workers, in a series of papers (see Benoit, 1950, for review), have dealt with the mechanism by which the pituitary is stimulated in the duck. Irradiation of the head and eyes stimulates the pituitary and growth of the testes, but when the head and eyes are covered and other parts of the body irradiated, the hypophysis is not stimulated (Benoit, 1937). When the eyes are enucleated and light introduced only through the orbit by way of a quartz rod, the pituitary is stimulated. The hypophysis can also be stimulated by irradiating the head even when the optic nerves are cut and also by stimulating directly the hypothalamus and hypophysis with light (Benoit, 1938 and 1950). Moreover, when areas of the central nervous system adjacent to the hypothalamus are stimulated with light, the pituitary is stimulated indirectly by way of the hypothalamus, according to Benoit and Kehl (1939).

Later, Benoit, Walter, and Assenmacher (1950) reported that various wave-lengths of light within the visible spectrum are effective in stimulating the pituitary by way of the hypothalamus, when the latter is irradiated directly. When, however, only the duck's head is irradiated, some of the colored lights were ineffective in stimulating the hypophysis. Red and orange lights stimulated the gland maximally, but the yellows, greens, and blues (wave lengths of 577, 546, and 436 mμ.) were relatively ineffective. (See also Benoit and Ott, 1938, and Chapter 16.) The difference in effect of the various lights, according to the authors, may be explained as follows. (1) The retina of the duck eye is less sensitive to yellow, green, and blue, and reflex stimulation of the pituitary through the eye by these colors is at a minimum. (2) The tissues surrounding the eye and orbital region absorb some of the colored light rays; the pituitary is, therefore, not stimulated by such light directly or indirectly by way of the central nervous system. The authors reported that red and orange rays penetrate these tissues readily, but blue rays only slightly. Light does not stimulate the duck pituitary when the pituitary stalk is sectioned, according to Benoit (1950, p. 467). Results based upon stalk sectioning, however, are open to question, as pointed out previously.

Visual (reflex) stimulation of the pigeon pituitary has been reported by Matthews (1939). Reflection of the pigeon's own image in a mirror or seeing other pigeons is sufficient to stimulate follicular growth and ovulation by way of the release of FSH and LH from the pituitary.

It was reported previously that the anterior lobe of the bird hypophysis is not directly innervated (Drager, 1945), but that prominent vascular channels extend into it. It appears, therefore, that the chicken hypophysis is stimulated by way of the hypothalamus humorally in the manner described by Harris for the rabbit.

Certain central nervous system depressants (barbiturates) are known to inhibit or delay ovulation in certain mammals (Everett and Sawyer, 1950), but they do not block ovulation in the hen (Bastian and Zarrow, 1952; Fraps and Case, 1953). In fact, they induce ovulation in some of the hens treated (Fraps and Case). Progesterone and barbiturates have a synergistic effect in inducing ovulation in the fowl. Fraps and Case suggested that barbiturate sedation may stimulate the pituitary neurohumorally to release the ovulating hormone. Recently, Nakajo (1952) interrupted broodiness in hens by electrical stimulation of the head. He believed that suppression of prolactin secretion by the pituitary was mediated by way of the hypothalamus.

There is evidence, however, that the anterior lobe can be stimulated by other routes. Progesterone, when injected or applied directly and in small amounts to the anterior lobe of the chicken hypophysis or to the muscle of the leg, evokes a release of the luteinizing hormone (Rothchild, 1949). McDermott, Fry, Brobeck, and Long (1950) demonstrated that the pituitary of the rat when transplanted to the eye releases ACTH if epinephrine is administered to the eye.

REFERENCES

Adams, A. Elizabeth   1946   Variations in the potency of thyrotrophic hormone of the pituitary in animals. Quart. Rev. Biol. 21:1.

Atwell, W. J.   1939   The morphogenesis of the hypophysis cerebri of the domestic fowl during the second and third weeks of incubation. Anat. Rec. 73:57.

Bailey, R. L., and R. E. Phillips   1952   Gonadotrophic potency of avian blood serum. Poultry Sci. 31:68.

Baldini, J. T., and M. X. Zarrow 1951 Ascorbic acid in the adrenal gland of the bobwhite quail. Poultry Sci. 30:906 (Abs.).

Bastian, J. W., and M. X. Zarrow 1952 Failure of nembutal to block ovulation in the hen. Proc. Soc. Exp. Biol. & Med. 79:249.

Bates, R. W., T. Loones, and O. Riddle 1935 Evidence from dwarf mice against the individuality of growth hormone. Proc. Soc. Exp. Biol. & Med. 33:446.

Bates, R. W., O. Riddle, and R. A. Miller 1940 Preparation of adrenotrophic extracts and their assay on two-day chicks. Endocrinol. 27:781–792.

Benoit, J. 1937 Facteurs externes de l'activité sexuelle. II: Étude du mécanisme de la stimulation par la lumière de l'activité testiculaire chez le canard domestique: Rôle de l'hypophyse. Bull. Biol. France, Belg.: 71:394.

Benoit, J. 1938 Action de divers éclairements localisés dans la région orbitaire sur la gonadostimulation chez le canard male impubère: Croissance testiculaire provoquée par l'éclairement direct de la région hypophysaire. Comp. Rend. Soc. Biol. 127:909.

Benoit, J. 1950 Traité de Zoologie, edited by P. P. Grassé. Tome XV: Oiseaux, p. 316. Masson & Co., Paris.

Benoit, J., and I. Assenmacher 1951 Étude préliminaire de la vascularisation de l'appareil hypophysaire du canard domestique. Archives d'Anatomie microscopique et de Morphologie expérimentale 40:27.

Benoit, J., and R. Kehl 1939 Nouvelles recherches sur les voies nerveuses photoréceptrices et hypophysostimulantes chez le canard domestique. Comp. Rend. Soc. Biol. 131:89.

Benoit, J., and L. Ott 1938 Action de lumières de différentes longueurs d'onde sur la gonado-stimulation chez le canard mâle impubère. Comp. Rend. Soc. Biol. 127:906–909.

Benoit, J., F. X. Walter, and I. Assenmacher 1950 Contribution à l'étude du réflexe opto-hypophysaire gonadostimulant chez le canard soumis à des radiations lumineuses de diverses longueurs d'onde. Journal de Physiologie (Bordeaux) 42:537–541.

Breneman, W. R. 1936 The effect on the chick of some gonadotrophic hormones. Anat. Rec. 64:211.

Breneman, W. R. 1944 The growth of the anterior lobe of the pituitary and the testes in the cockerel. Endocrinol. 35:456.

Breneman, W. R. 1945 The gonadotrophic activity of the anterior pituitary of cockerels. Endocrinol. 36:190.

Breneman, W. R. 1950 A study of the pituitary-gonad-comb relationship in normal, unilateral-castrated, and caponized chicks. J. Exp. Zool. 114:115.

Burrows, W. T., and T. C. Byerly   1936   Studies of prolactin in the fowl pituitary. I: Broody hens compared with laying hens and males. Proc. Soc. Exp. Biol. & Med. 34:841.

Byerly, T. C., and W. H. Burrows   1936   Studies of prolactin in the fowl pituitary. II: Effects of genetic constitution with respect to broodiness on prolactin content. Proc. Soc. Exp. Biol. & Med. 34:844.

Case, J. F.   1951   Adrenal cortical-anterior pituitary relationships during embryonic life. Presented at the New York Academy of Science Meetings, December, 1951.

Chen, G., F. K. Oldham, and E. M. K. Geiling   1940   Appearance of the melanophore-expanding hormone of the pituitary gland in developing chick embryo. Proc. Soc. Exp. Biol. & Med. 45:810.

DeLawder, A. M., L. Tarr, and E. M. K. Geiling   1934   The distribution in the chicken's hypophysis of the so-called posterior lobe principles. J. Pharm. & Exp. Thera. 51:142.

Drager, G. A.   1945   The innervation of the avian hypophysis. Endocrinol. 36:124.

Eufinger, W.   1939   Hormonale Beeinflussung der Legetätigkeit beim Huhn. Arch. f. Geflügelkunde 13:1.

Everett, J. W., and C. M. Sawyer   1950   A 24-hour periodicity in the "LH-release apparatus" of female rats, disclosed by barbiturate sedation. Endocrinol. 47:198.

Everett, J. W., C. M. Sawyer, and J. E. Markee   1949   A neurologic timing factor in control of the ovulatory discharge of LH in the cyclic rat. Endocrinol. 44:234.

Fraps, R. M.   1943   Potencies of anterior pituitary glands of mature chickens in the induction of ovulation in the hen. Anat. Rec. 87:443.

Fraps, R. M., and J. F. Case   1953   Premature ovulation in the domestic fowl under barbiturate sedation. Proc. Exp. Biol. & Med. 45:810.

Fraps, R. M., H. L. Fevold, and B. B. Neher   1947   Ovulatory response of the hen to presumptive luteinizing and other fractions free from fowl anterior pituitary tissue. Anat. Rec. 99:571 (Abs.).

Gorbman, A.   1941   Comparative anatomy and physiology of the anterior pituitary. Quart. Rev. Biol. 16:294.

Green, J. D.   1951   The comparative anatomy of the hypophysis with special reference to its blood supply and innervation. Am. J. Anat. 88:225.

Greep, R. O., and R. J. Barrnett   1951   The effect of pituitary stalk section on the reproductive organs of female rats. Endocrinol. 49:172.

Harris, G. W. 1948a Neural control of the pituitary gland. Physiol. Rev. 28:159.

Harris, G. W. 1948b Electrical stimulation of the hypothalamus and the mechanism of neural control of the adenohypophysis (anterior lobe). J. Physiol. 107:418.

Harris, G. W. 1949 Symposium of neuro-hormonal mechanisms. J. Endocrinol. 6:16 (Proc.).

Harris, G. W., and J. DeGroot 1950 Hypothalamic control of the secretion of adenocorticotrophic hormone. Fed. Proc. 9:57.

Herbert, S. K. 1939 The gonadotrophic and adrenotrophic hormones of the chicken hypophysis. J. Pharm. & Exp. Thera. 65:104.

Herrick, E. H., I. M. Eide, and M. R. Snow 1952 Vitamin E in pituitary gland function of fowls. Proc. Soc. Exp. Biol. & Med. 79:441.

Hill, R. T., A. B. Corkill, and A. S. Parkes 1934 Hypophysectomy of birds. II: General effects of hypophysectomy of fowls. Proc. Roy. Soc. London, B, 116:208.

Hill, R. T., and A. S. Parkes 1934 Hypophysectomy of birds. I: Technique, with a note on results. Proc. Roy. Soc. London, B, 115:402.

Jaap, R. G. 1935 Gonad-stimulating potency of individual pituitaries. Poultry Sci. 14:237.

Jailer, J. W., and N. F. Boas 1950 The inability of epinephrine or adrenocorticotrophic hormone to deplete the ascrobic acid content of the chick adrenal. Endocrinol. 45:312.

Kleinholz, L. H., and H. Rahn 1940 The distribution of intermedin: A new biological method of assay and results of tests under normal and Experimental conditions. Anat. Rec. 76:157.

Koch, W. 1935 Über den Einfluss von Prolan auf die Legetätigkeit der Vögel. Klin. Wschr. 14:1850.

Kumaran, J. D. S., and C. W. Turner 1949 The normal development of the testes in the White Plymouth Rock. Poultry Sci. 28:511.

Leonard, S. L. 1937 Luteinizing hormone in bird hypophyses. Proc. Soc. Exp. Biol. & Med. 37:566.

Li, C. H., H. M. Evans, and M. E. Simspon 1943 Adrenocorticotrophic hormone. J. Biol. Chem. 149:413.

Lyons, W. R., and E. Page 1935 Detection of mammotropin in the urine of lactating woman. Proc. Soc. Exp. Biol. & Med. 32:1049.

McDermott, W. V., E. G. Fry, J. R. Brobeck, and C. N. H. Long 1950 Mechanism of control of adrenocorticotrophic hormone. Yale J. Biol. & Med. 23:52.

McShan, W. H., and C. W. Turner 1936 Bioassay of galactin, the lactogenic hormone. Proc. Soc. Exp. Biol. & Med. 34:50.

Markee, J. E., C. H. Sawyer, and W. H. Hollinshead 1946 Activation of the anterior hypophysis by electrical stimulation in the rabbit. Endocrinol. 38:345.

Martindale, F. M. 1941 Initiation and early development of thyrotrophic function in the incubating chick. Anat. Rec. 79:373.

Matthews, L. H. 1939 Visual stimulation and ovulation in pigeons. Proc. Roy. Soc. London, B, 126:557.

Meyer, R. K., C. H. Mellish, and H. S. Kupperman 1939 The gonadotrophic and adrenotrophic hormones of the chicken hypophysis. J. Pharm. & Exp. Thera. 65:104.

Mitchell, J. B. 1929 Experimental studies of the bird hypophysis. I: Effects of hypophysectomy in the Brown Leghorn fowl. Physiol. Zool. 2:411.

Moszkowski, A. 1949 Pouvoir corticotrope et gonadotrope de l'hypophyse de l'embryon de poulet. Comp. Rend. Soc. Biol. 143:1332.

Nakajo, S. 1952 Effect of electrical stimulation of the head on broodiness of chickens. Poultry Sci. 31:337.

Nalbandov, A., and L. E. Card 1942 Hormonal induction of broodiness in roosters. Poultry Sci. 21:474 (Abs.).

Nalbandov, A., and L. E. Card 1943 Effect of hypophysectomy of growing chicks. J. Exp. Zool. 94:387.

Nalbandov, A., and L. E. Card 1946 Effect of FSH and LH upon the ovaries of immature chicks and low-producing hens. Endocrinol. 38:71.

Nalbandov, A., M. Hockhauser, and M. Dugas 1945 A study of the effect of prolactin on broodiness and on cock testes. Endocrinol. 36:251.

Nalbandov, A., R. K. Meyer, and W. H. McShan 1951 The role of a third gonadotrophic hormone in the mechanism of androgen secretion in chicken testes. Anat. Rec. 110:475.

Oakberg, E. F. 1951 Genetic differences in quantitative histology of the adrenal, organ weights, and inter-organ correlations in White Leghorn chickens. Growth 15:57.

Payne, F. 1940 Signet-ring or castration cells in the chick pituitary. Anat. Rec. 76:29.

Payne, F. 1942 The cytology of the anterior pituitary of the fowl. Biol. Bull. 82:79.

Payne, F. 1943 The cytology of the anterior pituitary of broody fowls. Anat. Rec. 86:1.

Payne, F. 1944 Pituitary changes in aging capons. Anat. Rec. 89:563.

Payne, F. 1946 The cellular picture in the anterior pituitary of normal fowls from embryo to old age. Anat. Rec. 96:77.

Payne, F. 1947 The effects of gonad removal on the anterior pituitary of the fowl from ten days to six years. Anat. Rec. 97:507.

Phillips, R. E. 1942 Comparative gonadotrophic potency of unfractionated extracts of poultry pituitaries. Poultry Sci. 21:161.

Rahn, H. 1939 The development of the chick pituitary with special reference to the cellular differentiation of the pars buccalis. J. Morph. 64:483.

Rahn, H., and B. T. Painter 1941 The comparative histology of the bird pituitary. Anat. Rec. 79:297.

Riddle, O. 1947 Endocrines and Constitution in Doves and Pigeons. Carnegie Institution of Washington, Publication 572.

Riddle, O., and R. W. Bates 1939 The preparation, assay, and actions of lactogenic hormones, in sex and Internal Secretions, edited by Edgar Allen. 2d ed., pp. 1088–1117. Williams & Wilkins Co., Baltimore.

Riddle, O., R. W. Bates, and S. W. Dykshorn 1932 A new hormone of the anterior pituitary. Proc. Soc. Exp. Biol. & Med. 29:1211.

Riddle, O., R. W. Bates, and E. L. Lahr 1935 Prolactin induces broodiness in the fowl. Am. J. Physiol. 111:352.

Riddle, O., and S. W. Dykshorn 1932 The secretion of crop milk in the castrate pigeon. Proc. Soc. Exp. Biol. & Med. 29:1213.

Riddle, O., and E. L. Lahr 1944 On broodiness of ring doves following implants of certain steroid hormones. Endocrinol. 35:255.

Riley, G. M., and R. M. Fraps 1942a Relationship of gonad-stimulating activity of female domestic fowl anterior pituitaries to reproductive activity. Endocrinol. 30:537.

Riley, G. M., and R. M. Fraps 1942b Biological assays of the male chicken pituitary for gonadotrophic potency. Endocrinol. 30:529.

Rothchild, I. 1948a A simplified technique for hypophysectomy of domestic fowl. Endocrinol. 43:293.

Rothchild, I. 1948b Notes on survival and body weight changes of adult hens following hypophysectomy. Endocrinol. 43:298.

Rothchild, I. 1949 An indication that the ovulating hormone release inducing action of progesterone is an indirect one. Fed. Proc. 8:135.

Sawyer, C. H., J. W. Everett, and J. E. Markee 1949a A neural factor in the mechanism by which estrogen induces the release of luteinizing hormone in the rat. Endocrinol. 44:218.

Sawyer, C. H., J. E. Markee, and B. F. Townsend 1949b Cholinergic and adrenergic components in the neurohumoral control of the release of LH in rabbits. Endocrinol. 44:18.

Schooley, J. P.   1939   Technique for hypophysectomy in pigeons. Endocrinol. 25:373.

Schooley, J. P., and O. Riddle   1938   The morphological basis of pituitary function in pigeons. Am. J. Anat. 62:314.

Schooley, J. P., O. Riddle, and R. W. Bates   1937   Effective stimulation of crop sacs by prolactin in hypophysectomized and in adrenalectomized pigeons. Proc. Soc. Exp. Biol. & Med. 36:408.

Schooley, J. P., O. Riddle, and R. W. Bates   1941   Replacement therapy in hypophysectomized juvenile pigeons. Am. J. Anat. 69:123.

Shellabarger, C. J.   1952   Pinealectomy vs. pineal injection in the young cockerel. Endocrinol. 51:152.

Stamler, J., C. Bolene, L. N. Katz, R. Harris, and R. Pick   1950   Influence of pancreatectomy on lipid metabolism and atherogenesis in the chick. Fed. Proc. 9:121.

White, A., H. R. Catchpole, and C. N. H. Long   1937   A crystalline protein with high lactogenic activity. Science 86:82.

Winchester, C. F.   1940   Growth and development. II: Seasonal metabolic and endocrine rhythms in the domestic fowl. Mo. Agr. Exp. Sta. Res. Bull. 315.

Zarrow, M. W., and I. G. Zarrow   1950   Ascorbic acid in the adrenal gland of the duck. Anat. Rec. 108 (Abs.).

CHAPTER 18

Gonadal Hormones

ANDROGEN is produced by the interstitial cells of the testis and ovary. The exact site of production of estrogen in birds has not been determined. It is generally conceded that the theca cells are the principal source of estrogen in mammals. The principal naturally-occurring androgen and estrogen are believed to be testosterone and estradiol. Progesterone is produced by the corpora lutea of the mammalian ovary, but the site of production in birds has not been established (see later section).

In recent years, a number of synthetic estrogens have become available, such as diethylstilbestrol, dianisylhexene, dienestrol, and many others. The structural formulas of some of the gonadal hormones are shown in Figure 65.

SECONDARY SEXUAL CHARACTERISTICS

Secondary sexual characteristics which differentiate male and female birds include differences in comb size, plumage color, structure of feathers, voice, and temperament. The gonadal hormones are responsible for many of these. Androgen produces comb growth in males and females. In the latter, where the comb is smaller, the androgen is produced by the interstitial cells of the medulla of the ovary (Taber, 1949 and 1951).

The size and shape of the feathers is influenced by the gonadal hormones and the thyroid hormone (see Chapter 19). The hackle and saddle feathers of the male are elongated and tapering in form and those of the female are shorter and blunt. This difference is not due to androgen, but is caused by estrogen. Castrated males (capons) and females (poulards) develop feathers malelike in structure except that they are longer (neutral type plumage).

The response of henny-feathered breeds to sex hormones is different. The male of this breed has the same type feather structure as the female. Henny feathering is dominant to normal feathering. When henny-feathered males are castrated, their plumage reverts to the neutral type. The plumage of the castrated female of the henny breed also reverts to the male or neutral type, as does that of normal females. It has been demonstrated by testicular grafts and hormone injections that the gonads of the hen-feathered male

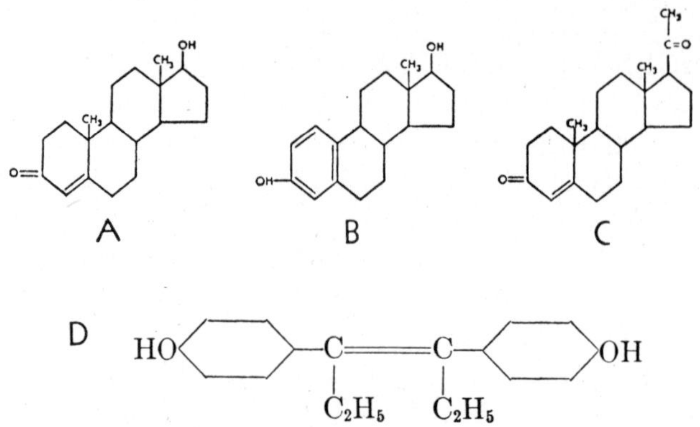

Figure 65. Gonadal hormones (steroids).
A, testosterone; B, alpha estradiol; C, progesterone; D, diethylstilbestrol.

produce androgen as do the gonads of normal males. Thus, the gene for henny feathering acts directly on the feather follicle but requires androgen for its expression. For details, see Benoit (1950), Hutt (1949), Greenwood and Blyth (1938a), and Nickerson (1946).

Color Changes in Birds

Certain breeds of chickens as well as other species of birds exhibit plumage dimorphism, and some of these differences are due to gonadal hormones (Benoit, 1950; Brown, 1950). In most species, the male is more brilliantly colored than the female. The plumage of the female castrate chicken (Brown Leghorn) reverts to that of the male in color, but the castrated-male plumage color is unchanged. The difference in male and female plumage color is therefore caused by the action of estrogen. In the African weaver finches, the neutral type is the hen plumage; the cock plumage is the result of pituitary hormones (Brown, 1950). Only in the herring gull does the cock type of plumage depend upon the action of androgens (Boss, 1943). The color of the beak of the weaver finch and the sparrow (Witschi and Woods, 1936) increases in intensity when androgen is injected.

In black breeds of chickens, the intensity of the black pigment is usually greater in the female, and this is due to estrogen. In certain crosses involving black and spangled birds, the female offspring may show more black and less spangling than in the males. The development of plumage color in the embryos of a number of breeds and studies on feather and skin grafting have been reviewed by Benoit (1950) and Hutt (1949).

Comb Growth

The dramatic effect of androgen upon comb growth has been demonstrated by a number of workers. Breneman (1938 and 1939) injected day-old chicks with testosterone propionate and dihydroandrosterone (0.6 to 2.5 mg. per day) for 5 to 10 days. The increase in comb size was tremendous, and some of the chicks began crowing as early as 7 days of age. Testes size was decreased. Kumaran and Turner (1949b) also demonstrated that treatment of the male with androgen decreases testes size and depresses spermatogenesis by suppressing the output of pituitary FSH. Dorfman and Dorfman (1948a) revealed that the comb of the White Leghorn is 15 times as sensitive to androgen as the combs of Rhode Island Reds and Barred Plymouth Rocks. Because of the variation in response to androgens in comb growth of different breeds (Dorfman and Dorfman, 1948b) and even strains within a breed (Campos and Shaffner, 1952), the use of the chick comb as an assay technique is subject to considerable error.

Deficiencies of vitamins A, D, and E, pantothenic acid, folic acid, nicotinic acid, choline, riboflavin, pyridoxine, and biotin do not influence the response of the chick comb to androgen (Haque, Lillie, Shaffner, and Briggs, 1949). The negative effect of folic acid was also confirmed by Zarrow, Koretsky, and Zarrow (1951).

Castration in Males and Females

Castration in the male, or caponization, is practiced commonly by poultrymen. Capons develop more slowly and put on more fat than the uncastrated male, particularly after five months of age. The amount of hemoglobin in the blood and the number of erythrocytes are influenced by androgen. Capons have the same number of red cells as females. Castrated females injected with androgen develop the number of red cells of a normal male (Juhn and Domm, 1930; Taber, Davis, and Domm, 1943; see also Chapter 1). Capons have a lower rate of metabolism than cocks by about 13.5 percent, according to Mitchell, Card, and Haines (1927).

Burmester and Nelson (1945) reported that the female chicken is more susceptible to lymphomatosis than the male, and capons are more susceptible than normal males. The results of these authors suggest that androgen is responsible for the increased resistance of normal males. When the capons were treated with androgen, their susceptibility was the same as that of normal males. Later work by Davis, Andrews, and Doyle (1951) suggests that androgen is not the sole factor involved in the lower incidence of the disease in males, but that hormone imbalance and possibly other factors are concerned.

Castration in the female is termed ovariectomy or ovariotomy; the castrate is known as a poulard. A general review of the effects of ovariectomy in the fowl was presented by Domm (1929 and 1939). The effects of sinistral and bilateral ovariectomy are different. Usually two operations are required for bilateral ovariectomy. In the first operation, the left ovary is removed (sinistral). Then the rudimentary right gonad hypertrophies to form an ovotestes. Soon after the sinistral operation and succeeding the next molt, the new plumage is malelike in color and structure; but later when the right gonad develops and secretes estrogen, the new plumage, following the next molt, may revert to the female type. Then the right gonad is removed, and the plumage reverts to male type again and remains this type. The operation is difficult to perform. Usually an electric cautery is used, and even with this instrument it is difficult to avoid lethal hemorrhages.

SEX REVERSAL

Crew (1923) reported a case of complete sex reversal in a hen. This female developed a tumor or ovotestis at the site of the left ovary. Spermatozoa were produced and the bird sired offspring.

The presence of the left ovary suppresses the development of the rudimentary right gonad, for when the left ovary is removed or diseased, the right gonad hypertrophies (both cortex and medulla) and develops into an ovotestis. If the female chick is ovariectomized sinistrally during the first 30 days of age, the subsequently hypertrophied right gonad may undergo normal spermatogenesis (Domm, 1929).

Hutt (1937) reported a case of gynandromorphism in the fowl, wherein the left side of the body was female in structure and the right side male in structure. The male side contained an ovotestis, and the female side, a nearly normal ovary. Hutt believed that this bird was originally a male, but that there was a loss of a sex chromosome in the two-cell cleavage stage, such that the female half of the bird developed from the cells which lost the chromosome.

In recent years a number of reports have appeared on the effects of androgen and estrogen on sexual development of the embryo (see review by Benoit, 1950). The hormones are injected into the egg before differentiation of the gonads (six to seven days). When estrogen is injected into zygotic females, the left ovary and the Wolffian ducts are usually not affected. The right oviduct, which normally is very small or degenerated at hatching time, persists and is hypertrophied, and so is the left oviduct. The zygotic male injected with estrogen develops an ovotestis on the left side, and sometimes on the right side, if the dose injected is large enough. With large doses, ovarian follicles with oöcytes may be present on the left side. In addition the left, and sometimes the right, oviduct may be present.

Testosterone injected into zygotic males has little effect except to increase the size of the Wolffian ducts and decrease slightly the size of the testes. In zygotic females the effects of testosterone are pronounced. The normal left ovary is transformed into an ovotestis and the right gonad (which normally degenerates) forms a testis, due to proliferation of the medullary tissue. Development of the left oviduct (Mullerian duct) is partially inhibited, but the right one is stimulated.

Estrogen injected into incubating eggs has pronounced effects upon the hatched and growing chick. Greenwood and Blyth (1938b) found that most of such females raised to maturity failed to lay eggs and most of the few eggs that were laid were devoid of shell or shell membranes. At autopsy, these birds showed two incompletely formed oviducts.

EFFECTS OF ESTROGEN ON THE OVIDUCT

The tremendous increase in size of the oviduct of the hen coincident with sexual maturity is attributable to the effects of estrogen, elaborated by the maturing ovary. The sensitivity of the avian oviduct is such that growth of the immature oviduct has been used as an assay method for estrogens (Kosin, 1942; Munro and Kosin, 1943 and 1946; Hertz, 1945; Jaap, 1945; Kar, 1947a; Dorfman and Dorfman, 1948c).

The chick oviduct may show a 40-fold increase in size following continued estrogen administration when the birds are fed a normal ration, but the response to estrogen is diminished if the ration is deficient in folic acid (Hertz, 1945). The diminished response is not due mainly to inanition, although this is a factor, but possibly to the fact that folic acid is involved in the enzyme system through which estrogen exerts its effect, according to Kline and Dorfman (1951). These investigators demonstrated that a deficiency of thiamine in the ration increases the response of the chick oviduct to all levels of estrogen, and so does a deficiency of nicotinic acid when moderate to low doses of estrogen are administered. But at very high levels, the oviduct response is reversed. Chicks deficient in riboflavin show a diminished oviduct response to estrogen, but this is due principally to inanition, because when the control birds were starved, there was little difference in the response of the two groups. Thiamine deficiency appears to interfere with estrogen inactivation and to produce an increased oviduct response, regardless of the effect of inanition (Kline and Dorfman).

The response of the chick oviduct to estrogen is not affected appreciably by deficiencies in riboflavin, pantothenic acid, choline, and vitamins A and D, but is influenced by folic-acid deficiency (Haque, Lillie, Shaffner, and Briggs, 1949).

Thyroxine and thiouracil, despite the fact that they inhibit the rise induced by estrogen in serum calcium, phosphorus, and some other constituents of the plasma, do not inhibit the hypertrophy of the oviduct produced by estrogens, according to Fleischmann and Fried (1945) and Common, Keefe, and Maw (1950). The latter workers disclosed that thiouracil enhances slightly the effects of estrogen in stimulating growth of the oviduct. Progesterone, however, reduces the effect of estrogen on the oviduct (Hertz, Larsen, and Tullner, 1947).

EFFECTS OF ESTROGEN ON PLASMA
AND TISSUE CONSTITUENTS

Blood Calcium and Phosphorus

Most investigators are agreed that total calcium and phosphorus increase as birds begin laying. The increase in calcium is principally in the nondiffusible fraction. (See Chapter 2.) Most of the phosphorus fractions are increased, particularly the lipid and protein phosphorus (Common, Bolton, and Rutledge, 1948; Fleischmann and Fried, 1945, on the chicken; McDonald and Riddle, 1945, on the pigeon; and others). That these increases result from the effects of estrogen has been demonstrated by a number of workers with pigeons, chickens, and ducks. Examples of the effects of estrogen on total calcium and phosphorus are shown in Table 36. The role of the parathyroids in causing these increases is discussed in Chapter 20.

Blood Lipids

The lipids of the blood increase with laying (see Chapter 2), and this increase is governed mainly by estrogen, which has been demonstrated in the chicken, duck, and pigeon (Table 37).

Lorenz (1938) and Entenman, Lorenz, and Chaikoff (1940), who injected estradiol benzoate (3.8 to 6.9 mg./kg.) into immature male and female chickens, reported tremendous increases in all the lipid fractions, approaching or exceeding the values they reported in laying females (also Chapter 2). Similar results have been obtained in cocks, capons, pigeons, and ducks (see Riddle, 1942; Benoit, 1950). Different estrogens vary in their lipogenic potencies (Lorenz and Bachman, 1947).

The effects of estrogen on proteins and blood sugar are discussed in Chapters 2 and 12 respectively.

Tissue Constituents

Estrogen increases plasma riboflavin, vitamin A, liver fat, and liver protein in the chicken (Common, Rutledge, and Bolton, 1947; Common, Bolton, and Rutledge, 1948). The liver weight of the pigeon is also increased by estrogen, approximately 80 percent (depending upon dosage), and the increase is due to the increase in the number and size of the liver cells (Clavert, 1944).

Fleischmann and Fried (1945) claimed that estrogen does not increase the amount of cholesterol in the tissues and that the in-

Table 36. Effects of estrogen (injected for five or more days) on serum calcium and phosphorus

Species, age, and treatment	Total serum calcium mg./100 ml.		Inorganic serum phosphorus mg./100 ml.	
	Control	Treated	Control	Treated
*Duck, mature Pekin male; estradiol, 1 mg. per day	10.4	52.4	2.4	9.9
†Pigeon, males and females, immature; estradiol, 0.25 to 5 mg. per day	10.5	28.9	4.3	6.6
‡Chicken, immature, both sexes; estradiol, 1 mg. per day	11.9	30.4	7.6	16.3
§Chicken, immature females; estradiol	12.5	49.8	7.3	16.0

* Landauer, Pfeiffer, Gardner, and Shaw (1941).
† McDonald, Riddle, and Smith (1945).
‡ Fleischmann and Fried (1945).
§ Common, Bolton, and Rutledge (1948).

crease observed in the plasma is not caused by changes in synthesis or destruction of cholesterol, but by alterations in the distribution of cholesterol between plasma and tissues. Stamler, Bolene, Dudley, and Levinson (1950) found, on the other hand, that diethylstilbestrol pellets implanted in six-week-old cockerels increase not only the cholesterol and fatty acids in the plasma, but also in the tissues. They studied the liver, kidney, heart, adrenals, gut, and lungs, and all showed an increased cholesterol content. All the visceral organs had increased amounts of lipid phosphorus, and all except the heart showed significant increases in total lipids and fatty acids. They concluded that estrogen increases lipid synthesis in the liver, but has little effect upon the destruction of lipids.

Thyroxine administered to the pigeon or chicken prevents the increases in plasma lipids, vitamin A, phosphorus, liver protein,

Table 37. Effects of estrogens on lipids of blood

Species and treatment	Total lipids, serum mg./100 ml.		Author
	Control	Treated	
Duck, male; estradiol, 1 mg. per day	448	3,136	Landauer *et al.* (1941)
Pigeon, both sexes, immature; estradiol, 0.25–0.5 mg. per day	468	1,775	McDonald & Riddle (1945)
Chicken, cock; stilbestrol, 4 mg. per day, 6 days	125	5,430	Zondek & Marx (1939)
Chicken, immature, estradiol, 3.8 to 6.9 mg. /kg.	415	2,261	Entenman *et al.* (1940)
Chicken, laying hen; Dianisylhexene, in feed	1,689	3,417*	Lorenz & Bachman (1947)

* Neutral fat.

and plasma proteins induced through estrogen injections (Fleischmann and Fried, 1945; McDonald, Riddle, and Smith 1945; Common *et al.*, 1947 and 1948; Sturkie, 1951) by decreasing the synthesis of, or increasing the destruction of, these. (See also Chapter 2.) Thiouracil appears to have the same effect as thyroxine, except that it does not decrease liver weight and liver protein, but actually increases them, even though it depresses serum proteins (Common, Keefe, and Maw, 1950).

That the liver is the principal organ concerned in the increased synthesis of lipids induced by estrogen was proven by Ranney and Chaikoff (1951), who demonstrated that estrogen does not induce lipemia in the hepatectomized fowl. The liver is also the principal site of formation of phospholipids in the fowl (Ranney, Chaikoff, and Entenman, 1951), as it is in the mammal (Chaikoff, Lindsay, Lorenz, and Entenman, 1948).

Estrogen and Ossification

Kyes and Potter (1934) noted that female pigeons have solid bones and males have marrow-filled bones. The condition of the bones in females is correlated with the size of the ovarian follicles and suggests that elaboration of estrogen by the ovaries accounts for the sex difference (see Gardner and Pfeiffer, 1942, for review). It has since been demonstrated that injections of estrogen increase ossification, particularly of endosteal bone in male pigeons, chickens, ducks, and sparrows (Pfeiffer and Gardner, 1938; Landauer, Pfeiffer, Gardner, and Shaw, 1941; McDonald, Riddle, and Smith, 1945). Usually the increase in plasma calcium precedes the hyperossification, indicating a lag in calcium deposition. There appears to be a species variation in the response, but some of the variation observed may be due to differences in dosages.

Thyroxine (injected) prevents or decreases the formation of medullary bone in the duck (Clavert, 1942) and the pigeon (McDonald, Riddle, and Smith) induced by estrogen. Injection of pigeons with alizarin demonstrated that calcium deposited in new bone is stained but that deposited on the egg shell is not (Gardner and Pfeiffer, 1942).

EFFECTS OF GONADAL HORMONES ON OUTPUT
OF PITUITARY HORMONES

Administration of estrogen and androgen to male and female birds depresses the output of pituitary gonadotrophins. Nalbandov and Baum (1948) reported that it is feasible to use estrogenized chicken males as test animals for assaying gonadotrophins, since they indicated that the effect of estrogen upon the output of pituitary gonadotrophins is equivalent to hypophysectomy. Kumaran and Turner (1949a) also concluded that estrogen administration to male chickens depresses the output of pituitary gonadotrophins, but has no appreciable effect upon the output of the other pituitary hormones except the adrenal hormones, which are stimulated. They showed that weights of the pituitary, thyroids, parathyroids, and pancreas are not affected by estrogen, but that the adrenals are enlarged. Hypertrophy of the adrenals of pigeons and chickens with estrogen has also been reported by Breneman (1942), Stamler *et al.* (1950), and Miller and Riddle (1939). Kar (1947b), however, reported no effects of estrogen on adrenal weight, but he observed an increase in size of the vacuoles of the cells of the cortex.

Androgen does not affect size of the chick adrenal, according to Kar (1947b) and Kumaran and Turner (1949b), and apparently has no appreciable effect upon the weights of the pituitary, thyroid, or parathyroids. Estrogen does not influence size of the thyroids or parathyroids of birds according to these investigators.

That estrogen depresses the secretion of prolactin by the pituitary is suggested by the work of Godfrey and Jaap (1950), demonstrating that broodiness in hens can be interrupted with estrogen.

Progesterone. Progesterone is produced by the maturing ovarian follicles and corpora lutea of mammals. Corpora lutea are absent in birds, and ovarian follicles of pigeons and chickens contain negative or insignificant amounts of progesterone, as shown by results from the McGinty test (Riddle and Schooley, 1944). Progesterone has been isolated from the blood of laying hens, nonlaying hens, and cocks, but not capons, suggesting that either the male or female gonad is concerned in its production, according to Fraps, Hooker, and Forbes (1948 and 1949). The authors state that they cannot exclude the possibility that the substance in avian blood, eliciting in the mammalian uterus (basis of test) the same reaction as progesterone, may not be progesterone. However, Hooker and Forbes (1949) tested 25 other substances believed most likely to duplicate the action of progesterone and failed. Progesterone has been isolated from organs other than the corpora lutea in mammals, particularly the adrenal.

Kar (1949) reported that progesterone injected into immature male pigeons for 30 days increases testicular weight and changes the epithelium of the tubules from the prepuberal state (one layer of cells) to the multilayered condition. The Leydig cells were also in-

creased. Kar concluded that progesterone stimulates the pituitary
to release FSH and LH.

EFFECTS OF ESTROGEN ADMINISTRATION ON FAT
DEPOSITION, GROWTH, AND STORAGE OF
ESTROGEN IN TISSUES

The blood lipids of the laying female are considerably higher
than in nonlaying females and in males, and most of the surplus fat
is deposited in the egg to form the yolk. Since the blood lipids of
males receiving estrogen are also increased, this suggested that the
surplus blood fat in males might be stored in the tissues, thus making the bird fatter and more desirable as a meat bird. The feasibility
of this idea has been tested by a number of investigators with varying results.

Most of the work has been done with synthetic estrogens such as
diethylstilbestrol, or its dimethyl ether (dianisylhexene), and
dienestrol diacetate. Diethylstilbestrol (DS) is effective when injected or implanted, but relatively ineffective when given orally
(Jaap and Thayer, 1944; Jaap, 1945; Lorenz, 1945b). Lorenz
(1945b) showed that when DS is implanted, about 2 mg. per week
had to be absorbed to give satisfactory results. Treatment for four
to six weeks was found in most cases to be optimum. The size of the
pellet implanted ranges from 15 to 25 mg., depending on the size
of the bird. The pellet is usually implanted in the skin, high on
the neck or head, with an implanter, a trocar and plunger device,
especially designed for the operation. Diethylstilbestrol may also
be implanted in the form of a paste.

Dianisylhexene and dienestrol are effective orally when fed at the
level of 0.01 percent or less of the feed for three to six weeks. Lorenz
and Bachman (1947) found that these estrogens gave satisfactory
results when fed at levels of 0.0033 percent, but more time was required to produce results than at higher levels. At the 0.01 level or
above, lipemia was produced, but not at the 0.0033 level.

Fat Deposition

Almost all investigators have reported that estrogen increases the
amount of fat deposited in the tissues, particularly abdominal fat,
and improves the grade of the carcass of males. This has been
demonstrated in broilers, roasters, and cocks.

An example of the improvement in market grade or quality is shown as follows (from Thayer, Jaap, and Penquite, 1945):

No. of birds	Treatment	Percent in each fat grade			
		AA+	AA	A	B
119 cockerels	Dianisylhexene (0.01 per-cent in feed for 19 days)	43	52	5	0
39 cockerels	Untreated (controls)	2	56	34	8

The improvement in grade is due to increased fat deposits and to changes in the skin. The skin of the treated birds is smoother and softer. Estrogen increases the deposits of abdominal and liver fat with lesser increases in other organs (Lorenz, 1945b):

No. of birds	Treatment	Abdominal fat—gm.	Muscle fat in		Gain in body wt. gm.
			Breast Percent	Leg Percent	
6	Pellet (20 mg. for 6 weeks)	32.1	1.13	2.16	640
12	Untreated	4.9	0.68	1.16	654

Gains in Weight

Table 38 shows the gains in weight of a number of estrogen-treated birds. This table does not include all results, but enough to show that the hormone has little effect upon gains. Although the gains are usually higher for the treated birds, in most cases the differences are not statistically significant. The slightly heavier weight of the treated birds is caused mainly by increased abdominal fat, and not true growth. Under some conditions, estrogen may depress growth. Estrogen administration to chickens tends to decrease metabolism (Bird, 1946) and activity, and the fattening effects may be attributed, in part, to these factors.

Tenderness of Flesh

It has been alleged that estrogen tenderizes the flesh of birds, particularly old birds. Few controlled tests have been made, however, on this point. Sturkie (1946a), who treated old cocks with estrogen, was unable to demonstrate appreciable improvement in tenderizing the meat. In further controlled cooking and tasting tests on hormonized and untreated cockerels (10 months of age)

Table 38. The effects of estrogen on gain in weight of chickens

Age of bird	Treatment	Av. gain in weight per bird gm.	Investigator
30 days	DS pellets (4 wks.)	952	Lorenz (1945a)
	Control	899	
30 days	DS pellets (5 wks.)	645	Lorenz (1945b)
	Control	640	
Growing cockerels	Dianisylhexene (0.01 percent—28 days)	459	Thayer *et al.* (1945)
	Control	419	
Cocks	Dianisylhexene (0.01 percent—28 days)	368	Thayer *et al.* (1945)
	Control	182	
Cockerels (17 wks.)	DS pellets (7 wks.)	546	Black & Booth (1946)
	Control	486	
Cockerels (12 wks.)	DS pellets (7 wks.)	1,210	Kelly & Roberts (1950)
	Control	1,142	
Cockerels (6 wks.)	DS pellets (6 wks.)	918	Andrews & Bohren (1947)
	Control	853	

and capons of the same age, little or no difference in flavor or eating quality could be detected (Sturkie, 1946b).

The tensile or shearing strength of the flesh of estrogen-treated birds, however, may be less than that of normal birds or birds receiving androgen (Herrick, 1945; Schnetzler, Andrews, and Hague, 1945).

Storage of Estrogen in Tissues

The liver and fatty tissues tend most readily to store estrogen. The possibility therefore exists that sufficient quantities of estrogen may be stored in the tissues to produce undesirable physiological

effects when such flesh is eaten, and thus render the meat unsafe
for human consumption. Experiments designed to test this possibility have been few and inconclusive.

Bird *et al.* (1947), on the basis of limited data, concluded that the
storage of estrogen in the liver and fat of estrogen-treated birds
was sufficient to cause definite changes in the vaginal smears of
postmenopausal women. Changes were exemplified by the disappearance of the basal type of cell and the appearance of the more
differentiated squamos type, with varying degrees of cornification.

Pooled livers from estrogen-treated chickens (which had been
fed the dimethyl ether of diethylstilbestrol and which according to
the authors assayed approximately 0.25 mg. of estrogen per liver)
were eaten by four women. Each woman consumed eight livers
per day for a period of six days, or a total of approximately 12 mg.
of the estrogen. The effects on the vaginal smears were definitely
positive in three of the patients, but questionable in the other one.
Only one patient consumed meat from birds fed another estrogen,
dienestrol diacetate. According to the assays, 1.2 mg. of estrogen
was ingested with the meat in a six-day period. The effect on the
vaginal smears was negative.

Gowe (1949) assayed (rat assay) the tissues of chickens which
had been fed 0.004 percent dienestrol diacetate for 13 weeks. According to his limited data, the livers of five birds stored less than
5 micrograms of the estrogen per liver. The muscle and skin, in
most cases, contained about 10 micrograms per 100 grams of tissue.

The results of Gowe and of Bird *et al.* are not comparable. The
assays of the former were made on dienestrol, and assays and
clinical studies of the latter were based mainly on hexestrol and the
dimethyl ether of diethylstilbestrol (DED). Moreover, the dosage
of DED fed to the chickens by Bird *et al.* was approximately three
times as great as the dienestrol in the Gowe experiments.

Gowe concluded that a person would have to consume inordinately large quantities of chicken skin and flesh every other day to
obtain a dose of estrogen (dienestrol) of the magnitude that is effective clinically. Even if the conclusions of Bird *et al.*, which are
based on meager data, are valid, one would have to consume unusually large portions of estrogen-treated chicken for several successive
days to produce a clinical effect. Statistically, the probability that
this would happen is remote. However, there is no information on

the possible deleterious effects of continued ingestion of small amounts of estrogen over extended periods of time.

Even less is known about the effects of ingestion of flesh from birds receiving the estrogen diethylstilbestrol, the one used commercially to fatten chickens. The limited data of Bird *et al.* suggest that a smaller amount of this estrogen and also of dienestrol is stored in the tissues than is the case with hexestrol or DED.

EFFECTS OF ANDROGEN ON GROWTH

Androgen, when administered in suitable quantities to animals, may stimulate growth and increase nitrogen retention (anabolism). (For reviews, see Kenyon, Knowlton, and Sandiford, 1944; Wilkins and Fleischmann, 1946.) Relatively little work has been done with birds, but data from Turner (1947) and Kumaran and Turner (1949b) indicate that growth may be stimulated in the chicken with suitable doses of androgen. Apparently dosage and age of bird are important factors because Turner (1948) has shown that growth may also be depressed with improper dosages.

The stimulating effects of androgen on growth in turkeys was demonstrated by Fraps, Olsen, and Marsden (1951). When immature and mature male turkeys were pretreated for 22 days with pregnant mare serum (PMS) and then administered testosterone propionate for 26 days, the gains were 10 to 14 percent greater than for the untreated birds. Pretreatment with PMS plus testosterone plus PMS produced gains 18 to 20 percent above control levels. The effects of testosterone alone without pretreatment with PMS were not determined.

REFERENCES

Andrews, F. N., and B. B. Bohren 1947 Influence of thiouracil and stilbestrol on growth, fattening, and feed efficiency in broilers. Poultry Sci. 26:447.

Benoit, J. 1950 Traité de Zoologie, edited by P. P. Grassé. Tome XV: Oiseaux, p. 419. Masson & Co., Paris.

Bird, S. 1946 The influence of ingested estrogens on feed intake, metabolic rate, and lipemia in male fowl. Endocrinol. 39:149.

Bird, S., L. I. Pugsley, and M. O. Klotz 1947 The quantitative recovery of synthetic estrogens from tissues of birds (Gallus domesticus); the response of the birds' testes, comb, and epidermis to estrogen and of humans to ingestion of tissues from treated birds. Endocrinol. 41:282.

Black, D. J. G., and R. G. Booth 1946 Capon production by the use of synthetic estrogen (stilbestrol). Vet. J. 102:41.

Boss, W. R. 1943 Hormonal determination of adult characters and sex behavior in herring gulls (Larus argentatus). J. Exp. Zool. 94:181.

Breneman, W. R. 1938 Relative effectiveness of testosterone-propion-ate and dihydroandrosterone-benzoate in the chick as indicated by comb growth. Endocrinol. 23:44.

Breneman, W. R. 1939 Effect of androgens on the chick. Proc. Seventh World's Poultry Congr., pp. 91–95.

Breneman, W. R. 1942 Action of diethylstilbestrol in the chick. Endocrinol. 31:179.

Brown, F. A. 1950 Chapter 22 in Comparative Animal Physiology, edited by C. L. Prosser. W. B. Saunders Co., Philadelphia.

Burmester, B. R., and N. M. Nelson 1945 The effect of castration and sex hormones upon the incidence of lymphomatosis in chickens. Poultry Sci. 24:509.

Campos, A. C., and C. S. Shaffner 1952 The genetic control of chick comb and oviduct response to androgen and estrogen. Poultry Sci. 31:567.

Chaikoff, I. L., S. Lindsay, F. W. Lorenz, and C. Entenman 1948 Production of atheromatosis in the aorta of the bird by administra-tion of diethylstilbestrol. J. Exp. Med. 88:373.

Clavert, J. 1942 Thesis. University of Algiers. (Abstracted in Rev. Canadienne de Biol. 3:15, 1944.)

Clavert, J. 1944 Action de la folliculine sur le foie du pigeon: Variation de poids du foie. Comp. Rend. Soc. Biol. 138:928.

Common, R. H., W. Bolton, and W. A. Rutledge 1948 The influence of gonadal hormones on the composition of the blood and liver of the domestic fowl. J. Endocrinol. 5:263.

Common, R. H., T. J. Keefe, and W. A. Maw 1950 Some biochemical effects of thiouracil on the response of the immature pullet to estrogen. Canadian J. Res. 28, D: 272.

Common, R. H., W. A. Rutledge, and W. Bolton 1947 The influence of gonadal hormones on serum riboflavin and certain other properties of blood and tissues of the domestic fowl. J. Endocrinol. 5:121.

Crew, F. A. E. 1923 Studies in intersexuality. II: Sex reversal in the fowl. Proc. Roy. Soc., B, 95:256.

Davidson, J. A., L. W. Wolterink, and E. P. Reineke 1946 Some effects of high dosage of synthetic estrogens in young turkeys. Poultry Sci. 25:400.

Davis, O. S., F. N. Andrews, and L. P. Doyle   1951   Studies in avian leucosis. V: An investigation of the possible relationship of sex hormones to visceral lymphomatosis. Am. J. Vet. Res. 11:428.

Domm, L. V.   1929   The effects of bilateral ovariotomy in the Brown Leghorn fowl. Biol. Bull. 56:459.

Domm, L. V.   1939   Chapter V in Sex and Internal Secretions, edited by Edgar Allen. 2d ed. Williams & Wilkins Co., Baltimore.

Dorfman, R. I., and A. S. Dorfman   1948a   Studies on the bioassay of hormones: The assay of testosterone propionate and androsterone by a chick comb inunction method. Endocrinol. 42:1.

Dorfman, R. I., and A. S. Dorfman   1948b   Studies on the bioassay of hormones: The relative reactivity of the comb of various breeds of chicks to androgen. Endocrinol. 42:7.

Dorfman, R. I., and A. S. Dorfman   1948c   Studies on the bioassay of hormones: The comparative oviduct response of various breeds of chicks to stilbestrol. Endocrinol. 42:102.

Entenman, C., F. W. Lorenz, and I. L. Chaikoff   1940   The endocrine control of lipid metabolism in the bird. III: Effects of crystalline sex hormones on blood lipids of birds. J. Biol. Chem. 134:495.

Fleischmann, W., and I. A. Fried   1945   Studies on the mechanism of the hypercholesterolemia and hypercalcemia induced by estrogen in immature chicks. Endocrinol. 36:406.

Fraps, R. M., C. W. Hooker, and T. R. Forbes   1948   Progesterone in blood plasma of the ovulating hen. Science 108:86.

Fraps, R. M., C. W. Hooker, and T. R. Forbes   1949   Progesterone in blood plasma of cocks and non-ovulating hens. Science 109:493.

Fraps, R. M., M. W. Olsen, and S. J. Marsden   1951   Augmentation by pregnant mares serum of body weight response of male turkeys to testosterone propionate. Proc. Soc. Exp. Biol. & Med. 77:356.

Gardner, W. U., and C. A. Pfeiffer   1942   Influence of estrogens and androgens on the skeletal system. Physiol. Rev. 23:139.

Godfrey, E. F., and R. G. Jaap   1950   Estrogenic interruption of broodiness in the domestic fowl. Poultry Sci. 29:356.

Gowe, R. S.   1949   Residual estrogens in the tissues of fowl treated with dienestrol diacetate. Poultry Sci. 28:666.

Greenwood, W. W., and J. S. S. Blyth   1938a   The influence of testis on sexual plumage in the domestic fowl. J. Genet. 36:501.

Greenwood, W. W., and J. S. S. Blyth   1938b   Experimental modification of the accessory sexual apparatus in the hen. Quart. J. Exp. Physiol. 28:61.

Haque, M. E., R. J. Lillie, C. S. Shaffner, and G. M. Briggs   1949   Response of vitamin-deficient chicks to the sex hormones. Poultry Sci. 28:914.

Herrick, E. H. 1945 Tensile strength of tissues as influenced by male sex hormones. Anat. Rec. 93:145.

Hertz, R. 1945 The quantitative relationship between stilbestrol response and dietary folic acid in the chick. Endocrinol. 37:1.

Hertz, R., C. D. Larsen, and W. W. Tullner 1947 Inhibition of estrogen-induced tissue growth with progesterone. J. National Cancer Institute 8:123.

Hooker, C. W., and T. R. Forbes 1949 Specificity of the intrauterine test for progesterone. Endocrinol. 45:71.

Hutt, F. B. 1937 Gynandromorphism in the fowl. Poultry Sci. 16:354.

Hutt, F. B. 1949 Genetics of the Fowl. McGraw-Hill Book Co., Inc., New York.

Jaap, R. G. 1945 Activity of synthetic estrogens on oral administration in the domestic fowl and turkey. Endocrinol. 37:369.

Jaap, R. G., and R. H. Thayer 1944 Oral administration of estrogens in poultry. Poultry Sci. 23:249.

Juhn, M., and L. V. Domm 1930 The relation of gonadal condition to erythrocyte number in fowls. Am. J. Physiol. 94:656.

Kar, A. B. 1947a Responses of the oviduct of immature female fowl to injection of diethylstilbestrol and the mechanism of perforation of the oviduct in the domestic fowl. Poultry Sci. 26:352.

Kar, A. B. 1947b The action of male and female sex hormones on the adrenals in the fowl. Anat. Rec. 97:551.

Kar, A. B. 1949 Testicular changes in tne juvenile pigeon due to progesterone treatment. Endocrinol. 45:346.

Kelly, K. G. R., and R. S. Roberts 1950 Stilbestrol implantation in cockerels. Vet. Rec. 62:44.

Kenyon, A. T., K. Knowlton, and I. Sandiford 1944 The anabolic effects of the androgens and somatic growth in man. Ann. Int. Med. 20:632.

Kline, I. T., and R. I. Dorfman 1951 Estrogen stimulation of the oviduct in vitamin deficient chicks. Endocrinol. 48:345.

Kosin, I. L. 1942 Observations on effect of esterfied androgen on sex eminence of the chick. Endocrinol. 30:767.

Kumaran, J. D. S., and C. W. Turner 1949a The endocrinology of spermatogenesis in birds. I: Effect of estrogen and androgen. Poultry Sci. 28:593.

Kumaran, J. D. S., and C. W. Turner 1949b The endocrinology of spermatogenesis in birds. II: The effect of androgens. Poultry Sci. 28:739.

Kyes, P., and T. S. Potter 1934 Physiological marrow ossification in female pigeons. Anat. Rec. 60:377.

Landauer, W., C. A. Pfeiffer, W. U. Gardner, and J. C. Shaw 1941 Blood serum and skeletal changes in two breeds of ducks receiving estrogens. Endocrinol. 28:458.

Lorenz, F. W. 1938 Effects of estrin on blood lipids of the immature fowl. J. Biol. Chem. 126:763.

Lorenz, F. W. 1945a The influence of diethylstilbestrol on fat deposition and meat quality in chickens. Poultry Sci. 24:128.

Lorenz, F. W. 1945b The fattening action of orally administered synthetic estrogens as compared with diethylstilbestrol pellet implants. Poultry Sci. 24:91.

Lorenz, F. W., and G. H. Bachman 1947 Lipemia and fat deposition in response to oral administration of synthetic estrogens. Poultry Sci. 26:419.

McDonald, M. R., and O. Riddle 1945 The effect of reproduction and estrogen administration on the partition of calcium, phosphorus, and nitrogen in pigeon plasma. J. Biol. Chem. 159:445.

McDonald, M. R., O. Riddle, and G. C. Smith 1945 Action of thyroxine on estrogen-induced changes in blood chemistry and endosteal bone. Endocrinol. 37:23.

Miller, R. A., and O. Riddle 1939 Stimulation of adrenal cortex of pigeons by anterior pituitary hormones. Proc. Soc. Exp. Biol. & Med. 41:518.

Mitchell, H. H., L. E. Card, and W. T. Haines 1927 The effect of age, sex, and castration on the basal heat production of chickens. J. Agr. Res. 34:945.

Munro, S. S., and I. L. Kosin 1943 Dramatic response of the chick oviduct to estrogen. Poultry Sci. 22:330.

Munro, S. S., and I. L. Kosin 1946 Relative potency of certain synthetic estrogens when administered orally to chicks. Am. J. Physiol. 147:582.

Nalbandov, A. V., and G. J. Baum 1948 The use of stilbestrol-inhibited males as test animals for gonadotrophic hormones. Endocrinol. 43:371.

Nickerson, M. 1946 Conditions modifying the expression of silver in the Silver Campine fowl. Physiol. Zool. 19:77.

Pfeiffer, C. A., and W. U. Gardner 1938 Skeletal changes and blood serum calcium level in pigeons receiving estrogens. Endocrinol. 23:485.

Ranney, R. E., and I. L. Chaikoff 1951 Effect of functional hepatectomy upon estrogen-induced lipemia in the fowl. Am. J. Physiol. 165:600.

Ranney, R. E., I. L. Chaikoff, and C. Entenman 1951 Site of formation of phospholipids in the bird. Am. J. Physiol. 165:596.

Riddle, O. 1942 Cyclic changes in blood calcium, phosphorus, and fat in relation to egg laying and estrogen production. Endocrinol. 31:498.

Riddle, O., and J. P. Schooley 1944 Tests indicating absence of progesterone in certain avian ovaries. J. Washington Acad. Sci. 34:341.

Schnetzler, E. E., F. N. Andrews, and S. M. Hague 1945 Influence of thiouracil and stilbestrol on fattening poultry. U.S. Egg and Poultry Magazine 51:554.

Stamler, J., C. Bolene, M. Dudley, and E. Levinson 1950 Effect of prolonged exhibition of diethylstilbestrol on plasma and tissue lipids in the chick. Endocrinol. 46:375.

Sturkie, P. D. 1946a The effect of estrogens upon the meat quality of old cocks and hens. Poultry Sci. 25:365.

Sturkie, P. D. 1946b Comparison of the gains in weight, fat deposition, and market quality of estrogen-treated cockerels and capons. Poultry Sci. 25:351.

Sturkie, P. D. 1951 Effects of estrogen and thyroxine upon plasma proteins and blood volume in the fowl. Endocrinol. 49:565.

Taber, E. 1949 Androgen production in the female Brown Leghorn fowl. Anat. Rec. 105:561.

Taber, E. 1951 Androgen secretion in the fowl. Endocrinol. 48:6.

Taber, E., D. E. Davis, and L. V. Domm 1943 Effect of sex hormones on the erythrocyte number in the blood of the domestic fowl. Am. J. Physiol. 138:479.

Thayer, R. H., R. G. Jaap, and R. Penquite 1945 Fattening chickens by feeding estrogens. Poultry Sci. 24:483.

Turner, C. W. 1947 Dried lactating cow manure in the ration of growing chickens. Poultry Sci. 26:143.

Turner, C. W. 1948 Oral effectiveness of androgens in fowls. Poultry Sci. 27:789.

Wilkins, L., and W. Fleischmann 1946 The influence of various androgenic steroids on nitrogen balance and growth. J. Clin. Endocrinol. 6:383.

Witschi, E., and R. P. Woods 1936 The bill of the sparrow as indicatory of the male sex hormone. J. Exp. Zool. 73:445.

Zarrow, M. X., I. B. Koretsky, and I. G. Zarrow 1951 Failure of folic acid antagonist to interfere with the action of testosterone propionate on the combs and testes of young cockerels. Endocrinol. 48:125.

Zondek, B., and L. Marx 1939 The induction of lipemia and calcemia in the cock by means of estrogenic hormone. Arch. Int. Pharm. Thera. 41:77.

CHAPTER 19

Thyroids

ANATOMY

THE thyroids are oval-shaped, paired organs situated on each side of the trachea at the entrance to the thoracic cavity (Figure 66). They are usually internal to the jugular veins and located in the angle formed by the divergence of the subclavian and common carotid arteries. Each gland receives arterial blood from a branch of the carotid (the thyroid artery) and is drained by veins which empty into the jugular (Kaupp, 1918).

The size of the glands varies considerably, depending upon a number of factors, such as season, environmental temperature, diet, age, and functional state. Schultze and Turner (1945) recorded the thyroid weights of a number of breeds of chickens from 5 weeks of age to maturity (26 weeks; see Table 39). They formulated equations describing the relationship between thyroid weight and body weight for several breeds (y = thyroid weight in milligrams and x = body weight in grams), as follows: $y = 0.35x^{1.05}$ and $y = 0.062x^{0.99}$ for White Plymouth Rock males and females respectively. For White Leghorn males, the equation is $y = 0.158x^{0.88}$. The equations apply to birds ranging in age from 2 to 27 weeks. The thyroid weights of Rouen and Pekin drakes average 68 and 112 mg. respectively per kilogram of body weight, according to Benoit (1950).

Riddle (1947) found considerable variation in the thyroid weights of pigeons and doves, depending upon the breed, age, and season. In adult pigeons of different breeds, the thyroid weights in percentage of body weight ranged from 0.0103 to 0.0253. The weights were usually greater in the fall and winter and less in summer, but there were exceptions. Thyroid weight, in general tends to increase with age of the bird (see also Chapter 21). Cruickshank (1929) and Galpin (1938) reported that the thyroids in chickens are heavier also in the fall and winter. Turner (1948a), however, reported little or no difference in thyroid weights of hens in the fall, winter, and early summer. That lower environmental temperature in the fall and winter is a factor in causing the increase in size is well known and will be discussed later.

Diet plays an important role in influencing thyroid size in animals and birds. A deficiency in iodine in the diet causes goiter or enlarged thyroids in chickens (Patton, Wilgus, and Harshfield, 1939). The effect of other nutrients or substances in the diet on the thyroid size of birds has received little attention. Greer (1950), in his review, states that Scheppleman in 1907 reported enlarged thyroids in geese fed an extremely high carbohydrate diet and that Korenchensky reported that deficiencies of vitamins A or B also enlarged the bird's thyroid. However, much of the earlier work is questionable, according to Greer. Soybean oil meal has goitrogenic activity when fed to chicks (Wilgus, Gassner, Patton, and Gustavson, 1941), and its activity is probably due to its low iodine content. Elemental iodine has a thyroxine-like action in the rat and the chick and completely inhibits the hypertrophy of the thyroid caused by thiouracil (Dvoskin, 1947a).

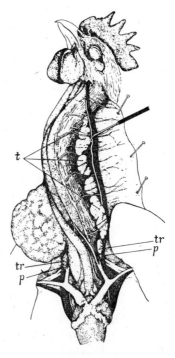

Figure 66. Location of thyroids (tr), parathyroids (p), and thymus (t) in the chicken. (From Nonidez and Goodale, *Am. J. Anat.*, 1927.)

HISTOLOGY

The thyroid gland consists of a capsule enclosing rounded follicles which are lined by a simple entodermal epithelium. The height

Table 39. Thyroid weights of White Plymouth Rock chickens
(Schultze and Turner, 1945)

Age of fowl weeks	Males		Females	
	Body weight gm.	Thyroid weight mg.	Body weight gm.	Thyroid weight mg.
5	238	9.7	245	10.93
7	379	18.9	309	19.52
9	573	42.2	529	39.50
11	806	35.6	824	50.80
13	1,072	44.5	977	47.00
18	1,456	60.8	1,345	81.50
22	2,173	125.4	1,750	119.80
26	2,545	152.0	1,851	105.2

and shape of these cells change with the activity of the gland. The follicles vary in size and may or may not contain colloid, depending upon their secretory state (Figure 67). Between the follicles within the connective tissue stroma are the interfollicular cells.

The increase in size of the thyroid may be due to an increase in cell size (hypertrophy) and/or number of cells (hyperplasia), with usually a decrease in colloid. These changes, however, may reflect either a hyper- or hypofunctioning gland. Thyroids stimulated by the thyrotrophic hormone (Rawson and Salter, 1940; Larson, Keating, Peacock, and Rawson, 1945a; and others) or low environmental temperature (Hoffman and Shaffner, 1950) show hyperplasia and hypertrophy and increased thyroxine formation or secretion. Goitrogenic substances, such as thiourea or thiouracil, also produce the same histological picture, but the gland does not form thyroxine (Figure 67).

The chick thyroid is very sensitive to the thyrotrophic hormone (TSH) and responds by an increase in size, but is particularly sensitive if increased height of epithelial cells serves as criterion of response. Cell height may increase 100 percent within 24 hours after a single injection of TSH, according to Smelser (1938) and Adams and Beeman (1942). The latter workers suggest that the

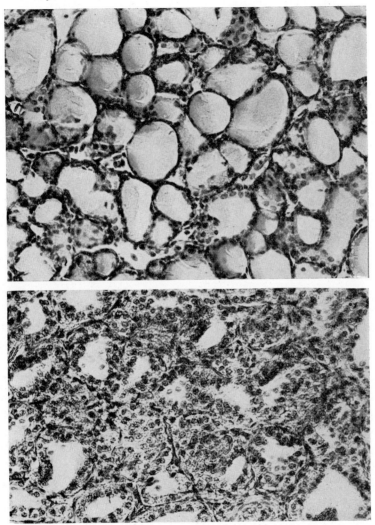

Figure 67. Thyroid gland of a normal chick showing colloid-filled
follicles (upper) and thyroid of a chick administered thiouracil (lower).
Increase in size and number of follicular cells and absence of colloid
are apparent in the lower figure. (From Larson *et al., Endocrinol.*, 1945a.)

unit of TSH should be the least amount required to give a 100
percent increase in cell height. Some workers claim that TSH can
be assayed by its effects in causing formation of colloid droplets
in thyroid slices *in vitro,* but Dvoskin (1947b) found that not only

TSH, but a number of other substances and conditions also cause this reaction. The increases in weight and cell height of the thyroid of chicks administered TSH and thiouracil are shown in Table 40.

It is apparent that both TSH and thiouracil cause thyroid enlargement, but TSH acts more quickly than thiouracil. It has a

Table 40. Effects of thiouracil and thyrotrophic hormone (Antuitrin T) on the mean cell height and weight of thyroids of chicks (two days old at beginning of treatment), from Larson, Keating, Peacock, and Rawson (1945a)

	Treatment (days)	Mean cell height (microns)	Weight of thyroids (mg.)	Weight of thyroids (mg./100 gm. body weight)
Controls (2 days old)	0	1.5	2.5	5.4
Controls (10 days old)	0	4.4	5.7	6.3
TSH (2 days old at start)	1	4.2	3.5	6.4
	7	9.4	20.2	28.1
1 unit daily	10	10.1	30.7	41.0
Thiouracil	3	1.9	2.8	5.7
0.1 percent in	7	6.5	6.9	9.2
water	10	8.9	11.3	14.0
	15	10.4	20.9	29.8

measurable effect within 24 hours, but the effect of thiouracil is not apparent until after five days.

Hypophysectomy causes a decrease in size and involution of the thyroid (see Chapter 17).

FORMATION OF THYROXINE

Relatively little work has been conducted upon the formation of thyroxine in the bird thyroid, but the meager data available (to be discussed later) suggest that it is formed in the same manner as in mammals. It is generally agreed that thyroxine is formed in the thyroid from tyrosine and diiodotyrosine. According to the scheme proposed by Harington and Barger (1927), tyrosine is iodinated to form diiodotyrosine, from which thyroxine is formed. Taurog, Tong, and Chaikoff (1950) demonstrated that the thyroids of rats and chickens also contain iodine in the form of mono-iodotyrosine. Tyrosine, which contains no iodine, has no thyroxine-like activity. The structural formula of thyroxine is:

$$\text{HO} \overset{\text{I}}{\underset{\text{I}}{\bigcirc}} \text{O} \overset{\text{I}}{\underset{\text{I}}{\bigcirc}} \text{CH}_2\text{CH(NH}_2) \\ \text{COOH}$$

L-thyroxine produces the effects of the functional thyroid, but D,L-thyroxine is only about one-half as active physiologically (Reineke and Turner, 1945a). The thyroxine circulating in the blood appears to be bound to protein, and in amounts so low as to make it difficult to detect by present chemical methods.

The embryonic chick thyroid begins its production of thyroxine by the 10th to 12th day of development, as shown by morphological and cytochemical tests (Sun, 1932; Hopkins, 1935) and by the uptake of radioactive iodine (Hansborough and Khan, 1951).

Iodine Uptake

The thyroids of animals and birds have a strong affinity for iodine, which is necessary for the formation of thyroxine. Low iodine uptake prevents or reduces the formation of thyroxine. In recent years, considerable information upon the uptake of iodine and its role in the formation of thyroxine has been gained through the use of radioactive iodine administered to animals (see Chaikoff and Taurog, 1948; Hevesy, 1948).

Radioactive iodine, usually I^{131}, is administered, and its rate of uptake by the thyroid and other organs can then be measured by appropriate instruments, such as the Geiger counter, which records the radioactive rays emanating from the tissue. Studies of this nature in the chicken have been conducted in recent years by Larson *et al.* (1945a and 1945b), Keating *et al.* (1945), Wolterink, Lee, and Groschke (1950), and Epstein and Wolterink (1949). It was

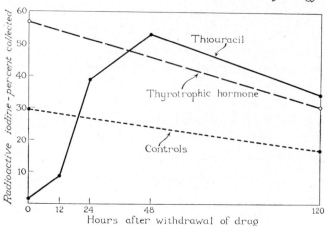

Figure 68. The effects of thiouracil and thyrotrophic hormone
on the collection of radioactive iodine (I^{131}) by the chick thyroid.
(From Larson *et al., Endocrinol.,* 1945a.)

shown previously that TSH and thiouracil cause hypertrophy and
hyperplasia of the thyroid. The effects of these substances upon the
uptake of radioactive iodine are shown in Figure 68. The thyroids
stimulated by TSH collected 56.5 percent of the injected dose as
compared to 29.6 percent for the control chicks, and only 1.9 percent for those receiving thiouracil. After withdrawal of thiouracil,

Table 41. Effect of thiouracil on the distribution of the radioactive
iodine in the thyroid of chicks. The total iodine should equal organic and
inorganic iodine; the discrepancy (about 9%) is due to error in the
method. From Larson, Keating, Peacock, and Rawson (1945b)

Treatment	Radioactive iodine in percent of injected dose		
	Total iodine	Organic iodine	Inorganic iodine
I Thiouracil	1.2	0.1	1.0
II Thiouracil	0.7	0.1	0.4
III Control	6.7	4.7	0.6
IV Control	9.7	6.9	0.8

the iodine uptake increased above that of the control glands. Since the thyroids of the thiouracil-treated birds were greatly enlarged, this cannot be considered as hyperfunction. In terms of weight of thyroids, the collection of iodine by the thiouracil-stimulated gland is not increased.

In later studies, Larson *et al.* (1945b) fractionated the radioactive iodine of the thyroids into inorganic and organic iodine or that

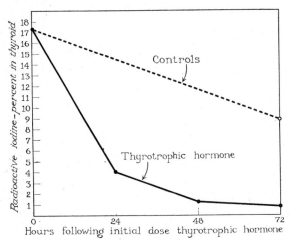

Figure 69. Disappearance of radioactive iodine (I^{131}) in the thyroids of chickens.

The thyrotrophic hormone increases the rate of disappearance of iodine from the gland. (From Keating *et al., Endocrinol.,* 1945.)

bound to protein. Here they found that thiouracil does not decrease the uptake of inorganic iodine, but prevents the gland from binding it to protein, or decreases the organic iodine (Table 41). This has been demonstrated also in mammals (see Chaikoff and Taurog, 1948).

Thus, thiouracil acts by interfering with the synthesis of thyroxine, probably by inhibiting necessary enzymatic reactions. Dempsey (1944), by histologic techniques, has shown that normally the enzyme peroxidase is present in the thyroid cells and disappears after thiouracil administration. There is a loss also of alkaline phosphatase.

That TSH not only increases the uptake of iodine, but also the formation of thyroxine in the gland has been demonstrated in mammals and also in chickens by Keating *et al.* (1945). They reported that the disappearance of radioactive iodine from the chick thyroid (evidence of the formation of thyroxine and release from the gland) is greatly increased in the thyroid stimulated by TSH (Figure 69). The output of iodine or disappearance of radioactive iodine from the thyroids of chicks is retarded when estrogen is administered for a period of two weeks, and the output of iodine in chicks deficient in vitamin B_{12} is also retarded (Epstein and Wolterink, 1949).

THYROXINE SECRETION RATE

Methods of Determination

Metabolic rate is a means of measuring wide differences in thyroid activity and is used clinically to diagnose hypo- and hyperthyroidism (see Chapter 9). But metabolism tests are not sensitive enough to measure changes in thyroid activity within the physiological norm. Methods which are more sensitive have received much attention in recent years. Some workers have considered the amount of circulating thyroxine (protein-bound iodine) as the best indication of thyroid activity (see Salter, 1950), but the minute amounts present in the blood make difficult its accurate chemical determination. Another method of determining thyroxine secretion that has been used extensively is the method used by Dempsey and Astwood (1943) for rats and modified slightly by Mixner, Reineke, and Turner (1944) for the chicken.

This method involves the use of a goitrogenic agent, such as thiourea or thiouracil, which causes thyroid enlargement and inhibits thyroxine formation. By subcutaneous injection of graded doses of thyroxine, the weight of the thyroid is reduced in thiouracil- or thiourea-treated animals, and the weight reduction is proportional to the thyroxine dosage. Thus, the establishment of a normal thyroxine-thyrotrophin equilibrium by injections of thyroxine results in a thyroid weight equal to that in control animals. The quantity of thyroxine required to bring about this change is considered to be an estimate of the normal thyroid secretion rate by the glands of a particular group of animals.

Each group of animals to be tested is divided into subgroups, preferably 10 or more per group. One group receives the basal ration alone; one group receives the basal ration plus 0.1 percent thiouracil in the feed; the remaining subgroups receive the thiouracil and injected D,L-thyroxine in increasing amounts. The number of such groups depends upon the range of thyroxine secretion expected. In most cases, three to four groups are sufficient.

The assay period is usually two to four weeks in White Leghorn chickens (depending upon the age) and three to five in heavier

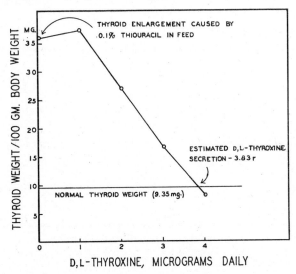

Figure 70. Method of plotting data to determine thyroxine secretion rate of the fowl.
    Data are for four-week-old White Leghorn cockerels. (From Schultze and Turner, *Mo. Agr. Exp. Sta. Res. Bull.* 392, 1945.)

breeds. At the end of this period, the birds are killed and the thyroids of each group are weighed. The weights (averages) of these groups are then plotted, as shown in Figure 70. The amount of thyroxine injected per day which is required to produce average thyroid weights the same as those of the control group is considered the amount normally secreted by the glands. The values so derived represent the average secretion rate of the group, and not of a given individual in the group. The amount secreted may be plotted against thyroid weight per total body weight in adult

Table 42. Thyroxine secretion rate of growing chickens
(Schultze and Turner, 1945)

Breed	Age weeks	Av. body weight gm.	D,L-Thyroxine secreted	
			Per chick daily	Per 100 gm. body weight
			in micrograms	
White Leghorn	1–2	70.7	1.94	2.76
cockerels	4	148.3	3.83	2.58
"	6	343.4	7.55	2.20
"	7	469.7	11.35	2.42
"	9	663.0	14.40	2.17
"	12	1,008.0	16.50	1.64
"	20	1,193.0	20.00	1.68
"	24	1,426.0	23.50	1.65
"	27	1,536.0	25.00	1.63
White Rock	4–7	410.0	8.10	1.98
cockerels	8–11	837.0	13.00	1.55
"	10–13	1,164.0	18.80	1.62
"	19–22	2,069.0	29.50	1.43
"	23–26	2,427.0	35.00	1.44
Pullets	4–7	360.0	8.75	2.43
"	8–11	776.0	14.30	1.84
"	10–13	974.0	18.00	1.84
"	19–22	1,637.0	26.00	1.59
"	23–26	1,931.0	29.00	1.50

birds of the same breed and age, or it may be plotted in terms of thyroid weight per 100 grams of body weight for growing birds. Since the thyroxine secreted by the gland is in the L-form and this form is twice as active physiologically as the D,L-form (that injected), all determinations should be halved to obtain the equivalent amount produced by the glands.

This method assumes that the differences in thyroid weights reflect differences in thyrotrophin release from the pituitary. However, other factors may influence thyroid size, particularly the amount of iodine in the diet and also heredity; these should be considered in applying the test. The accuracy of this method has recently been compared with thyroid·activity as determined by the radio-iodine turnover method in rats (Wolterink and Lee, 1950). The difference in thyroxine secretion observed between these methods, 4 percent, was not statistically significant.

The amount of D,L-thyroxine required to maintain body weight in chicks whose thyroids are destroyed with radio-iodine is approximately the same as the amount normally secreted by the thyroid as determined by the thiouracil-thyroxine technique (Winchester, Comar, and Davis, 1949).

Thyroxine Secretion Rate of Growing Birds

The data on growing chickens are taken from Schultze and Turner (1945; see Table 42). Their White Leghorn males had a slightly higher secretion rate per unit of body weight than White Plymouth males, and White Plymouth Rock females had a slightly higher rate than males. No data are given on growing White Leghorn females. The secretion rate of 15-week-old cockerels was higher than capons of the same age. Odell (1952), however, reported no difference in the secretion rates of White Leghorn cockerels and capons at 25 days of age. The greatest increase in secretion rate usually occurs during the period of greatest growth (4 to 12 weeks). Metabolic rate is also highest during this period (Chapter 9).

Ducks. The thyroxine secretion rate of ducks is much higher than that in growing chickens and appears to be correlated with the faster growth rate in the duck (Biellier and Turner, 1950; Hoffman, 1950). See Table 43.

Hoffman reported the thyroxine secretion rate of three-week-old Pekin ducks weighing 520 grams to be 18.7 micrograms per bird, or 3.8 micrograms per 100 grams of body weight.

Biellier and Turner presented equations showing the relationship of thyroxine secretion rate of the duck to body weight as follows: ($y =$ micrograms of D,L-thyroxine and $x =$ body weight in grams): Male $= y = 0.0262x^{1.01}$; Female $= y = 0.0104x^{1.15}$. The normal thyroid weight of the duck is greater in relation to body weight than in other bird species studied.

The thyroxine secretion rate of growing turkeys is of the same magnitude as that of growing ducks (see later section).

Table 43. Thyroxine secretion rate in Pekin ducks
(Biellier and Turner, 1950)

Age weeks	Average body weight, grams male	female	Micrograms of D,L-Thyroxine per bird male	female	per 100 gm. body wt. male	female
0–3	488	524	13.9	14.0	2.85	2.67
3–6	1,198	1,254	34.0	37.0	2.84	2.95
6–9	1,691	1,617	43.2	48.0	2.55	2.97
9–12	1,885	1,813	60.0	61.4	3.18	3.39

Secretion Rate Influenced by Season and Rate of Egg Production

The thyroxine secretion rate of laying pullets varies with rate of production (Booker and Sturkie, 1950). The rate for pullets laying two-egg sequences averaged 10.85 micrograms of D,L-thyroxine per day, and for pullets laying four eggs in sequence, 13.75 micrograms per day.

Turner (1948b) studied the effects of season upon thyroid secretion rate in two-year-old birds (White Leghron hens) in their second year of production. His results follow:

Date tested	Body weight gm.	D,L-*Thyroxine* secretion per day (microgram)
November	1,915	12.00
January	1,965	11.85
March	2,011	11.75
May	1,915	10.05
July	no assay	—

These results indicate that secretion is greatest in the fall and winter and least in warm weather. The figures are based on an average of 10 birds, and some of the differences are not significant. Turner did not relate his studies to rate of production.

Reineke and Turner (1945b) measured the secretion rate of White Plymouth Rock chicks at two weeks of age during varying intervals throughout the year. Maximum secretion levels, equivalent to 2.7

micrograms of D,L-thyroxine in females and 2.45 in males per 100 grams of body weight, were observed in October and November. Secretion declined thereafter to 2.1 and 1.95 micrograms in females and males respectively during February and early March. During the latter part of March, secretion declined further to 0.9 and 0.75 micrograms for females and males and remained at a low level until August. During October the secretion rose again toward the normal winter levels. The authors state that these findings somewhat limit the usefulness of the chick for the assay of thyroidal substances by the thiouracil technique. During the fall and winter, the method is satisfactory when thyroid enlargement with thiouracil is at a maximum. During the spring and summer, however, the range of thyroid weight response is too small to permit any distinction other than gross differences in the thyroidal potency of test substances. They found that the thyroid weights of the chicks when secretion was highest (fall and winter) were also greater than in the spring and summer. They concluded that the seasonal rhythm in activity of the chick thyroid must be mediated by way of the anterior pituitary, and Winchester (1940) has shown that the thyrotrophin content of hen pituitaries is higher in winter than in summer. That the seasonal change in thyroid activity is not wholly a matter of change in environmental temperature has been demonstrated by Winchester.

Light and Thyroid Secretion

The effects of different quantities and qualities of light upon thyroid activity in the baby chick have been studied by Kleinpeter and Mixner (1947). Thyroxine secretion rate is not affected appreciably by the quality of light, but is influenced by the amount of light. Birds receiving 24 hours of light have higher secretion rates than those receiving 12 hours.

Genetic Differences in Thyroid Secretion Rate

Mixner and Upp (1947) have recently studied the secretion rates of thyroids of the Wallace hybrid chicks and standard-bred chicks. The first step in producing the hybrid is to inbreed closely each of two breeds of chickens for a number of generations. The two inbred strains of each breed are then crossed to form the single hybrids, which are, in turn, crossed to produce the double hybrid. These workers tested secretion rate of (1) single crosses, (2) double crosses, and (3) standard-bred chicks. Thyroxine secretion of the double hybrid was about 30 to 40 percent higher than that of the single cross and the standard-bred chicks. The single crosses were no higher than the standard breds.

Smyth and Fox (1951) demonstrated that progeny from Broadbreasted Bronze and Jersey Buff turkeys exhibit a higher thyroxine secretion rate than either parent, as follows:

	D,L-*Thyroxine, micrograms per 100 gm. body weight (males and females)*
Crossbred poults	2.98
Jersey Buff poults	2.76
Bronze poults	2.72

El-Ibiary and Shaffner (1950) were able to select strains of chicks differing markedly in their response to thiouracil and presumably in thyroid activity. They selected breeders on the basis of the enlargement of the thyroids following administration of thiouracil. The first-generation offspring of the high- and low-responding parents also showed a difference in this respect. The thyroid weights of the high-responding and low-responding progeny were 161.8 and 95.0 mg. respectively.

Genetically determined slow- and rapid-growing strains of chickens exhibit differences in thyroid secretion rate (Glazener, Shaffner, and Jull, 1949) as follows:

Breed	Type of growth	D,L-*Thyroxine, micrograms per bird per day*		
		3–6 wks. of age	*6–9 wks.*	*9–12 wks.*
New Hampshire	rapid	—	23.4	27.1
	slow	—	18.8	26.0
Barred Rock	rapid	18.9	26.6	—
	slow	13.4	23.0	—

The difference in secretion rate occurs at the periods of greatest growth.

The thyroxine secretion rates of genetically determined slow- and rapid-feathering strains of Rhode Island Red chicks are not significantly different (Boone, Davidson, and Reineke, 1950). Expressed as micrograms of D,L-thyroxine per 100 grams of body weight, the rates for the slow-feathering males and females were 1.55 and 1.50 respectively, and for the rapid-feathering males and females, 1.62 and 1.60. The rate of feathering in the slow-feathering strain, however, was significantly increased when thyroprotein was administered.

ROLE OF THE THYROID IN MOLTING

Although the mechanism for the control of molting in birds is not understood, it is known that several factors are involved. The fact that activity of the thyroid influences the molt has been reported by a number of investigators (see Blivaiss, 1947b, and Fleischmann, 1947, for reviews). Molting can be induced with large doses of thyroxine or desiccated thyroid. Van der Meulen (1939) produced molting in laying hens within seven to eight days by feeding desiccated thyroid and showed that it was easier to produce the molt at the normal molting time than at other periods. He concluded that the normal periodical molt is due to an increase in thyroid activity, which in turn is dependent upon the variation in output of the thyrotrophic hormone. The data of Perek and Sulman (1945) would seem to support this view, since they demonstrated that the metabolism of molting hens is higher than that of nonmolting hens (Chapter 9). But the higher metabolic rate may not be due solely to greater thyroxine secretion, but to greater heat loss because of a loss of feathers, a secondary effect. Thyroidectomy does not prevent molting in the duck (Hühn, 1949), nor does thiouracil in laying hens, but the drug delays the onset of the molt (Glazener and Jull, 1946b).

Van der Meulen believed that the laying cycle and molting are controlled by separate mechanisms. He held that gonadotrophins elaborated by the pituitary in the laying hen tend to suppress or reduce the output of thyrotrophin, but that when the rate of laying decreases or ceases, the output of gonadotrophins decreases with a consequent increase of thyrotrophin and thyroid activity, which brings on the molt. There is little experimental evidence to support this view. He conceded, however, that other factors may be involved.

THYROIDECTOMY

Thyroidectomy has been performed in ducks, geese, pigeons, and chickens by a number of workers, but it is apparent from some of the reports that the operation is difficult and in some cases unsuccessful. The technique for removal of the glands has been described in the pigeon by Marvin and Smith (1943), in the duck by Benoit and Aron (1934), in the goose by Lee and Lee (1937), and in the chicken by Parkes and Selye (1937) and Winchester (1939).

The parathyroids are usually attached to the thyroids in the chicken, but are separated in the duck, goose, and pigeon. The removal of the thyroids in the latter species is therefore relatively simple, but removal in the chicken without disturbing the parathyroids may be difficult.

Winchester, Comar, and Davis (1949) have described a technique for destroying the chick thyroid by injecting large doses of radioactive I^{131}. They coined the term radio-thyroid-ecrexis for this operation. Their results indicate that about 6 millicuries of I^{131} per 100 grams of body weight over a period of 24 days are necessary for complete destruction of the gland. This treatment may damage the parathyroids, according to these workers, and possibly other structures.

Effects of Thyroidectomy on Growth and Sexual Development

Growth is retarded by thyroidectomy in birds, as it is in mammals. Blivaiss (1947b) thyroidectomized female chicks at 10 days of age and studied rate of growth to 12 months of age. The average body weight of the operated birds at one month of age averaged 84.5 percent of that of the normal birds, and only 64.3 percent of the normals at 12 months of age. The thyroidectomized hens have a squat, dwarflike appearance and are somewhat obese, showing excessive deposits of fat in the neck, back, breast, and viscera (Figure 71). The skeleton and particularly the bones of the wings and legs are shortened. The liver of the duck is more than doubled in size after ablation of the thyroids (Benoit, 1950).

The reproductive system of thyroidectomized female chickens at

10 to 12 months of age is in a juvenile state, and this condition persists in some as late as two years (Blivaiss, 1947b). The left ovary at 7 months of age weighs only about 10 percent of normal. Ovulation never occurred in the operated birds, some of which were under observation for two years. Winchester (1939) reported that egg production in females, thyroidectomized at or near maturity, is from 10 to 28 percent of normal. Complete ablation of the thyroids in adults decreases egg production 65 to 75 percent, and in those incompletely thyroidectomized, the production is 66 percent

Figure 71. Normal (left) and thyroidectomized (right) Brown Leghorn female. Bird was thyroidectomized at 10 days of age. (From Blivaiss, *J. Exp. Zool.*, 1947.)

of normal, according to Taylor and Burmester (1940). The amount of calcium deposited on the shell of the egg is decreased also. The growth of the comb of the thyroidectomized female is greatly retarded (Blivaiss, 1947b). At 12 months of age, comb size of the operated birds is only 5 percent of normal. Similar results were observed by Blivaiss (1947a) in the thyroidectomized male.

Decrease in size of the gonads of cocks and drakes also occurs with ablation of the thyroids. Benoit and Aron (1934 and later) reported that thyroidectomy in adult cocks and drakes causes a reduction of 80 to 90 percent in size of the testes within 11 to 20 days after the operation. Blivaiss (1947a) and Woitkewitsch (1940) have observed similar effects in the chicken.

The depressed growth and gonadal development of thyroidectomized birds may be due to a reduction in the output of gonadotrophic (Benoit, 1936) and growth hormones from the pituitary, because of decreased activity and metabolism of the pituitary itself, or to the lowered rate of response of all body tissues to hormonal and other stimuli, from lack of thyroxine.

Effects of Thyroidectomy and Thiouracil on Feathers

The effects of hypothyroidism, produced by thiouracil and thyroidectomy upon feather structure, growth, and color have been studied by many investigators. Blivaiss (1947a and 1947b) has reviewed much of this work.

Figure 72. Saddle feathers (the two at left) and wing coverts (the two at right) of Brown Leghorn females.

The first and third are those of a normal hen, the second and fourth of a thyroidectomized hen. (From Blivaiss, *J. Exp. Zool.*, 1947.)

Thyroidectomy decreases the growth rate of feathers and produces changes in their structure. The feathers of both male and female become fringed and elongated, and there is a loss of barbules (Figure 72). This occurs not only in chickens, but also in pigeons and ducks (Greenwood and Blyth, 1929; Parkes and Selye, 1937; Chu, 1940). The color changes depend in part upon the original color of the plumage, and there is great variation in the reports of the different investigators. Blivaiss (1947b) states that most of the previous observations on color changes in Brown Leghorns were based upon incomplete removal of the thyroids. In his incompletely thyroidectomized birds, he reports changes in color the same as those who allegedly removed all of the gland.

In the Brown Leghorn, there is a loss of the black, brown, and yellow melanins, which are replaced by light reddish-brown pigment (Blivaiss). The reports of color changes in black or barred breeds are variable, some showing changes and others no changes after thyroidectomy. Administration of thiouracil to Brown Leghorns causes about the same changes in the feathers as does thyroidectomy (Juhn, 1946).

That injections of thyroxine reverse the changes in feather structure and color produced by thyroidectomy has been demonstrated by several investigators (Juhn and Barnes, 1931; Fraps, 1938; Chu, 1940; Emmens and Parkes, 1940).

ANTITHYROID SUBSTANCES AND THEIR EFFECTS

There are a number of substances which produce enlargement of the thyroids and inhibition of thyroxine formation. These are termed goitrogens or antithyroid agents. For a consideration of these and their effects, particularly on domestic animals and birds, consult reviews by Blaxter, Reineke, Crampton, and Petersen (1949) and Sadhu (1948).

Thiourea and thiouracil are the most commonly used goitrogens for birds. They are equally effective in producing hypertrophy of the thyroids, but thiourea is toxic when fed at levels of 0.15 percent, whereas thiouracil is nontoxic for the chicken over a wide range of dosages.

Chicks fed 0.1 percent thiouracil for 10 days have thyroids 5 to 7 times larger than normal. When fed thiouracil for 10 weeks, the chick glands may be 45 times the size of normal thyroids (Astwood, Bissell, and Hughes, 1944). The hypertrophy of the thyroids with thiouracil is relatively greater in young, growing birds (Schultze and Turner, 1945), and it is more marked when thiouracil is administered with estrogen (Andrews and Bohren, 1947; Selle and Selle, 1948) or low levels of thyroprotein (Moreng and Shaffner, 1949). The explanation for the synergistic effect is not known.

Effects of Thiouracil on Growth and Fat Deposition

Since thiouracil depresses metabolic rate and activity, it appeared that it might be effective in increasing the deposition of fat in the tissues and improving finish in market birds and thus have an important application to the poultry industry. A number of experiments have been conducted on its use, but the effects have been rather variable. Some have reported increased gains in weight and feed efficiency, and others have reported no gains or decreased gains. Most of the experiments, however, show that thiouracil tends to improve the market grade of the carcass.

Kempster and Turner (1945) fed 0.2 percent thiouracil to 10-day-old chicks for 16 days (Lot I). No effects were reported on gain in weight, feed consumption, or economy of gains. A second group of birds, aged 8 weeks, were fed for 5 weeks (Lot II) with no effect on these characteristics, but the treatments did improve the market grade or quality of the carcasses as follows:

	Lot I		Lot II	
	Controls	Treated	Controls	Treated
Grade A, percent	9.4	40.0	50	85
Grade B, percent	40.6	46.7	36	10
Grade C, percent	48.4	13.3	14	5
Rejects, percent	1.8	0	0	0

Thiouracil fed at levels of 0.025, 0.05, 0.10, and 0.2 percent to 6-week-old Barred Rock chickens for 8 weeks tends to reduce rate of gain, but the differences are not significant except for the males. The treated birds require less feed per pound of gain than the controls, and the market quality of the carcasses is improved (Andrews and Schnetzler, 1946).

Andrews and Bohren (1947) fed 0.2 percent thiouracil to 6-week-old White Plymouth Rock chickens for 6 weeks. The rate of gain was significantly reduced, but there was an improvement in market quality, and the average gain per unit of feed consumed was not changed by the treatment. When stilbestrol and thiouracil were administered, the average gain was significantly greater than that of the controls.

Mixner, Tower, and Upp (1946) fed thiouracil to males from 16 to 20 weeks of age. The average gains for the treated and control birds were 1.31 and 0.90 pounds respectively. Feed consumption per pound of gain was 25 percent less in the treated birds. Such favorable effects have not been reported by other workers. Glazener and Jull (1946a) reported that thiouracil decreases both growth rate and feed consumption of broilers and does not improve the market quality of the carcass.

Later work by Moreng and Shaffner (1949) and Shaffner (1951) indicates that thiouracil depresses gains in weight in chickens except when fed at low levels (0.05 to 0.012 percent), and at these levels the improvement in fat deposition and carcass grade is slight. They reported, however, marked improvement in fat deposition, and in gain and feed efficiency in some cases, when both thiouracil and thyroprotein were fed at levels which induced very mild hypothyroidism.

Thiouracil fed at the level of 0.1 percent for six months does not materially affect egg production or fertility and hatchability in chickens, but higher levels (0.3 percent) reduce these (McCartney and Shaffner, 1949a).

Goitrous Chicks from Hypothyroid and Hyperthyroid Dams

Chicks hatched from dams made hypothyroid with thiouracil (Andrews and Schnetzler, 1945; McCartney and Shaffner, 1949a) or hyperthyroid with thyroprotein (Wheeler and Hoffman, 1948a, 1949, and 1950; McCartney and Shaffner, 1949a) have enlarged and hypoactive thyroids. The thyroids of chicks hatched from eggs injected with thyroxine or thyroprotein are reduced in size, and this suggests that thyroxine curtails the production of TSH by the the embryonic pituitary as it does in the adult gland (Booker and Sturkie, 1949). Thus, the goitrous thyroids are not due to thyroxine transmitted from the hyperthyroactive dams to the eggs and chicks.

Wheeler and Hoffman demonstrated that potassium iodide when injected into incubating eggs produces goiter in the chicks, and they thought that the thyroprotein used may have contained inorganic iodide. But in later experiments where iodide-free thyroprotein was fed to hens, goitrous chicks were also obtained. This enigma therefore still awaits a satisfactory solution.

HYPERTHYROIDISM

Compounds containing thyroidal activity have been synthesized. One of these, iodocasein or thyroprotein, is prepared by iodinating casein (Reineke, Williamson, and Turner, 1943). The thyroidal activity of this substance usually assays approximately 3 percent D,L-thyroxine. It is relatively inexpensive in comparison to pure thyroxine, and this, plus its lower thyroidal activity, make it particularly suitable for oral administration and for inducing a prolonged and mild state of hyperthyroidism.

The effects of hyperthyroidism and iodocasein upon growth and reproduction in domestic animals and birds have been studied extensively in recent years and have been reviewed by Blaxter *et al.* (1949).

Hyperthyroidism and Growth

Rhode Island Red chicks grown for 12 weeks on diets containing 0.025 to 0.2 percent iodocasein show slightly greater gains in weight, require less feed per unit of gain, and feather more rapidly, according to Parker (1943). Similar results were reported by Irwin, Reineke, and Turner (1943), who fed iodocasein at the 0.08 percent level; but when the level in the diet was increased to 0.1 percent, gains were depressed (Turner, Irwin, and Reineke, 1944). Wheeler and Hoffman (1949b) reported no effect upon gain in weight when 0.02 percent iodocasein was fed.

The variation in results obtained with thyroprotein depends, in part, upon the level fed and the resulting degree of hyperthyroidism induced. It is well known that moderate to extreme ovaractivity of the thyroid causes losses in body weight, but very mild hyperthyroidism may increase gains in weight.

Hyperthyroidism and Egg Production

It is known that activity of the thyroid gland decreases in hot weather and with age. Since egg production also declines under these conditions, a number of investigators have attempted to prevent the decline by administering thyroactive compounds. Most of the earlier workers used desiccated thyroid tissue of varying and questionable potency, and this may account for some of the variation in their results. For a review of the earlier work, consult Schneider (1939) and Blaxter *et al.* (1949). In evaluating the results obtained with thyroactive substances, the fact should be borne in mind that the responses vary considerably with dosage, and this may account for some of the variation reported in the literature. Many have reported that large doses of thyroid tissue or thyroxine will produce molting and a cessation of laying.

As early as 1925, Crew reported remarkable rejuvenation in very old hens (five to eight years of age) and an increase in egg production following the administration of moderate doses of desiccated thyroid. Similar results were obtained by Zawadowsky *et al.* (1928). Cole and Hutt (1928), who fed desiccated thyroid in small but effective doses to yearling hens for four months, reported no effect on egg production. With the advent of iodinated casein (thyroprotein), a number of reports have appeared concerning its effect on egg production in chickens; the results have been somewhat variable and, in some cases, conflicting.

Turner and Kempster (1948), like Crew, reported rejuvenation and increased egg production in old hens fed 10 gm. of thyroprotein per 100 pounds of feed. Such hens fed continuously thyroprotein from the second through the fifth year laid 11.2 percent more eggs in the third year, 25.7 percent more in the fourth year, and 52.7 percent more eggs in the fifth year than control birds of the same ages. Therefore, the older the bird and presumably the less active the thyroid is normally, the greater is the effect of thyroxine.

Turner, Irwin, and Reineke (1945), who fed thyroprotein at three different levels to White Leghorn hens during their second year of production, also reported an increase in number of eggs laid. The three groups received 5, 10, and 20 grams of thyroprotein per 100 pounds of feed. The rates of egg production for the three groups of birds for the year period were 38.1, 40.6, and 30.7 percent respectively, as compared to 22.6 percent for the controls. Twenty grams appeared to be an excessive amount, as weight loss and mortality were higher at this level. The production of the group stimulated most (40.6) is considerably greater than that of the controls, but this figure cannot be considered high. In fact, a production of 40 percent in untreated two-year-old hens is not unusual. Most of the increased production in these experiments occurred during the summer months when normally thyroid activity is at a minimum.

In another group of naturally low producing birds (White Plymouth Rock pullets), Turner (1948c) was able to increase egg production by feeding thyroprotein throughout the first laying year. The 21 surviving control females averaged 139.6 eggs per bird per year as compared to 182.8 eggs for the 32 treated birds.

Moore and Rees (1948, in England) reported a 25 percent increase in egg production of hens receiving thyroprotein. The production of the control birds, however, was low.

On the other hand, thyroprotein did not increase egg production in two-year-old hens, according to McClymont, Greaves, and Duncan (1951). These birds received 20 grams of thyroprotein per 100 pounds of feed during the months of December to May inclusive (which is summertime in Australia, where the tests were conducted). This dosage, however, is not considered optimum by Turner *et al.*

The effects of thyroprotein on egg production in youg birds in their first year of egg production are also inconsistent. Turner, Kempster, Hall, and Reineke (1945) fed iodocasein (10 gm. per 100 pounds of feed) to Rhode Island Red pullets for an entire laying year and found that average production for the year was 69.8 percent, as compared to 62.8 percent for the controls. The production from October to May was approximately the same for the controls and the treated birds, but thereafter production was higher in the treated birds, even though it dropped during the summer months in both groups. The results of Hutt and Gowe (1948) indicate, on the contrary, that thyroprotein does not increase annual egg production in White Leghorn pullets. Actually, during the first four months, the treated birds laid fewer eggs than the controls, but after May 1, the treated birds laid slightly more eggs. The thyroprotein had no measurable effect upon body weight, egg weight, viability, or shell strength. Gutteridge and associates (1946 and 1947) reported that thyroprotein had no effect on egg production, even when administered toward the end of the laying year, when presumably thyroid activity is normally lowest.

The variable results obtained with thyroprotein suggest that rate of egg production is related to thyroid activity, but that other hormones and other factors may influence egg production more, particularly in young birds.

Hyperthyroidism and Organ Size

Mild hyperthyroidism induced by feeding iodinated casein for 8 to 10 months decreases thyroid weight of hens from 30 to 50 percent, but has no consistent effect upon the weights of the pituitary, thymus, pancreas, adrenals, or other organs (Turner, 1948b). Larger doses (0.04 to 0.5 percent) of thyroprotein in the feed produces heart enlargement and slight decreases in pituitary and gonad weights of 12-week-old male and female chicks (Irwin, Reineke, and Turner, 1943). Only very large doses (0.5 percent) produce adrenal hypertrophy.

EFFECTS OF ALTERED THYROID ACTIVITY ON PLASMA CONSTITUENTS

Thyroxine tends to prevent or inhibit the estrogen-induced increase in plasma lipids, calcium, and plasma proteins of birds (see Chapters 2, 15, and 19). Preliminary reports by Common, Keefe, and Maw (1950) suggest that thiouracil is also effective in preventing the rise in plasma proteins induced by estrogen.

Riddle and Dotti (1936) noted that in pigeons thyroidectomy does not appreciably affect the ability of estrogens to raise plasma calcium. Clavert (1942), however, reported that ablation of the thyroids in ducks reduces the hypercalcemic effect of estrogen, but that this effect is restored when thyroxine is injected. Thyroidectomy in the drake increased plasma cholesterol, fatty acids, and phospholipids (Benoit and Bogdanovitch, 1937). Administration of thiouracil to turkeys also increases the plasma lipids from 65 to 85 percent (Reineke, Davidson, Wolterink, and Barrett, 1946). Thiouracil is not stored in the tissues, according to Pipes and Turner (1948).

Thyroidectomy decreases, and thyroxine increases, blood sugar of the bird (see Chapter 12). The effects of thyroxine upon blood cells, blood pressure, and heart rate are discussed in Chapters 1, 3, and 4.

REFERENCES

Adams, E. A., and E. A. Beeman 1942 The reaction of the chick thyroid to frog and mouse anterior pituitaries. Endocrinol. 31:128.

Andrews, F. N., and B. B. Bohren 1947 Influence of thiouracil and stilbestrol on growth, fattening, and feed efficiency in broilers. Poultry Sci. 26:447.

Andrews, F. N., and E. E. Schnetzler 1945 The effect of feeding thiouracil to hens upon the thyroid gland of chicks. Endocrinol. 37:382.

Andrews, F. N., and E. E. Schnetzler 1946 Influence of thiouracil on growth and fattening in broilers. Poultry Sci. 25:124.

Astwood, E. B., A. Bissell, and A. M. Hughes 1944 Inhibition of the endocrine function of the chick thyroid. Fed. Proc. 3:2.

Benoit, J. 1936 Rôle de la thyroïde dans la gonado-stimulation par la lumière artificielle chez la canard domestique. Comp. Rend. Soc. Biol. 123:243.

Benoit, J. 1950 Traité de Zoologie, edited by P. P. Grassé. Tome XV: Oiseaux, p. 290. Masson & Co., Paris.

Benoit, J., and M. Aron 1934 Sur le conditionnement hormonique du développement testiculaire, chez les oiseaux, résultats de la thyroïdectomie. Comp. Rend. Soc. Biol. 116:221.

Benoit, J., and S. B. Bogdanovitch 1937 Sur la teneur du sang en acides gras, phosphore lipidique, et cholestérol chez le canard domestique, après injection d'extraits préhypophysaires et après thyroïdectomie. Comp. Rend. Soc. Biol. 125:891.

Biellier, H. V., and C. W. Turner 1950 The thyroxine secretion rate of growing White Pekin ducks. Poultry Sci. 29:248.

Blaxter, K. L., E. P. Reineke, E. W. Crampton, and W. E. Petersen 1949 The role of thyroidal materials and synthetic goitrogens in animal production and an appraisal of their practical use. J. Animal Sci. 8:307.

Blivaiss, B. B. 1947a Interrelation of thyroid and gonad in the development of plumage and other sex characters in Brown Leghorn roosters. Physiol. Zool. 20:67.

Blivaiss, B. B. 1947b Development of secondary sexual characters in the thyroidectomized Brown Leghorn hen. J. Exp. Zool. 104:267.

Booker, E. E., and P. D. Sturkie 1949 The effect of thyroxine and iodinated casein on the development of the chick thyroid. Poultry Sci. 28:147.

Booker, E. E., and P. D. Sturkie 1950 Relation of rate of thyroxine secretion to rate of egg production in the domestic fowl. Poultry Sci. 29:240.

Boone, M. A., J. A. Davidson, and E. P. Reineke 1950 Thyroid studies in fast and slow-feathering Rhode Island Red chicks. Poultry Sci. 29:195.

Chaikoff, I. L., and A. Taurog 1948 The Use of Isotopes in Biology and Medicine: A Symposium (P. W. Wilson in charge of Publications), p. 292. University of Wisconsin Press, Madison.

Chu, J. P. 1940 The endocrine system and plumage types. III: Further experiments on the relation between the thyroid gland and plumage patterns in domestic fowls and ducks. J. Genetics 39:493.

Clavert, J. 1942 Thesis. University of Algiers. (Abstracted in Rev. Canadienne de Biol. 3:15, 1944.)

Cole, L. J., and F. B. Hutt 1928 Further experiments in feeding thyroid to fowls. Poultry Sci. 7:60.

Common, R. H., T. J. Keefe, and W. A. Maw 1950 Some biochemical effects of thiouracil on the response of the immature pullet to estrogen. Canadian J. Res., D, 28:272.

Crew, F. A. E. 1925 Rejuvenation of the aged fowl through thyroid medication. Proc. Roy. Soc. Edinburgh 45:252.

Cruickshank, E. M. 1929 The iodine content of the thyroid and ovary of the fowl during growth, laying, and molting periods. Biochem. J. 23:1044.

Dempsey, E. W. 1944 Fluorescent and histochemical reactions in the rat thyroid gland at different states of physiological activity. Endocrinol. 34:27.

Dempsey, E. W., and E. P. Astwood 1943 Determination of the rate of thyroid hormone secretion at various environmental temperatures. Endocrinol. 32:509.

Dvoskin, S. 1947a The thyroxine-like action of elemental iodine in the rat and chick. Endocrinol. 40:334.

Dvoskin, S. 1947b The spontaneous formation of intracellular colloid droplets in surviving chick thyroid tissue. Endocrinol. 41:403.

El-Ibiary, H. M., and C. S. Shaffner 1950 Genetic responses to induced goiter in chickens. J. Heredity 41:246.

Emmens, C. W., and A. S. Parkes 1940 The endocrine system and plumage types. II: The effects of thyroxine injections to normal, caponized, and thyroidectomized caponized birds. J. Genetics 39:485.

Epstein, D. I., and L. F. Wolterink 1949 The effect of estrogen on the chick thyroid. Poultry Sci. 28:763.

Fleischmann, W. 1947 Comparative physiology of the thyroid hormone. Quart. Rev. Biol. 22:119.

Fraps, R. M. 1938 Germinal basis of thyroxine and female hormone effect on barb origin in saddle feathers. Proc. Soc. Exp. Biol. & Med. 38:206.

Galpin, N. 1938 Factors affecting the hatching weight of Brown Leghorn chickens. Proc. Roy. Soc. Edinburgh 58:98.

Glazener, E. W., and M. A. Jull 1946a Effects of thiouracil, desiccated thyroid, and stilbestrol derivatives on various glands, body weight, and dressing appearance in the chicken. Poultry Sci. 25:236.

Glazener, E. W., and M. A. Jull 1946b Effect of thiouracil on naturally occurring molt in the hen. Poultry Sci. 25:533.

Glazener, E. W., C. S. Shaffner, and M. A. Jull 1949 Thyroid activity as related to strain differences on growing chickens. Poultry Sci. 28:834.

Greenwood, A. W., and J. S. S. Blyth 1929 An experimental analysis of the plumage of the Brown Leghorn fowl. Proc. Roy. Soc. Edinburgh 49:313.

Greer, M. A. Nutrition and goiter. Physiol. Rev. 30:513.

Gutteridge, H. S., and M. Novikoff 1947 The effect of natural and synthetic vitamin D_2 and D_3 and of thyroprotein on egg shell quality. Poultry Sci. 26:210.

Gutteridge, H. S., and J. M. Pratt 1946 The effects of vitamins D_2 and D_3 and iodinated casein on shell quality. Poultry Sci. 25:89.

Hansborough, A. L., and M. Khan 1951 The initial function of the chick thyroid gland with the use of radioiodine (I^{131}). J. Exp. Zool. 116:447.

Haque, M. E., R. J. Lillie, C. S. Shaffner, and G. M. Briggs 1948 Effect of vitamin deficiencies in New Hampshire chicks injected with high doses of thyroxine. Endocrinol. 42:273.

Harington, C. R., and G. Barger 1927 Chemistry of thyroxine; constitution and synthesis of thyroxine. Biochem. J. 21:169.

Hevesy, G. 1948 Radioactive Indicators. Interscience Publishers, Inc., New York.

Hoffman, E. 1950 Thyroxine secretion rate and growth in the White Pekin duck. Poultry Sci. 29:109.

Hoffman, E., and C. S. Shaffner 1950 Thyroid weight and function as influenced by environmental temperature. Poultry Sci. 29:365.

Hopkins, M. L. 1935 Development of the thyroid gland in the chick embryo. J. Morph. 58:585.

Huhn, E. 1949 Seasonal changes in the thyroid gland and effects of thyroidectomy in the mallard in relation to molt. Am. J. Physiol. 158:337.

Hutt, F. B., and R. S. Gowe 1948 On the supposed effect of iodocasein upon egg production. Poultry Sci. 27:286.

Irwin, M. R., E. P. Reineke, and C. W. Turner 1943 Effect of feeding thyroactive iodocasein on growth, feathering, and weights of glands of young chicks. Poultry Sci. 22:374.

Juhn, M. 1946 Effect of thiouracil on the juvenile plumages of Brown Leghorn fowl. Endocrinol. 39:14.

Juhn, M., and B. O. Barnes 1931 The feather germ as an indicator for thyroid preparations. Am. J. Physiol. 98:463.

Kaupp, B. F. 1918 The Anatomy of the Domestic Fowl. W. B. Saunders Co., Philadelphia.

Keating, F. R., Jr., R. W. Rawson, W. Peacock, and R. D. Evans 1945 The collection and loss of radioactive iodine compared with the anatomic changes induced in the thyroid of the chick by the injection of thyrotrophic hormone. Endocrinol. 36:137.

Kempster, H. L., and C. W. Turner 1945 The effect of feeding thiouracil on the fleshing of New Hampshire broilers. Poultry Sci. 24:94.

Kleinpeter, M. E., and J. P. Mixner 1947 The effect of the quantity and quality of light on the thyroid activity of the baby chick. Poultry Sci. 26:494.

Larson, R. A., F. R. Keating, Jr., W. Peacock, and R. W. Rawson 1945a A comparison of the effects of thiouracil and of injected thyrotrophic hormone on the collection of radioactive iodine and the anatomic changes induced in the thyroid of the chick. Endocrinol. 36:149.

Larson, R. A., F. R. Keating, Jr., W. Peacock, and R. W. Rawson 1945b The effect of thiouracil on the collection of radioactive iodine by the thyroid of the chick. Endocrinol. 36:160.

Lee, M., and R. C. Lee 1937 Effect of thyroidectomy and thyroid feeding in geese on the basal metabolism at different temperatures. Endocrinol. 21:790.

McCartney, M. G., and C. S. Shaffner 1949a The influence of altered metabolism upon fertility and hatchability in the female fowl. Poultry Sci. 29:67.

McCartney, M. G., and C. S. Shaffner 1949b Chick thyroid size and incubation period as influenced by thyroxine, thiouracil, and thyroprotein. Poultry Sci. 28:223.

McClymont, G. L., H. Greaves, and D. C. Duncan 1951 No response in egg production to feeding thyroprotein. Agr. Gazette New South Wales 62:46 (abstracted in Animal Breeding Abs. 19:384, 1951).

Marvin, H. N., and G. C. Smith 1943 Technique for thyroidectomy in the pigeon and early effect of thyroid removal on heat production. Endocrinol. 32:87.

Mixner, J. P., E. P. Reineke, and C. W. Turner 1944 Effect of thiouracil and thiourea on the thyroid gland of the chick. Endocrinol. 34:168.

Mixner, J. P., B. A. Tower, and C. P. Upp 1946 The effect of feeding thiouracil on the body weight of New Hampshire cockerels. Poultry Sci. 25:536.

Mixner, J. P., and C. W. Upp 1947 Increased rate of thyroxine secretion by hybrid chicks as a factor in heterosis. Poultry Sci. 26:389.

Moore, A. C., and H. G. Rees 1948 The effect of iodized protein on the laying capacity of hens. Vet. J. 104:156.

Moreng, R. E., and C. S. Shaffner 1949 A thiouracil-thyroprotein treatment for fattening poultry. Poultry Sci. 28:504.

Nonidez, J. F., and H. D. Goodale 1927 Histological studies on the endocrines of chickens deprived of ultraviolet light. Am. J. Anat. 38:319.

Odell, T. T. 1952 Secretion rate of thyroid hormone in White Leghorn castrates. Endocrinol. 51:265.

Parker, J. E. 1943 Influence of thyroactive iodocasein on growth of chicks. Proc. Soc. Exp. Biol. & Med. 52:234.

Parkes, A. S., and H. Selye 1937 The endocrine system and plumage types. I: Some effects of hypothyroidism. J. Genetics 34:298.

Patton, A. R., H. S. Wilgus, and G. S. Harshfield 1939 The production of goiter in chickens. Science 89:162.

Perek, M., and F. Sulman 1945 The basal metabolic rate in molting and laying hens. Endocrinol. 36:240.

Pipes, G. W., and C. W. Turner 1948 The retention of goitrogens in the blood and tissues of several domestic animals. Mo. Agr. Exp. Sta. Res. Bull. 422:36.

Rawson, R. W., and W. T. Salter 1940 Microhistometric assay of thyrotrophic hormone in day-old chicks. Endocrinol. 27:155.

Reineke, E. P., J. A. Davidson, L. F. Wolterink, and F. N. Barrett 1946 The effect of thiouracil on fattening turkeys. Poultry Sci. 25:410.

Reineke, E. P., and C. W. Turner 1945a The relative thyroidal potency of L and D,L-thyroxine. Endocrinol. 36:200.

Reineke, E. P., and C. W. Turner 1954b Seasonal rhythm in the thyroid hormone secretion of the chick. Poultry Sci. 24:499.

Reineke, E. P., M. B. Williamson, and C. W. Turner 1943 The effect of progressive iodination followed by incubation at high temperature on the thyroidal activity of iodinated proteins. J. Biol. Chem. 147:115.

Riddle, O. 1947 Endocrines and constitution in doves and pigeons. Carnegie Institution of Washington, Publication 572.

Riddle, O., and L. B. Dotti 1936 Blood calcium in relation to anterior pituitary and sex hormones. Science 84:557.

Robblee, A. R., C. A. Nichol, W. W. Cravens, C. A. Elvehjem, and J. G. Halpin 1948 Relation between induced hyperthyroidism and an unidentified chick growth factor. Proc. Soc. Exp. Biol. & Med. 67:400.

Sadhu, D. P. 1948 Physiological mechanism of experimental goitrogenesis. Am. J. Physiol. 152:150.

Salter, W. T. 1950 Chemical Developments in Thyroidology. Charles C Thomas, Springfield, Ill.

Schneider, B. A. 1939 Effects of feeding thyroid substances. Quart. Rev. Biol. 14:289.

Schultze, A. B., and C. W. Turner 1945 The determination of rate of thyroxine secretion of certain domestic animals. Mo. Agr. Exp. Sta. Res. Bull. 392.

Selle, J. E., and R. Y. Selle 1948 Effect of diethylstilbestrol on the thyroid glands of chicks receiving thiouracil. Science 107:394.

Shaffner, C. S. 1951 Feed efficiency of broilers as influenced by mild hyperthyroidism. Proc. Ninth World's Poultry Congr. 2:43.

Smelser, G. K. 1938 Chick thyroid responses as a basis for thyrotrophic hormone assay. Endocrinol. 23:429.

Smyth, J. R., Jr., and T. W. Fox 1951 The thyroxine secretion rate of turkey poults. Poultry Sci. 30:607.

Sun, T. P. 1932 Histo-physiogenesis of the glands of internal secretion —thyroid, adrenal, parathyroid, and thymus—of the chick embryo. Physiol. Zool. 5:384.

Taurog, A., W. Tong, and I. L. Chaikoff 1950 The monoiodotyrosine content of the thyroid gland. J. Biol. Chem. 184:83.

Taylor, L. W., and B. R. Burmester 1940 Effect of thyroidectomy on production, quality, and composition of chicken eggs. Poultry Sci. 19:326.

Turner, C. W. 1946 Comparison of the effect of feeding thiobarbital and thiouracil on the thyroid gland of the chick. Poultry Sci. 25:517.

Turner, C. W. 1948a Effect of age and season on the thyroxine secretion rate of White Leghorn hens. Poultry Sci. 27:146.

Turner, C. W. 1948b Effect of thyroprotein-feeding on the gland and organ weights of two-year-old White Leghorn hens. Poultry Sci. 27:155.

Turner, C. W. 1948c Feeding thyroprotein and sex hormones to laying hens. Poultry Sci. 27:613.

Turner, C. W., M. R. Irwin, and E. P. Reineke 1944 Effect of feeding thyroactive iodocasein to Barred Rock cockerels. Poultry Sci. 23:242.

Turner, C. W., M. R. Irwin, and E. P. Reineke 1945 Effect of the thyroid hormone on egg production of White Leghorn hens. Poultry Sci. 24:171.

Turner, C. W., and H. L. Kempster 1947 Effect of mild hyperthyroidism on seasonal and yearly egg production of fowls with advancing age. Am. J. Physiol. 149:383.

Turner, C. W., H. L. Kempster, N. M. Hall, and E. P. Reineke 1945 The effect of thyroprotein on egg production. Poultry Sci. 24:522.

Van der Meulen, J. B. 1939 Hormonal regulation of molt and ovulation. Proc. Seventh World's Poultry Congr., p. 109.

Wheeler, R. S., and E. Hoffman 1948a Goitrous chicks from thyroprotein-fed hens. Endocrinol. 42:326.

Wheeler, R. S., and E. Hoffman 1948b The value of thyroprotein in starting, growing, and laying rations. Poultry Sci. 27:509.

Wheeler, R. S., and E. Hoffman 1949 Goitrogenic action of iodide and the etiology of goiter in chicks from thyroprotein-fed hens. Proc. Soc. Exp. Biol. & Med. 72:250.

Wheeler, R. S., and E. Hoffman 1950 The etiology of goiter in chicks from thyroprotein-fed hens; negative role of inorganic iodide. Poultry Sci. 29:306.

Wilgus, H. S., Jr., F. X. Gassner, A. R. Patton, and R. G. Gustavson 1941 The goitrogenicity of soybeans. J. Nutrition 22:43.

Winchester, C. F. 1939 Influence of thyroid on egg production. Endocrinol. 24:697.

Winchester, C. F. 1940 Growth and development. II: Seasonal metabolic and endocrine rhythm in the domestic fowl. Mo. Agr. Exp. Sta. Res. Bull. 315.

Winchester, C. F., C. L. Comar, and G. K. Davis 1949 Thyroid destruction by I^{131} and replacement therapy. Science 110:302.

Woitkewitsch, A. A. 1940 Sex differences in the activity of gonads in thyroidectomized fowl. Comp. Rend. Acad. Sci. URSS 27:738.

Wolterink, L. F., and C. C. Lee 1950 Relationship between thyroid activity as assayed by the thiouracil-thyroxine method and by the thyroid turnover of radio-iodine in pair-fed rats. Fed. Proc. 9:134.

Wolterink, L. F., C. C. Lee, and A. C. Groschke 1950 The effect of a deficiency of vitamin B_{12} on iodine turnover in the chick thyroid. Fed. Proc. 9:138.

Zawadowsky, B. M., L. P. Liptschina, and E. N. Radsiwon 1928 Über den Einfluss der Hyperthyreodisierung auf das Legen der Hühner. Arch. Entwicklungsmech. Organ. 113:419.

CHAPTER 20

Parathyroids, Thymus, Pancreas

ANATOMY OF PARATHYROIDS

THERE are usually four parathyroid glands in the chicken, pigeon, and duck—two on each side, attached to or near the posterior pole of the thyroid gland. In the chicken, the pair on each side consists of a larger lobe, parathyroid three, which is developed from the third visceral pouch, and a smaller one, parathyroid four, which is developed from the fourth visceral pouch (Schrier and Hamilton, 1952). The two lobes are usually fused, and the larger lobe is usually attached to, but sometimes separated from, the posterior pole of the thyroid. In some instances, the smaller lobe may be in contact with the thyroid, with the larger lobe behind the smaller one (Nonidez and Goodale, 1927). See Figure 66, Chapter 19.

In the pigeon, the two parathyroids on each side are located outside of the thyroid and are entirely separated from it, and they may be separated from each other (Smith, 1945). The glands make contact with the jugular veins and carotid arteries and receive branches from these vessels.

Nonidez and Goodale (1927) reported accessory parathyroid tissue in the chicken, which was found in the caudal lobe of the thymus and in the thymus tissue under the thyroid and also in the ultimobranchial bodies. Campbell and Turner (1942), who serially sectioned thyroids of seven-day-old chicks, found no traces of parathyroid tissue. Smith (1945) sectioned and studied the thyroids of a number of pigeons and found no accessory parathyroid tissue.

HISTOLOGY AND SIZE

The chief cells of the parathyroids of birds are arranged in cords, like those of mammals, but there are no oxyphils, according to

Benoit (1950) and Benoit, Clavert, and Cabannes (1944a and 1944b). The cords of the chief cells are elongated in the duck (Benoit), but may be somewhat irregular and may anastomose freely in the chicken (Nonidez and Goodale). The cords are separated by a thin connective tissue stroma, abounding in capillaries. The appearance of the cord cells varies with the physiological state of the gland, according to Benoit (1950). The nucleus may stain very lightly and the cytoplasm may be vacuolated with relatively few granules, or the nucleus may be more chromatic and the cytoplasm may be granular and relatively free of vacuoles, indicating a more active condition of the cells.

In chickens, ducks, and pigeons deprived of ultraviolet light or vitamin D or fed rations deficient in calcium, the parathyroids undergo hypertrophy and hyperplasia, more than doubling in size in many cases, but this is usually followed by regression in size (Marine, 1924; Nonidez and Goodale, 1927; Higgins and Sheard, 1928; Oberling and Guerin, 1933). Ducks kept in darkness for several months exhibit parathyroids 10 times the normal size (Benoit, 1950).

Benoit, Clavert, and Cabannes (1944a) reported that hypophysectomy in the duck causes regression in size of, and an arrest of mitosis in, the parathyroids, but this condition is not permanent as the cells may later show signs of activity.

Anterior pituitary extracts injected into intact chicks have no effect upon the histology of the parathyroids (Campbell and Turner, 1942). Administration of estrogen to intact ducks causes hypertrophy of the parathyroids, according to Benoit, Clavert, and Cabannes (1944b), but other workers (see Chapter 18) have shown that injected estrogens do not affect parathyroid size in male chicks.

The weights of the parathyroids show considerable variation (Table 44). The data of Nonidez and Goodale and of Hollander and Riddle (1945) show an inverse relationship between the amount of ultraviolet light and parathyroid size. The data of Turner suggest that seasonal changes may also influence size of the glands apart from amount of light. He reported a gradual increase in weight of the parathyroids of laying hens from September of one year to July of the following year. Thus, the weights increased from September to January when the amount of natural light was de-

Table 44. Weights of parathyroids of birds

Species, age, sex, treatment	Body weight gm.	Para-thyroid weight, mg.	Para-thyroid weight in mg./kg. of body wt.	Author
Chicken				
White Leghorn, male, normal	642	4.0	6.2	Kumaran & Turner (1949b)
White Leghorn, male, normal	957	5.8	6.0	"
White Leghorn, male, normal	1,339	8.4	6.2	"
White Leghorn, male, normal	2,000	16.3	8.15	Kumaran & Turner (1949a)
White Leghorn, 6 wks., no sunlight, no vitamin D	—	50.0	—	Nonidez & Goodale (1927)
White Leghorn, 6 wks., sunlight	—	22.0	—	"
White Leghorn, laying hen (Sept.)	1,883	14.5	7.7	Turner (1948)
White Leghorn, laying hen (Nov.)	1,861	15.9	8.5	"
White Leghorn, laying hen (Jan.)	2,043	19.2	9.4	"
White Leghorn, laying hen (March)	2,007	27.2	13.6	"
White Leghorn, laying hen (May)	2,043	33.5	16.4	"
White Leghorn, laying hen (July)	1,725	54.5	31.4	"
Pigeon				
2 months, male and female, sunlight	321	3.4	10.3	Hollander & Riddle (1945)
23 months, male and female, sunlight	390	3.7	9.5	"
3 months, rickets	239	28.5	118.0	"
Duck				
Rouen, male	—	—	9.4	Benoit, 1950
Rouen, female	—	—	10.7	"

creasing, but the weights increased most from March to July when natural light was increasing.

PARATHYROIDECTOMY

Parathyroidectomy has been performed in the chicken, pigeon, and duck. Doyon and Jouty (1904), who destroyed the parathyroids of chickens with heated forceps, reported severe tetanic seizures followed by death after a few hours. In some cases, tetany did not develop. Nonidez and Goodale (1927), who removed the parathyroids in a few chickens, did not report tetany. However, there was a marked depression in activity for a period of 10 days. These workers believed that the presence of accessory parathyroid tissue, which they found, was responsible for their results. They state that the results of Doyon and Jouty are questionable since their crude technique may have produced some of the symptoms which they observed. Neither of these workers reported blood calcium values. Other workers, including Allara in 1885, Launov in 1885, and Moussu in 1897, claim to have parathyroidectomized chickens without tetany resulting, according to Benoit, Stricker, and Fabiani (1941). It is therefore not clear from the work on the chicken whether the conflicting results obtained were due to poor technique or to the presence of accessory parathyroid tissue. Further studies on the chicken are necessary.

Hutt and Boyd (1935) reported a case of tetany in a laying hen which they believed resulted from parathyroid insufficiency.

The parathyroids have been successfully removed in the duck. The duck develops classical symptoms of tetany and usually dies within 20 to 30 hours after the operation. The operation results in a decrease in blood calcium and an increase in phosphorus, shown as follows (Benoit, Fabiani, Grangaud, and Clavert, 1941):

	Total blood calcium mg./100 ml.	Inorganic phosphorus mg./100 ml.
Before operation	13.75	1.5
16 hours after	4.50	5.9
26 hours after	4.00	7.5

Smith (1945) described a technique for parathyroidectomy in

pigeons and, like Riddle, Rauch, and Smith (1945), Riddle and McDonald (1945), and McDonald and Riddle (1945), has reported on the effects of the operation. These authors showed that the pigeon develops tetany, but that this can be prevented by the administration of calcium or aluminum hydroxide. In most of their experiments, the parathyroidectomized birds were thus treated, and the changes observed in blood calcium and phosphorus were slight. In those not receiving calcium, the decrease in blood calcium was great and mainly in the diffusible fraction. The increase in phosphorus was also in the diffusible fraction.

EFFECTS OF PARATHORMONE

On Blood Calcium

The drop in blood calcium and development of tetany in parathyroidectomized ducks and pigeons can be prevented by administering parathormone. Injection of parathormone into normal or hypophysectomized male and female pigeons increases serum calcium considerably, according to Riddle and Dotti (1934). The normal duck (male), however, is rather resistant to the effects of the hormone on blood calcium. As much as 100 units per day elevates blood calcium very slightly, according to Landauer, Pfeiffer, Gardner, and Shaw (1941).

The effect of parathormone on normal chickens appears to depend on the age and sex of the bird. The hormone is without effect upon the blood calcium of nonlaying (Collip, 1931) or molting hens (Macowan, 1932), but calcium is elevated in pullets within 15 to 19 hours after a single injection of the hormone, according to Macowan. Knowles, Hart, and Halpin (1935) increased the blood calcium of immature pullets and nonlaying hens with 1 to 3 cc. of parathormone (Lilly), but they got no response in cocks or capons. This work was confirmed by Deobald, Lease, Hart, and Halpin (1936), who showed that nonlaying hens, starved of calcium, failed to respond to parathormone. Altman (1938), who injected 2 to 4 cc. of parathormone (Squibb) intramuscularly over a two-day period to immature pullets, reported an increase of 47.17 percent in blood calcium. The controls increased 20.4 percent over the same period.

Avery, Scott, and Conrad (1940a) studied the effects of parathormone (Lilly) on the blood calcium of laying hens, molting hens, immature pullets, and cockerels. Their results are shown as follows:

Group	No.	Before injection	Mg. total blood Ca/100 ml. 19 hrs. after injection (1.5 cc./kg.)
Immature pullets	6	8.20	8.61
Molting hens	6	8.82	8.92
Laying hens	6	17.54	18.30
Cockerels	6	7.59	8.62

The values after injection were slightly higher, but not significantly so. The control values were also higher 19 hours after the beginning of the experiment. Even after parathormone was injected daily for seven days, no increase in blood calcium occurred, and the hormone had no effect upon the calcium balance of molting hens (Avery, Scott, and Conrad, 1940b). The hens were in positive balance before and remained so after a series of injections of parathormone. Parathormone is without effect upon blood calcium of month-old chickens (Campbell and Turner, 1942).

The physiology of calcium deposition on the shell and of bone formation are discussed further in Chapter 15.

It is interesting to note that most of the positive results with parathormone were obtained in laying females, in which presumably the ovaries are secreting estrogen; this suggests that parathormone and estrogen have synergistic effects and that the latter plays a major role in the mobilization of calcium.

It was demonstrated in Chapters 2 and 18 that estrogen increases the blood calcium of males and females and of castrates with intact parathyroids. In parathyroidectomized male or female pigeons, Riddle and co-workers have reported that estrogen elicits the same rise in blood calcium and phosphorus as when the parathyroids are present. Most of their experiments were on immature males and females, and their birds received calcium or aluminum hydroxide to prevent tetany. The blood calcium response to estrogen in hypophysectomized pigeons was the same as in normals, and neither of these operations affected the increased endosteal bone formation induced by estrogens.

In the parathyroidectomized duck, estrogen does not elevate blood calcium (Benoit, Fabiani, Grangaud, and Clavert, 1941; Benoit, Stricker, and Fabiani, 1941; Benoit, 1950). This is demonstrated graphically in Figure 73. When estrogen is injected intramuscularly in the intact duck, blood calcium is elevated over five times within two days. Ablation of the parathyroids at this point causes a marked drop in calcium within the next 24 hours, even if the estrogen is again injected.

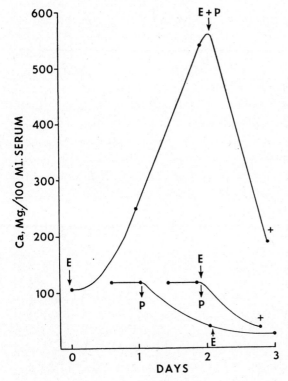

Figure 73. Effects of estrogen (E) and parathyroidectomy (P) on blood calcium of the duck.

Estrogen (10 mg. estradiol) increases calcium of normal duck (upper curve, E). The duck was parathyroidectomized and given 5 mg. of estrogen (E and P at peak of curve), and calcium dropped. The lower curves show that blood calcium drops after parathyroidectomy even when estrogen is administered. (From Benoit, Fabiani, Grangaud, and Clavert, *Comp. Rend. Soc. Biol.*, 1941, slightly modified.)

The hypophysis and thyroids play a secondary role in the hypercalcemia induced by estrogen, according to Benoit (1950). The removal of either of these glands diminishes the increase in calcium of the blood produced by estrogen and the drop in blood calcium following parathyroidectomy. Hypophysectomy in the pigeon, as in some mammals, has little or no effect upon blood calcium of males or immature females, according to Riddle and collaborators. Anterior pituitary extract injected into intact chicks has no effects upon blood calcium level, but the thyrotrophic hormone may lower it (Altman and Hutt, 1938).

Effects of Estrogen and Parathormone on Bone Formation

Although estrogen increases the formation of medullary bone, the parathyroids also play an important role in this process, according to Benoit (1950 and earlier). Estrogen causes proliferation of the framework or protein matrix of new bone, but parathormone is necessary for the deposition of calcium salts on the matrix, contrary to the work of Riddle, Rauch, and Smith (1945) for the pigeon. In certain mammals, the parathyroids are not considered necessary for ossification, since estrogen induces bone formation in the absence of the glands (Baker and Leek, 1946). Benoit (1950) showed that the drake, on a diet deficient in calcium and at the same time receiving injections of estrogen, continues to form new medullary bone (matrix); there is hypercalcemia, but the calcium comes from reabsorption of old bone, and finally calcium salts are no longer deposited in the new matrix. Injection of parathormone also causes decalcification. In the laying hen or pigeon, Bloom, Bloom, and McLean (1941) concluded that bone is being formed and destroyed continually and that the cells concerned in the formation and breakdown of bone are the same cells, but exhibiting different functional states.

Action of Parathormone

It is known that in certain mammals excretion of calcium, although increased during tetany, does not parallel the fall in blood calcium, while blood phosphorus rises markedly and its excretion is decreased in tetany. Calcium will not relieve the tetany of rabbits, in which phosphorus in the blood is greatly elevated. These facts lend support to the view that the rise in blood phosphorus may be as important in the pathogenesis of tetany as the fall in blood calcium and that the kidney is involved. It is generally accepted that parathormone regulates the excretion of phosphorus by the kidney. That this may be true also in birds is suggested by the fact that aluminum hydroxide, which prevents tetany in the pigeon, acts, according to Riddle and colleagues, by restricting the absorption of phosphorus from the intestine and thus preventing the phosphorus from reaching excessive levels after parathyroidectomy. They showed that prolonged administration of aluminum hydroxide to pigeons prevented or reversed the changes (or increase) in filterable phosphorus after removal of the glands.

STRUCTURE OF THYMUS

The thymus is at its maximum in the young chick in which it exists in the form of lobulated bodies extending the entire length of the neck. It diminishes in size with age, and only remnants of it may be found in adult birds, or it may be absent. The main portion of the thymus is derived from the entodermal lining of the third visceral pouch. This thickening elongates to form in the chick an epithelial cord extending along the jugular vein. A small portion, thymus four, is derived from a corresponding part of the fourth pouch and fuses with thymus three. The gland in the chicken is similar histologically to that of mammals. The gland consists of a connective tissue capsule and is divided into lobules by connective tissue septa. The entodermal cells of the solid epithelial cords become changed into a stellate reticulum, and in this reticulum appear small cells, the thymocytes, which resemble small lymphocytes. These cells are probably true lymphocytes of mesenchymal origin which invade the entodermal epithelium.

FUNCTION

The thymus is sometimes classified as an endocrine organ, although it is by no means certain that this classification is justified. Its function is in doubt in mammals and birds.

Removal of the thymus in chickens has no ill effects. Maughan (1938) showed that thymectomy in the chicken has no effect on growth, blood calcium, bone formation, egg production, or egg size or shell thickness. Morgan and Grierson (1930) also found that removal of the gland has no effect on egg production and size of egg laid. Riddle and Krizenecky (1931), who thymectomized pigeons, observed no ill effects.

PANCREAS

The pancreas of the bird, like that of the mammal, has both endocrine and exocrine functions. It produces the hormone insulin

and pancreatic juice. Insulin and its role in the regulation of carbohydrate metabolism in the bird is discussed in Chapter 12. The
function of pancreatic juice in digestion is discussed in Chapter 11.

ANATOMY AND HISTOLOGY

The pancreas of the bird is an elongated, lobulated gland located
in the loop of the duodenum. The gland of the chicken has three
lobes, according to most investigators (see Calhoun, 1933, for review). These are the dorsal and ventral lobes and a third, smaller
lobe, the splenic lobe, extending toward the spleen. The dorsal
and ventral lobes have one and two excretory ducts respectively,
which open into the intestine at the junction of the duodenum and
jejunum, beside the two bile ducts (see Figure 36, Chapter 10).
Most observers state that the splenic lobe has no excretory duct.

The pancreas is supplied with arterial blood from the anterior
and posterior pancreaticoduodenal arteries, which run along the
duodenal loop, supplying the duodenum and pancreas. The anterior artery is a branch from the hepatoduodenal, which arises beyond the splenic artery. The posterior pancreatic artery is a branch
of the right gastric. The pancreas is drained by the pancreaticoduodenal vein, which courses in the duodenal loop and collects
blood from the duodenum as well as the pancreas. The pancreatic
vein empties into the gastroduodenal, which in turn empties into
the hepatic portal (Hyman, 1932). The abdominal viscera, and
probably the pancreas, receive parasympathetic fibers from the
vagus and sympathetic fibers from the celiac ganglion. Some weights
of the pancreas of the fowl are shown as follows:

Species and sex	Body weight gm.	Pancreas weight gm.	Pancreas wt. as % body wt.	Author
White Plymouth Rock, males	420	1.553	0.37	Kumaran & Turner (1949c)
"	906	2.455	0.27	"
"	2,005	3.400	0.17	Kumaran & Turner (1949d)
White Leghorns, adult females	1,520–2,159	2.76–4.58	0.13–0.22	Oakberg & Lucas (1949)

The gland is larger per unit of body weight in small birds than
in larger ones. Within a given age and weight group, weights of

the pancreas are fairly constant and show less variation than the other endocrine organs. Hypophysectomy causes a decrease in weight of the pancreas in pigeons, and likewise in the intestine and other nonendocrine organs (Schooley, Riddle, and Bates, 1941), and probably is not a specific effect. Starvation also decreases the size of the pancreas, and hypophysectomy reduces considerably feed consumption and body weight.

The pancreas is divided into lobes and lobules, but interlobular septa are indistinct and there is little intralobular connective tissue present in the gland of the chicken (Calhoun, 1933; Batt, 1940). The lobules are composed of short tubules or acini, as in the mammal. The acinar cells are low-columnar and have a granular cytoplasm. The acinar cells, the exocrine portion of the pancreas, produce pancreatic juice containing enzymes. Batt has described zymogen granules in the acinar cells of chickens like those present in mammals. Distributed irregularly among the acini are the islet cells of Langerhans, which produce insulin (Figure 74).

There are two main types of islet cells in the chicken pancreas, the alpha and beta cells, and three cell types in the pigeon gland, according to Miller (1942), who describes them as follows. The alpha cells of the pigeon have oval or round nuclei and many large red cytoplasmic granules (stained with Heidenhain's azan). The beta cells, the largest, have spherical nuclei, showing diffuse scant chromatin and small cytoplasmic granules which stain yellow. The delta cells, the smallest of the three, are variously shaped and the nuclei stain rather densely, with the small cytoplasmic granules staining blue. The beta cells are believed to produce insulin. The distribution of cells in an islet is such that the delta and alpha cells form one islet, and the beta and delta another.

Hypophysectomy in the pigeon results in an increase in size of the alpha cells, but the beta cells become smaller and less well granulated, and many degenerate. The number of delta cells is also decreased. It was shown that these changes are due to starvation rather than the operation, because when the operated birds were force-fed, no cell changes occurred.

Miller also demonstrated that the beta cells could be stimulated by overfeeding of normal birds and by prolactin, partial pancreatectomy, and corticotrophin, while gonadotrophins and thyrotrophin had no effect. In contrast, large doses of insulin caused a marked atrophy of the beta cells. Atrophy of the beta cells follows fasting of normal birds. Castration in chickens and ducks increases the number and size of the islet cells. Alloxan administered to animals causes necrosis of the islet cells, but does not have this effect in birds (see Chapter 12).

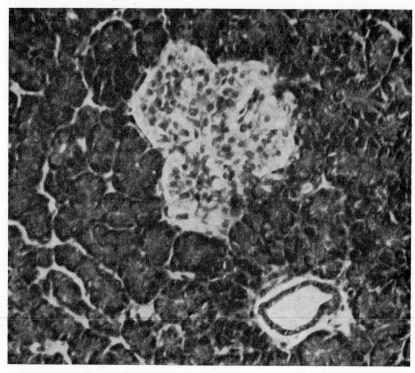

Figure 74. Cross section of pancreas of chicken showing islet cells (light staining) and acinar cells (dark staining), with excretory duct at lower right. (Courtesy of Dr. A. M. Lucas.)

The distribution of the alpha and beta islet cells in chickens of various ages has been studied by Oakberg (1949). In the pancreas of the one-day-old chick, the number of alpha and beta cells average 150 and 3500 respectively, and at 100 days of age, 2000 and 29,000 respectively. The number of alpha cells then remains fairly constant up to 300 days, but the beta cells increase to 40,000. The alpha cells are most numerous in the proximal part of the gland, but the beta cells are distributed throughout the gland. Lucas (1947) reported inclusion bodies in the beta cells of most chickens more than 40 days of age, but none in birds less than 30 days. Their significance is unknown.

PANCREATECTOMY

The pancreas is supplied by blood vessels which also supply the adjacent parts of the intestines. Sprague and Ivy (1936) have shown that destruction of these vessels in the duck results in gangrene of the duodenum and death. Therefore, in removing the pancreas, care must be taken to avoid impairing the blood supply to the duodenum. Some have attempted to remove the pancreas without disturbance to the intestine, but it is difficult to remove all fragments of pancreatic tissue. Others, aware of this difficulty, have removed the pancreas and duodenum en masse and then anastomosed the intestinal ends. The latter is a difficult operation and involves possible complications resulting from the removal of about 20 percent of the small intestine. With either type of operation, the bird is deprived of pancreatic juice, and this may result in inanition and ultimate death.

Pancreatectomy has been performed in the duck by Minkowski (1893), Kausch (1896 and 1897), Paton (1905), Weintraud (1894), Fleming (1919), Seitz and Ivy (1929), Sprague and Ivy (1936), and Mirsky, Nelson, Grayman, and Korenberg (1941); in the goose by the first three cited above; in the pigeon by Minkowski and by Riddle (1937); in the chicken by Giaja (1912), Koppanyi, Ivy, Tatum, and Jung (1926), and Batt (1940); and in the owl by Nelson, Elgart, and Mirsky (1942). The results of the operation appear to be least successful in the pigeon, but it has been performed only on a few birds.

Most birds recover rapidly following the operation and remain in a fair state of health for several days; they then begin to lose weight, and most of them (ducks) die within six weeks to four months (Seitz, 1930). The weight loss in depancreatized chickens is 27 percent seven weeks after the operation, despite normal food consumption (Batt, 1940). Ultimate death is attributed to impaired digestion, resulting from loss of pancreatic juice. The weight loss in pancreatectomized ducks can be prevented by feeding pan-

creatin or raw pancreas (Mirsky *et al.*, 1941), but not in the case
of the depancreatized owl (Nelson *et al.*, 1942). Other workers have
demonstrated that ligation of the pancreatic ducts of birds produces
the same effects on health and body weight as removal of the
pancreas.

The effects of pancreatectomy on carbohydrate regulation are
discussed in Chapter 12.

REFERENCES

Altman, M.   1938   Doctoral thesis. Cornell University.
Altman, M., and F. B. Hutt   1938   The influence of estrogens in the egg
    yolk upon avian blood calcium. Endocrinol. 23:793.
Avery, T. B., H. M. Scott, and R. M. Conrad   1940a   Effect of para-
    thyroid preparation on the blood calcium of the fowl. Poultry Sci.
    19:321.
Avery, T. B., H. M. Scott, and R. M. Conrad   1940b   Effect of para-
    thyroid preparation on the calcium metabolism of the fowl. Poultry
    Sci. 19:324.
Baker, B. L., and J. H. Leek   1946   The relationship of the parathyroid
    gland to the action of estrogen on bone. Am. J. Physiol. 147:552.
Batt, H. T.   1940   The pancreas of the fowl. Thesis. University of
    Toronto.
Benoit, J.   1950   Traité de Zoologie, edited by P. P. Grassé. Tome XV,
    Oiseaux, p. 297. Masson & Co., Paris.
Benoit, J., J. Clavert, and R. Cabannes   1944a   Étude histo-physio-
    logique de la parathyroïde du canard domestique. I: Conditionne-
    ment partiel de son activité par la préhypophyse. Comp. Rend. Soc.
    Biol. 138:1071.
Benoit, J., J. Clavert, and R. Cabannes   1944b   Étude histo-physio-
    logique de la parathyroïde du canard domestique. II: Modifications
    histologiques déterminées par le traitement à la folliculine. Comp.
    Rend. Soc. Biol. 138:1074.
Benoit, J., G. Fabiani, R. Grangaud, and J. Clavert   1941   Suppression
    par la parathyroïdectomie de l'action hypercalcémiante du dipro-
    pionate d'oestradiol chez le canard domestique. Comp. Rend. Soc.
    Biol. 135:1606.
Benoit, J., P. Stricker, and G. Fabiani   1941   Technique et résultats de
    la parathyroïdectomie chez la canard domestique. Comp. Rend. Soc.
    Biol. 136:1600.
Bloom, W., M. A. Bloom, and F. C. McLean   1941   Calcification and

ossification: Medullary bone changes in the reproductive cycle of female pigeons. Anat. Rec. 81:443.

Calhoun, M. L. 1933 The microscopic anatomy of the digestive tract of Gallus domesticus. Iowa State Coll. J. Sci. 7:261.

Campbell, I. L., and C. W. Turner 1942 The relation of the endocrine system to the regulation of calcium metabolism. Univ. Mo. Res. Bull. 352.

Collip, J. B. 1931 Physiology of the parathyroid gland. Canadian Med. Assoc. J. 24:646.

Deobald, H. J., E. J. Lease, E. P. Hart, and J. G. Halpin 1936 Studies on the calcium metabolism of laying hens. Poultry Sci. 15:179.

Doyon, M., and A. Jouty 1904 Ablation des parathyroïdes chez l'oiseaux. Comp. Rend. Soc. Biol. 66:11.

Fleming, G. B. 1919 Carbohydrate metabolism in ducks. J. Physiol. 53:236.

Giaja, J. 1912 Sur la glycémie chez le poulet. Comp. Rend. Soc. Biol. 73:102.

Higgins, G. M., and C. Sheard 1928 The effects of selective solar irradiation on the parathyroid glands of chickens. Am. J. Physiol. 85:299.

Hollander, W. F., and O. Riddle 1945 On partial mechanism associated with parathyroid enlargement in pigeons. Am. Nat. 79:451.

Hutt, F. B., and W. L. Boyd 1935 Idiopathic hypoparathyroidism and tetany in the fowl. Endocrinol. 19:398.

Hyman, L. H. 1932 A Laboratory Manual for Comparative Vertebrate Anatomy. University of Chicago Press, Chicago.

Kausch, W. 1896 Über den Diabetes Mellitus der Vögel nach Pankreasexstirpation. Arch. f. Exp. Path. u. Pharm. 37:274.

Kausch, W. 1897 Der Zuckerverbrauch im Diabetes Mellitus des Vögels nach Pankreasexstirpation. Arch. f. Exp. Path. u. Pharm. 39:219.

Knowles, H. T., E. B. Hart, and J. G. Halpin 1935 The variations in the calcium level of the blood of the domestic fowl. Poultry Sci. 14:83.

Koppanyi, T., A. C. Ivy, A. L. Tatum, and F. T. Jung 1926 Absence of permanent diabetes following pancreatectomy in the domestic fowl. Am. J. Physiol. 76:212.

Kumaran, J. D. S., and C. W. Turner 1949a The endocrinology of spermatogenesis in birds. I: Effects of estrogen and androgen. Poultry Sci. 28:593.

Kumaran, J. D. S., and C. W. Turner 1949b The endocrinology of spermatogenesis in birds. II: Effects of androgens. Poultry Sci. 28:739.

Kumaran, J. D. S., and C. W. Turner 1949c The normal development of the testes in the White Plymouth Rock. Poultry Sci. 28:511.

Kumaran, J. D. S., and C. W. Turner 1949d The endocrinology of spermatogenesis in birds. III: Effect of hypo- and hyperthyroidism. Poultry Sci. 28:653.

Landauer, W., C. A. Pfeiffer, W. W. Gardner, and J. C. Shaw 1941 Blood serum and skeletal changes in two breeds of ducks receiving estrogens. Endocrinol. 28:458.

Lucas, A. M. 1947 Intranuclear inclusions in the islands of Langerhans in chickens. Am. J. Path. 23:1005.

McDonald, M. R., and O. Riddle 1945 The effect of reproduction and estrogen administration on the partition of calcium, phosphorus, and nitrogen in pigeon plasma. J. Biol. Chem. 159:445.

Macowan, M. M. 1932 Observations on the ductless glands, the serum calcium, and egg laying in the fowl. Quart. J. Exp. Physiol. 31:383.

Marine, P. 1924 Parathyroid hypertrophy and hyperplasia in fowls. Proc. Soc. Exp. Biol. & Med. 11:117.

Maughan, G. H. 1938 Some effects of thymus removal in chickens. Am. J. Physiol. 123:319.

Miller, R. A. 1942 Effects of anterior pituitary preparations and insulin on islet cells of pigeon pancreas. Endocrinol. 31:535.

Minkowski, O. 1893 Untersuchungen über den Diabetes Mellitus nach Exstirpation des Pankreas. Arch. f. Exp. Path. u. Pharm. 31:85.

Mirsky, A., N. Nelson, I. Grayman, and M. Korenberg 1941 Studies on normal and depancreatized domestic ducks. Am. J. Physiol. 135:223.

Morgan, A., and M. Grierson 1930 Effects of thymectomy on young fowls. Anat. Rec. 47:101.

Nelson, N., S. Elgart, and I. A. Mirsky 1942 Pancreatic diabetes in the owl. Endocrinol. 31:119.

Nonidez, F. J., and H. D. Goodale 1927 Histological studies on the endocrines of chickens deprived of ultraviolet lights. I: Parathyroids. Am. J. Anat. 38:319.

Oakberg, E. F. 1949 Quantitative studies of pancreas and islands of Langerhans in relation to age, sex, and body weight in White Leghorn chickens. Am. J. Anat. 84:279.

Oakberg, E. F., and A. M. Lucas 1949 Variations in body weight and organs: Body weight ratios of inbred lines of White Leghorn chickens in relation to mortality, especially from lymphomatosis. Growth 13:319.

Oberling, C., and M. Guerin 1933 Les modifications des parathyroïdes dans les ostéites par carence chez la poule. Comp. Rend. Assoc. Anat. 28:489.

Paton, W. 1905 The effect of adrenaline on sugar and nitrogen excretion in urine of birds. J. Physiol. 32:59.

Riddle, O. 1937 Carbohydrate metabolism in pigeons. Cold Spring Harbor Symposia on Quantitative Biol. 5:362.

Riddle, O., and L. B. Dotti 1934 Action of parathyroid hormone in normal and hypophysectomized pigeons. Proc. Soc. Exp. Biol. & Med. 32:507.

Riddle, O., and J. Krizenecky 1931 Failure of thymectomy to reveal thymus function. Am. J. Physiol. 97:343.

Riddle, O., and M. R. McDonald 1945 The partition of plasma calcium and inorganic phosphorus in estrogen-treated normal and parathyroidectomized birds. Endocrinol. 36:48.

Riddle, O., V. M. Rauch, and G. C. Smith 1945 Action of estrogen on plasma calcium and endosteal bone formation in parathyroidectomized pigeons. Endocrinol. 36:41.

Schooley, J. P., O. Riddle, and R. W. Bates 1941 Replacement therapy in hypophysectomized juvenile pigeons. Am. J. Anat. 69:123.

Schrier, J. E., and H. L. Hamilton 1952 An experimental study of the origin of the parathyroids and thymus glands in the chick. J. Exp. Zool. 119:165.

Seitz, I. J. 1930 On the respiratory quotient of depancreatized ducks. Am. J. Physiol. 93:686 (Abs.).

Seitz, I. J., and A. C. Ivy 1929 The effects of pancreatectomy in ducks. Proc. Soc. Exp. Biol. & Med. 26:463.

Smith, G. C. 1945 Technique for parathyroidectomy in pigeons. Anat. Rec. 92:81.

Sprague, R., and A. C. Ivy 1936 Studies in avian carbohydrate metabolism. Am. J. Physiol. 115:389.

Turner, C. W. 1948 Effects of thyroprotein on the gland and organ weights of two-year-old White Leghorn hens. Poultry Sci. 27:155.

Weintraud, W. 1894 Über den Pancreas: Diabetes der Vögel. Arch f. Exp. Path. u. Pharm. 34:303.

CHAPTER 21

Adrenals

ANATOMY

THE adrenals of birds are paired, oval-shaped organs which are anterior and medial to the cephalic lobe of the kidneys, just anterior to the bifurcation of the posterior vena cava. In mammals, the glands are divided into distinct zones, the outer cortex and the inner medulla (chromaffin tissue). These tissues have different origins, as they do in birds. In most birds, the chromaffin tissue is not located in the center of the gland, but is intermingled with the interrenal tissue which does not form a true cortex as in mammals. Hence, the use of the term interrenal instead of cortex for birds (Hartman and Brownell, 1949).

The interrenal cells arise from the peritoneal epithelium (mesothelium) ventral and medial to the mesonephros and dorsal to the hind gut. Their origin is mesodermal. The chromaffin cells arise from the sympathetic trunks on each side of the embryonic aorta and migrate into the gland (Hays, 1914). The chromaffin cells stain very darkly with iron hematoxylin or osmic acid. With chromic acid, the granules of these cells stain brown, and this is known as the chromium reaction. These cells are thought to carry adrenaline, because the granules of these cells, in mammals at least, yield a greenish color with ferric chloride, and a similar reaction is given by the blood of the adrenal vein.

The blood supply of the fowl adrenal is shown in Figure 75. The left gland receives arterial blood from the adrenal artery and arteries branching from the renal artery; the right gland is supplied by branches of the renal artery. The adrenals are drained by two veins, one from each gland, which empty into the posterior vena cava (Hays).

Many nerve fibers penetrate the adrenals of birds, and most of them are unmyelinated, according to Giacomini (quoted by Hartman and Brownell). Some of the nerve trunks located in the capsule give off fibers which run between the various chromaffin cells near the periphery and then penetrate the interior. The nerve fibers never enter the interrenal, but do enter the chromaffin tissue.

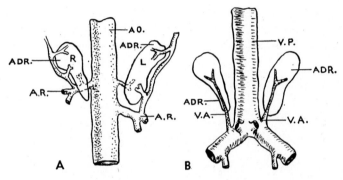

Figure 75. Diagram of arteries (A) and veins (B) of the adrenals of the fowl.

AO., aorta; ADR., R and L, right and left adrenals; A.R., renal artery with branches (adrenal arteries) shown entering the glands; V.P., posterior vena cava; V.A., adrenal vein. (From Hays, *Anat. Rec.*, 1914, slightly modified.)

HISTOLOGY

Histological studies have been made on the adrenals of chickens (Uotila, 1939; Nalbandov and Card, 1943; Kar, 1947a and 1947b), pigeons (Miller and Riddle, 1942), ducks (Benoit, 1950), and many wild species of birds (Hartman, Knouff, McNutt, and Carver, 1947; Hartman and Brownell, 1949; Knouff and Hartman, 1951). The adrenals are enclosed by a thin capsule containing blood vessels and nerves. The interrenal tissue of all birds studied thus far, including many wild species, is not zonated, except in the brown pelican, in which the interrenal tissue is organized into three zones that correspond in position and general appearance, but not in relative proportions, to the three zones of the mammalian adrenal (Knouff and Hartman). In all other species, the interrenal tissue may extend from the periphery far into the gland, but the relative distribution of the chromaffin and cortical tissues varies with the different species (Hartman *et al.*, 1947).

The interrenal cells are arranged in cords or strands, and the cells are less chromatic than the chromaffin cells. The cytoplasm of the cortical cells contain mitochondria and lipid droplets, and the relative proportions of these vary under different conditions of activity of the gland (Figure 76). Subsequent to hypophysectomy the interrenal tissue atrophies, exhibiting shrunken lipid-filled cells and golgi bodies with a decrease in mitochondria (Miller and Riddle, 1942; Benoit, 1950).

The cortex of the male chicken adrenal comprises 40 percent of the gland, according to Kar (1947a), and 44.2 percent, according to Sauer and Latimer (1931). The interrenal tissue of the female gland amounts to 71 percent, according to Kar. In proportion to body weight, females have 30 percent more cortical tissue than males (Sauer and Latimer). In immature chickens, there is slightly more chromaffin than interrenal tissue (Elliott and Tuckett, 1906). More extensive studies involving three different lines of White Leghorn males and four lines of females, 120 days of age (Oakberg, 1951), reveal that the amounts of interrenal and chromaffin tissue in males are approximately the same but that there is slightly more interrenal tissue (52 percent) in the female gland. The interrenal tissue in percent of body weight averaged 0.0043 for the males and 0.005 for the females. Some of the individual lines exhibited considerable variation in the relative proportions of interrenal and chromaffin tissues. Approximately 65 percent of the adrenal of male and female pigeons (Miller and Riddle, 1939a) is composed of interrenal tissue, and 85 to 90 percent of the gland in pelicans (Knouff and Hartman, 1951).

HORMONES OF THE ADRENAL

Little is known concerning the physiology of the adrenals of birds. In 1927, extracts from the animal adrenal cortex were prepared by Hartman and also by Rogoff and Stewart (see Hartman and Brownell, 1949), which prolonged the lives of adrenalectomized animals. Such extracts from the bird adrenal have not been prepared, but it is known that extracts from the mammalian adrenal

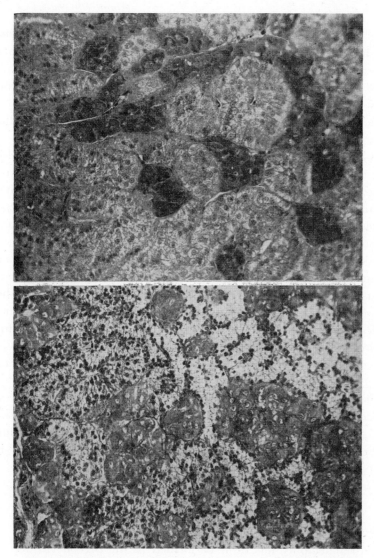

Figure 76. Cross sections of the adrenals of normal (upper) and hypophysectomized (lower) ducks.

In the upper figure are shown the prominent cortical or interrenal cells (light staining) and the chromaffin cells (darker staining) arranged in islets, as well as blood vessels. In the lower figure, the adrenal of the duck 47 days after hypophysectomy shows signs of involution and degeneration of the interrenal cells, which are filled with lipids. (From Benoit, in *Traité de Zoologie*, edited by P. P. Grassé, Tome XV, Figures 249 and 250, Masson & Co., Paris, 1950.)

will also maintain life in adrenalectomized birds, and the effects of such extracts in the intact bird are similar to those in mammals. Extracts of the adrenals and liver of man and of the cat, dog, rat, and guinea pig produce cortisone in media containing desoxycorticosterone acetate (DCA) and certain other substances, but the chicken adrenal does not (Seneca, Ellenbogen, Henderson, Collins, and Rockenbach, 1950).

Crude extracts of the cortex contain a number of fractions which are necessary for the health and well-being of the animal. A considerable number of steroids have been isolated in pure form from the mammalian adrenal cortex, but only some of these show physiological activity. Some of them are corticosterone, 11-desoxycorticosterone, 17-hydroxycorticosterone (Kendall's Compound F), 17-hydroxy-11-dehydrocorticosterone (Kendall's Compound E, or cortisone), and others. These substances are less active than crude adrenal extracts which contain all fractions. There is evidence to show that certain adrenal steroids not oxygenated at carbon atom 11 affect mainly mineral metabolism and the distribution of sodium, chloride, and potassium in the cells, plasma, and tissues. The C-11 oxygenated steroids (cortisone, etc.) are concerned in the metabolism of carbohydrates and fats.

The fact that the pituitary is concerned in the release of cortical hormones in birds, as in mammals, is discussed in Chapter 17.

It is presumed that the medulla of the bird adrenal produces adrenaline, but isolation of this hormone from the bird gland has apparently not been demonstrated.

ADRENALECTOMY

Technique of Operation and General Effects

Adrenalectomy has been performed in the pigeon (Miller and Riddle, 1943), duck (Parkes and Selye, 1936; Bulbring, 1940; Benoit, 1950 and earlier), and chicken (Parkins, 1931; Parkes and Selye, 1936; Herrick and Torstveit, 1938; Herrick and Finerty, 1941; Hewitt, 1947). The operation is difficult because of the close connection of the gland with the friable vena cava. It is best performed in males or immature females. The highly vascular ovary of the adult female makes it unusually difficult to remove the left adrenal without fatal hemorrhage.

The glands may be removed by splitting the capsule and removing the tissue with a cannula attached to a suction pump. Remaining fragments may be destroyed by applying ferric chloride solution (Selye, 1949). Parkins (1931), after clamping and dissecting away as much of the gland as possible, used an electric cautery to destroy the remaining portion of the gland. Herrick and Torstveit (1938) removed both glands in two different operations. Others have removed both at one time.

Completely adrenalectomized ducks and chickens usually die 6 to 20 hours after the operation without replacement therapy. Bulbring (1940) showed that life could be maintained in the duck with cortical extracts or DCA. The mean survival time was proportional to the logarithm of dose of cortical extract injected. The requirement of cortical extract to maintain life was higher in the spring when the testes were growing and lower in castrates. When testosterone was administered to castrates, however, their survival time was not changed, suggesting that androgen is not a factor. Cortical extracts in oil, 0.05 to 3.0 cc., had to be injected at four-hour intervals to maintain life, while daily injections of 5 mg. DCA were sufficient. NaCl was not used.

Herrick and Torstveit (1938) reported that the typical signs of adrenal insufficiency as observed in mammals do not appear in the chicken soon after the operation. The birds appear normal until shortly before death when muscle weakness is the principal symptom observed. These authors injected cortical extract (Eschatin) for two to three days after the operation and from then on administered NaCl by injection or in the drinking water. Birds thus treated lived from a few to 82 days. Parkins, who claims to have completely adrenalectomized chickens, reported an average survival time of 80 days without replacement therapy. During the acute stages following the operation, uric acid in the blood increased from a normal of about 3 mg. to 11.8 mg. per 100 ml. There was also a slight decrease in blood sugar (Chapter 12).

The adrenalectomized pigeon can be maintained for nine days on NACl. Cortical extracts or DCA not only maintain life but restore feed consumption and body weight to normal levels (Miller and Riddle, 1943).

Effects on Gonads

Adrenalectomy causes a marked reduction in the size of the testes and combs of chickens within two to four days after the operation. Histological studies show the seminiferous tubules reduced in size and the cells in a state of degeneration. Herrick and Finerty (1941) demonstrated that adrenalectomy causes pronounced changes in the pituitary. Within 30 to 50 days after the operation (birds maintained on cortical extracts and salt), the testes were one-half of normal size, and the pituitary revealed an increase in the number of degenerating basophils, approximately three times that of the normal gland. The pituitaries of castrates with intact adrenals revealed few degenerating basophils. The workers concluded that adrenalectomy causes degeneration of the testes indirectly, by decreasing the production of gonadotrophins from the pituitary.

Hewitt (1947) demonstrated also that adrenalectomy decreases testes size in the male fowl; in the female it prevented the hypertrophy of the rudimentary right gonad, or development of an ovotestis and production of androgen which normally occur in the ovariectomized fowl with intact adrenals.

Tumors of the suprarenal cortex of female mammals may result in the production of androgen and the assumption of masculine characteristics (virilism). This has also been reported in chickens by McGowen (1936).

FACTORS AFFECTING ADRENAL SIZE

Within and between species, the size of the adrenals of birds varies considerably with age, sex, state of health, and other factors. Hartman and Brownell (1949) reported the adrenal weights of 20 species of birds (exclusive of the chicken, pigeon, and duck) and showed that the adrenal weights in percentage of body weight ranged from 0.0085 percent for the downy woodpecker to 0.0405 for the brown pelican. Among these species, there was no sex difference in size. The variation within individuals of some of the same species was great. The adrenal weights of some species of birds are shown in Figure 77 and Table 45.

In proportion to body weight, the size of the adrenals is larger in embryos and young birds. Crile and Quiring (1940) and others have shown that in chicks weighing 40 to 50 grams the adrenals are approximately twice as large, in proportion to body weight, as in

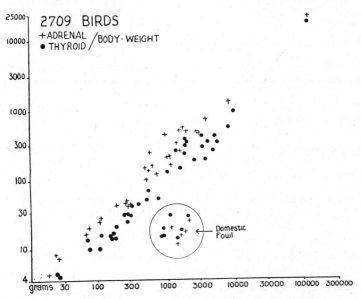

Figure 77. The relationship of body weight to adrenal and thyroid weights of birds.

Ordinates represent adrenal and thyroid weights in milligrams, and abscissae, body weight in grams. (From Quiring, *Growth*, 1951.)

chicks weighing 300 grams. There is no difference in the size of the right and left adrenals in chickens, according to Sauer and Latimer (1931).

Riddle (1923) claimed that the male pigeon adrenal is slightly heavier than that of the nonlaying female, but that the glands of the females enlarge preceding and during ovulation and regress in size following ovulation (see table). Nagel (according to Riddle) stated that adrenal size in pigeons, ducks, and chickens did not vary with reproductive cycle. Data from a number of sources on the

Table 45. Adrenal weights of chickens and pigeons

Species, sex, and age	Body weight gm.	Adrenal weight gm.	Adrenal wt. as % of body wt.	Author
Chicken, embryo, 10 days	—	—	0.040	Venzke (1943)
Chicken, embryo, 21 days	—	—	0.024	
White Leghorn, male, 4 wks.	272.3	—	0.0127	Breneman (1942)
White Leghorn, male, 8 wks.	642.0	0.071	0.0110	Kumaran & Turner
White Leghorn, male, 14 wks.	1,339.0	0.123	0.0090	(1949)
White Leghorn, male	2,079.0	0.106	0.0051	Sauer & Latimer
White Leghorn, female	1,641.0	0.094	0.0057	(1931)
White Leghorn, male, 3 mos.	—	0.086	0.0082	Kar (1947a and
White Leghorn, male, 3 mos., castrate	—	0.1146	0.0112	1947b)
White Leghorn, male, 4 mos.	—	0.1756	0.0107	Oakberg (1951)
White Leghorn, female, 4 mos.	—	0.1280	0.0102	
Brown Leghorn, male, 11 mos.	—	—	0.0177	Juhn & Mitchell
Brown Leghorn, male, 11 mos. castrate	—	—	0.0154	(1929)
Brown Leghorn, female, 11 mos.	—	—	0.0182	
Black Minorca, female, 3 yrs.	2,400.0	0.142	0.0060	Elliott & Tuckett
Black Minorca, male, 3 yrs.	3,570.0	0.101	0.0030	(1906)
Pigeon, male, adult	344.0	0.0199	—	Riddle (1923)
Pigeon, female, 108 hrs. before ovulation	308.0	0.0163	—	
Pigeon, female, during ovulation	341.0	0.0358	—	
Pigeon, female, 108 hrs. after ovulation	317.0	0.0162	—	

chicken show that on a body-weight basis there is no real difference in adrenal size of males and females. The relationship between adrenal size and reproductive cycle in the chicken has received scant attention. There is, as a matter of fact, little data to show that circulating estrogens or androgens in the sexes under different conditions affect adrenal size. In the discussion of the effects of androgen and estrogen on adrenal size (see Chapter 18), it is shown that small doses of estrogen have no effect but that large doses cause some enlargement. Androgen has no effect on size of adrenals.

Castration of the male chicken results in enlarged adrenals; this is caused mainly by hyperplasia of interrenal tissue (Kar, 1947b), which can be prevented if testosterone or estrogen is injected. Juhn and Mitchell (1929), however, reported no difference in the adrenal size of males and castrates.

Effects of Stress, Hormones, and Chemicals

Various stress reactions in mammals cause adrenal hypertrophy and an outpouring of cortical hormones (see review of Tepperman, Engel, and Long, 1943). Very little work of this nature has been reported for birds.

Adrenal hypertrophy can be induced with thyroxine in the intact and hypophysectomized pigeon (Miller and Riddle, 1939a and 1942). Bates, Riddle, and Miller (1940) reported no change in adrenal weights of chicks injected for five days with thyroxine. Later work by Irwin and co-workers and by Turner (see Chapter 19) reveals that dosage is an important factor in the response of the adrenal. Mild hyperthyroidism induced by small doses in chickens does not affect adrenal size, but large doses cause enlargement. Hypothyroidism resulting from the administration of 0.1 percent thiouracil or from thyroidectomy causes adrenal hypertrophy in the chicken according to Morris (1953), but the mechanism involved is not known.

Substances which usually cause the alarm reaction in animals and an outpouring of cortical hormones and hypertrophy of the adrenals have little effect in the young chick, according to Bates, Riddle, and Miller (1940). They injected chicks for five days with thyroxine, insulin, desoxycorticosterone acetate, copper sulfate, potassium chloride, and formaldehyde; only formaldehyde, and in large doses, caused adrenal enlargement, and the effect was decreased only slightly in hypophysectomized chicks. More recent work by Jailer and Boas and by others (see Chapter 17), however, indicates that the chick adrenal does respond (enlarges) to ACTH and epinephrine.

Insulin injections for four days to pigeons (60 units per day) increased adrenal size over 100 percent in intact birds and to a lesser extent in those hypophysectomized (Miller and Riddle, 1941). Formaldehyde, ACTH, and other anterior pituitary hormones increase adrenal size in the pigeon, while DCA decreases it and causes a marked atrophy of the interrenal tissue (Miller and Riddle, 1942).

Pigeons infested with ascarids or infected with tuberculosis have enlarged adrenals (Riddle, 1923). Avian leucosis in the chicken causes hypertrophy and hyperplasia of the adrenals and thyroids, and the change in the adrenal is mainly in the interrenal tissue (Arvy and Gabe, 1951). Adrenal enlargement resulting from vitamin B_1 deficiency has been reported in pigeons (Beznak, 1923) and in chickens. Fasting also causes enlargement of the adrenals (Sure, 1938).

Effects of Epinephrine and Cortical Hormones

Compound E (cortisone), Compound F, and DCA when injected into chick embryos cause a marked reduction in growth and development, and the effect of cortisone is more pronounced than that of Compound F (Karnofsky, Stock, and Rhoads, 1950; Sames and Leatham, 1951). Since certain other chemicals and viruses also decrease embryonic growth, the effect of cortical hormones is probably not a specific one.

Selye and Friedman (1941) reported that a number of steroid hormones, and particularly DCA, causes testicular atrophy in the chick, possibly by suppression of pituitary gonadotrophins. DCA also causes hypoplasia of the developing gonads of the chick embryo (Vannini, 1947). Whether or not cortical hormones have an androgenic effect in birds is questionable. Hooker and Collins (1940) reported that DCA increased comb growth slightly, but was considerably less effective than testosterone in the capon. Paschkis (1941), however, reported negative results. Adrenaline or epinephrine injected into the sparrow (Perry, 1941) or the chicken (Wheeler, Search, and Andrews, 1942) causes atrophy of the testes, probably in the same manner as DCA.

Large doses of DCA given to chicks produce nephrosclerosis

(Selye, 1942) and cardiac hypertrophy and hypertension (Stamler, Pick, and Katz, 1951).

Adrenal cortical extract (ACE) injected into the adult chicken produces lymphopenia and leucocytosis, with the increase occurring mainly in the heterophils (see Chapter 1). Cortical hormones and ACTH cause a reduction in eosinophils in certain mammals, but apparently have no effect upon the eosinophils of birds (Chapter 1).

Cortical extracts and Compound F, but not cortisone, produce marked hyperglycemia in normal or depancreatized chicks and increase the lipemia induced by cholesterol, according to Stamler (1952). See also Chapter 12.

Adrenaline or epinephrine affects the bird much the same as mammals. It increases heart rate and blood pressure (Chapters 3 and 4) and mobilizes blood sugar (Chapter 12). Its effects upon respiration, motility of the digestive tract, and other organs are discussed in the particular chapters concerned.

REFERENCES

Arvy, L., and M. Gabe   1951   État des glandes endocrines au cours de l'érythroblastose aviaire transmissible (leucose aviaire). Comp. Rend. Acad. Sci., Paris 232:260.

Bates, R. W., O. Riddle, and R. A. Miller   1940   Preparation of adreno-trophic extracts and their assay on two-day chicks. Endocrinol. 27:781.

Benoit, J.   1950   Traité de Zoologie, edited by P. P. Grassé. Tome XV: Oiseaux, p. 305. Masson & Co., Paris.

Beznak, A.   1923   Die Rolle der Nebennieren bei Mangel an Vitamin B. Biochem. Z. 141:1.

Breneman, W. R.   1942   Action of diethylstilbestrol in the chick. Endocrinol. 31:179.

Bulbring, E.   1940   The relation between cortical hormone and the size of the testis in the drake, with some observations on the effect of different oils as solvents and on DCA. J. Pharm. & Exp. Thera. 69:52.

Crile, G., and D. P. Quiring   1940   A record of body weight and certain organ and gland weights of 3,690 animals. Ohio J. Sci. 40:219.

Elliott, T. R., and I. Tuckett   1906   Cortex and medulla in the supra-renal glands. J. Physiol. 34:322.

Hartman, F. A., and K. A. Brownell   1949   The Adrenal Gland. Lea & Febiger, Philadelphia.

Hartman, F. A., R. A. Knouff, A. W. McNutt, and J. E. Carver   1947   Chromaffin patterns in bird adrenals. Anat. Rec. 97:211.

Hays, V. J.   1914   The development of the adrenals in the bird. Anat. Rec. 8:451.

Herrick, E. H., and J. C. Finerty   1941   The effect of adrenalectomy on the anterior pituitaries of fowls. Endocrinol. 27:279.

Herrick, E. H., and O. Torstveit   1938   Some effects of adrenalectomy in fowls. Endocrinol. 22:469.

Hewitt, W. F.   1947   The essential role of the adrenal cortex in the hypertrophy of the ovotestis following ovariectomy in the hen. Anat. Rec. 98:159.

Hooker, C. W., and V. J. Collins   1940   Androgenic action of DCA. Endocrinol. 26:269.

Juhn, M., and J. B. Mitchell, Jr.   1929   On endocrine weights in Brown Leghorns. Am. J. Physiol. 88:177.

Kar, A. B.   1947a   The adrenal cortex, testicular relations in the fowl: The effect of castration and replacement therapy on the adrenal cortex. Anat. Rec. 99:177.

Kar, A. B.   1947b   The action of male and female sex hormones on the adrenals in the fowl. Anat. Rec. 97:551.

Karnosfky, D. A., C. C. Stock, and C. P. Rhoads   1950   The effect of adrenal steroids on growth of chick embryo. Fed. Proc. 9:290.

Knouff, R. A., and F. A. Hartman   1951   A microscopic study of the adrenal of the brown pelican. Anat. Rec. 109:161.

Kumaran, J. D. S., and C. W. Turner   1949   The endocrinology of spermatogenesis in birds. II: Effect of androgens. Poultry Sci. 28:739.

McGowen, J. P.   1936   Suprarenal virilism in a domestic hen; its possible significance. J. Exp. Biol. 13:377.

Miller, R. A., and O. Riddle   1939a   Stimulation of adrenal cortex of pigeons by anterior pituitary hormones. Proc. Soc. Exp. Biol. & Med. 41:518.

Miller, R. A., and O. Riddle   1939b   Rest, activity, and repair in cortical cells of the pigeon adrenal. Anat. Rec. 75:103.

Miller, R. A., and O. Riddle   1941   Cellular response to insulin in suprarenals of pigeons. Proc. Soc. Exp. Biol. & Med. 47:449.

Miller, R. A., and O. Riddle   1942   The cytology of the adrenal cortex of normal pigeons and in experimentally induced atrophy and hypertrophy. Am. J. Anat. 71:311.

Miller, R. A., and O. Riddle   1943   Effects of prolactin and cortical hormones on body weight and food intake of adrenalectomized pigeons. Proc. Soc. Exp. Biol. & Med. 52:231.

Morris, D. M. 1953 Adrenal hypertrophy in the White Leghorn cockerel after treatment with thiouracil and thyroidectomy. Science 117:61.

Nalbandov, A. V., and L. E. Card 1943 Effect of hypophysectomy of growing chicks. J. Exp. Zool. 94:387.

Oakberg, E. F. 1951 Genetic differences in quantitative histology of the adrenal organ weights and interorgan correlations in White Leghorn chickens. Growth 15:57.

Parkes, A. S., and H. Selye 1936 Adrenalectomy of birds. J. Physiol. 86:35 (Proc.).

Parkins, W. M. 1931 An experimental study of bilateral adrenalectomy in the fowl. Anat. Rec. 51:39.

Paschkis, K. E. 1941 Androgenic action of DCA. Proc. Soc. Exp. Biol. & Med. 46:366.

Perry, J. C. 1941 The antagonistic action of adrenaline on the reproductive cycle of the English sparrow, Passer domesticus. Anat. Rec. 79:57.

Quiring, D. P. 1951 Studies in the comparative anatomy of the endocrine system. Growth 15:121.

Riddle, O. 1923 Studies on the physiology of reproduction in birds. XIV: Suprarenal hypertrophy coincident with ovulation. Am. J. Physiol. 66:322.

Sames, G. L., and J. H. Leathem 1951 Influence of DCA and cortisone acetate on body weight of chick embryos. Proc. Soc. Exp. Biol. & Med. 78:231.

Sauer, F. C., and H. B. Latimer 1931 Sex differences in the proportion of cortex and medulla in the chicken suprarenal. Anat. Rec. 50:289.

Selye, H. 1942 Production of nephrosclerosis by overdosage with desoxycorticosterone acetate. Canadian Med. Assoc. J. 47:515.

Selye, H. 1949 Textbook of Endocrinology. 2d ed. Acta Endocrinologica, Inc., Montreal.

Selye, H., and S. Friedman 1941 The action of various steroid hormones on the testis. Endocrinol. 28:129.

Seneca, H., E. Ellenbogen, E. Henderson, A. Collins, and J. Rockenbach 1950 The *in vitro* production of cortisone by mammalian cells. Science 112:524.

Stamler, J. 1952 Effects of adrenal steroid F in depancreatized, cholesterol-fed cockerels. Fed. Proc. 11:153.

Stamler, J., R. Pick, and L. N. Katz 1951 Effects of corticoids and ACTH on fluid exchange, blood pressure, glycemia, cholesterolemia, and atherogenesis in chicks. Fed. Proc. 10:131.

Sure, B.   1938   Influence of avitaminosis on weights of endocrine glands. Endocrinol. 23:575.

Tepperman, J., F. L. Engel, and C. N. H. Long   1943   A review of adrenal cortical hypertrophy. Endocrinol. 32:373.

Uotila, U. U.   1939   On the fuchsinophile and pale cells in the adrenal cortex tissue of the fowl. Anat. Rec. 75:439.

Vannini, E.   1947   The effects of desoxycorticosterone acetate on the development of the gonads of the chick embryo. Bol. Sòc. Ital. Biol. Sper. 23:240 (abstracted in Animal Breeding Abs. 18:104, 1950).

Venzke, W. G.   1943   Endocrine gland weights of chick embryos. Growth 7:265.

Wheeler, N. C., G. L. Search, and F. N. Andrews   1942   The effect of epinephrine upon semen production in the domestic fowl. Endocrinol. 30:369.

INDEX